MW00667490

/13

The Encyclopedia of

Alternative Agriculture

for Urban and
Semi-Rural Communities

NEW CENTURY EDITION

Book 1

Vol. 1 No. 1-12

Vol. 2 No. 1-12

Richard Alan Miller

06-13-13

By

Dr. Richard Alan Miller

The Encyclopedia of

Alternative Agriculture

For Urban & Semi-Rural Communities

NEW CENTURY EDITION

Book 1

Vol. 1 No. 1-12 & Vol. 2 No. 1-12

By

Dr. Richard Alan Miller

THE ENCYCLOPEDIA OF ALTERNATIVE AGRICULTURE:
for Urban and Semi-Rural Communities

NEW CENTURY EDITION

10-digit ISBN 0988337916
13-digit ISBN 978-0-9883379-1-6
Manufactured in the United States of America

Published by
OAK Publishing
1212 SW 5th Street, Grants Pass, OR 97526

Illustrator
Connie Nygard

Designer/Editor
Elleyne Kase

Editor
Dan Dawson

Cover Photo:
Tagetes patula L. Marigold
The big markets lie in *Tagete erecta L.* (African cultivar),
as a poultry feed additive—dyes the yoke.
http://en.wikipedia.org/wiki/Tagetes

For general information on our other products and
services, please contact OAK Publishing at 541-476-5588
or visit us at www.richardalamiller.com.

OAK Publishing
Organization for Advancement of Knowledge

Table of Contents

Foreward

The Herb Market Report was a monthly publication spanning from January of 1985 through September of 1993. This unique and comprehensive report covers a wide range of pertinent topics for active and potential herb farmers. The articles are in depth, concerning all aspects of herb production, processing and marketing. This well researched and written information will be found nowhere else in regard to the scope and comprehensiveness of the articles.

The author, Richard Alan Miller, is a world renowned agricultural consultant and researcher on the forefront and 'cutting edge' of the sciences related to botanicals and their practical cultivation, use and marketing. Connie Nygard, whose beautiful artwork graces these pages, is a graduate of the Corcoran School of Art. Her wonderful illustrations may also be found in The Magical and Ritual Use of Aphrodisiacs and The Potential of Herbs as a Cash Crop.

It has been my pleasure knowing Rick both as a friend and, more importantly, as a source of information and illumination for well over a decade. It is with great pleasure and a measure of gratitude that I have undertaken the task of assembling this small portion of his extensive works so that others may continue to benefit from them.

Dan Dawson

Editor

Dr. Richard Alan Miller

Introduction

Things cycle, like music and our diets. Cycles are like metaphors, especially when organized by a Physicist. From that perspective, my "take" on things is unique and has a more "timeless" element to it. And my background was not from Agronomy, but from the hard sciences with a focus on Processing and Marketing.

Like the original Foxfire series of books, this is a set of "classical approaches" for basic small farm agriculture. Back in the early 80s, this information was not easily found. It was considered "lost information" in most libraries." So this is where I started my homework, by writing a newsletter.

> The Herb Market Report newsletters were written
> before computers, or before the internet.

The Herb Market Report newsletters were written before computers, or before the internet. Many of the graphs or addresses have obviously changed over the years. But then, those aspects are easily rebuilt (internet and computer) using the "key word" topics (as a metaphor). Rather than spend time updating that aspect, I felt it more important to address your options and diversity.

> This set of newsletters will teach the basics
> for how to "small farm" field crops correctly,
> and be successful.

So while the data charts may be old, the information about the herbs themselves is still valid. This set of newsletter will teach the basics for how to "small farm" field crops correctly, and be successful.

Dr. Richard Alan Miller

Economic Outlooks for the 21st. Century

The actual monitoring of herb and spice imports into the United States is quite limited. While the USDA Foreign Agricultural Service has published data, other monitoring systems (like Chemical Marketing Reporter) show import figures into the Port of New York to be twice those reported by FAS for the entire nation.

Other major Ports of Entry, like San Antonio, TX, do not even formally monitor the amount of crops brought in from Mexico, Central and South America. Why are there not more detailed studies on the actual dollars involved? One reason is because most herbs and spices are treated as "non-storable" commodities. Their individual total gross sales are usually quite small and uninteresting as trade.

Some, however, have such significant gross volumes in sales that they are often grouped for stock and trade on some of the Exchanges. One export example from the United States is the red peppers (including paprika, used to color hot dogs). Another would be garlic and onion. The next question that arises is what constitutes an herb or spice? These examples seem like they are foods.

In an important study made last year by this author, it was shown that products imported (in this category of markets) which could be grown, manufactured, or otherwise processed on the West Coast of the United States was in excess of $20 billion.

The herb and spice trade has several distinct markets. For simplicity, they are often referred to as foods, drugs, cosmetics, and dried florals. As food, most herbs and spices are not the primary ingredient, but used to enhance. To monitor the amount of basil, for example, used in the manufacture of pesto is almost impossible. The oregano used on pizza is another example.

The USDA FAS has published data to indicate that the United States now imports more than ten times the spices that they export. For example, the United States imports of just selected dried condiments, seasonings, and flavoring materials in

X

Dr. Richard Alan Miller

1987 were valued at nearly $439 million. Meanwhile, exports of specific spices and seasonings (including dehydrated onion and garlic) were valued at $62.7 million.

The important point to remember is that these figures are often in conflict with other reported import figures, and they only reflect those markets where herbs and spices are sold as foods. These figures do not reflect those crops which might be marketed as pharmaceuticals (drugs), cosmetics, or even the growing decorative floral markets.

In an important study made last year by this author, it was shown that products imported (in this category of markets) which could be grown, manufactured, or otherwise processed on the West Coast of the United States was in excess of $20 billion, more than 40 times what might be indicated by current available studies. Why are we importing with such large figures when our economy needs to export?

```
The markets are large for these types of
crops, and are growing at an annual rate of
more than 20 percent in some cases.
```

The primary reason is that most spices and herbs require special handling and are labor-intensive. Third World countries, with very cheap labor, can afford to subsidize these types of crops as their market niche in world economy. However, as world economic standards become more uniform, the ability to compete becomes possible.

The markets are large for these types of crops, and are growing at an annual rate of more than 20 percent in some cases. A typical example is psyllium hulls, now used as a major source for dietary fiber. In 1989 one company brought in more than $100 million from India, while a major cereal manufacturer has announced that they planned to spend more than $40 million in advertising its use in their cereals in 1990.

Other new crops with good market futures include comfrey for cattle feed and pyrethrum as an organic insecticide. While the market potentials for these types

Dr. Richard Alan Miller

crops are staggering, new farm methods are needed to make them feasible and in volumes sufficient to meet world demand. Most of the mechanized machinery or technology to farm these types of crops competitively in the United States already exists. The problem is how to get access to the markets.

Despite these obvious potentials for rural economic development and growth in small farm agriculture, almost all herbs are imported. Many come from Mexico and South America, but others arrived from as far away as Romania, Yugoslavia and Poland. Much of the peppermint and spearmint leaf comes from Egypt and Bulgaria, whereas orange peel is imported from Haiti and Spain. As shipping costs go up and demand increases, prices also increase.

Many herbs bring prices that are far higher than could be expected from the cost of production. Farm prices, in general, range from $600 to $2,500 per ton. One to three tons per acre is the average harvest. This kind of return rivals that of the most lucrative farm crops; yet, once established, herbs will continually produce this high return with lower continuing cash requirements. The primary investment is labor.

> If present trends continue, the herb
> and spice markets should continue to
> grow for many years.

Proximity to the market is also less important than with other commodities. Partly, this is true because once they are dried, herbs are relatively easy and light-weight to store and transport. Also, these higher prices make it feasible to ship over long distances. A 10-ton load of herbs is often worth $10,000, whereas a similar load of wheat is generally worth $2,000 (or less).

If present trends continue, the herb and spice markets should continue to grow for many years. Herbs should have greater potential as cash crops in areas that are not suited to the more familiar farm crops. Areas with limited water and poorer soil can produce as much income per acre with herbs as the most fertile areas with abundant water-producing traditional farm crops.

Dr. Richard Alan Miller

In addition, the investment requirements are lower when growing herbs. The primary investment is labor. And since the total volumes used by specific end users are less than the major crops, smaller farm ventures are favored. These markets are well suited to the need for diversification in agriculture. Machinery costs are less and chemical costs are almost nonexistent in their production.

Since recorded history, the country which controlled spice trade has also controlled world trade. This is true even today. With only slight modification in farm practices and technology, the United States has an opportunity to compete in these commodities. They will also strengthen rural economic development by favoring the small farm and agricultural diversification.

Cottage Industries; A market perspective.

Lack of new products and low consumer confidence in product quality this last year has impacted the growth of herb and spice industry. Future success will be driven by the creation of innovative, effective products with proven clinical support and patent protection. This is not a raw material industry as much as it is best suited for the development of cottage industries.

Those wanting to live in rural communities are left with opportunities other than as raw material suppliers. That would be OK except for the fact that the markets for herbs and spices are limited. The marketing and sales, however, is driven by the (consistent) quality of the raw materials used in the cottage industry.

> Always begin a market program around a
> specific "idea" (like an Indian Herbal
> Coffee, or herbal steroid).

Niche marketing is created by availability. This means a "new idea," not a new product (or raw material). The "niche" is the idea, not the product itself. The market is not about the raw material itself, but the quality of raw materials used to make "something."

For herbs and spices, the first rule is: Always begin a market program around a specific "idea" (like an Indian Herbal Coffee, or herbal steroid). This is your "cottage industry" idea. Then, to guarantee the continued purchase and growth of that cottage industry, grow your own fields needed to supply its needs (focusing on quality).

This is called "vertical integration," where you might also have a small processing plant to put your various raw materials into a form for their final use. This might mean further cleaning of contaminates, or processing it into better forms for use in your final product. The operant standard here is that "when you want it done right, do it yourself."

I've found that processing is as important
as the raw material itself.

Your "in house" ability can also be used for outside customers, also seeking your processing. I've found that processing is as important as the raw material itself. A good processor can clean up problems, and often make things work (when they might not have otherwise). It allows the farmer some latitudes with overall farm costs and procedures.

Niches also imply diversification of ingredients and a balance of options (when markets wane or rise). Peppermint is primarily grown for the oil, but some have found that when world oil prices drop, they can often process their product as leaf (for the tea industry) for a better return. However, the grower that makes the real money in this industry is the one who also sells his peppermint as part of a blend of herbal teas (like Country Spice Tea) from his farm.

Economic forces, federal farm policies, and consumer choices are causing small farmers to look at the business of farming in new ways. Today's successful farmers are, of necessity, increasingly becoming small business entrepreneurs.

Many small farm experts and policy makers across the nation believe that local value-added agricultural food production where farmers assume more processing

Dr. Richard Alan Miller

steps and sell through direct marketing techniques – is a critical strategy to sustain many small farmers and their communities. The world's agricultural trade is rapidly shifting from commodities to products. Consumers are demanding products with traits to meet their specific needs. Global competition is intense.

To survive in today's dynamic market, small farmers must interpret market signals accurately. They must carefully consider what mix of crops and other agricultural products will maintain crop diversity and flexibility, and provide more value-added farm income.

Value-Added Definition

Value-added means adding features – desirable to customers – to a raw agricultural, marine, aqua cultural, or forestry material used to make a product. Drying, canning, juicing, combining ingredients, handcrafting, and unique packaging and marketing techniques can add value.

Everyone who adds value to a product as it goes from farm to consumer gets paid. Vertical integration – the farmer doing production, processing, and distributing – can be good for those farmers who are willing and able.

Many farmers have not gone into value-added food products because they are concentrating on what they have traditionally done best – producing a commodity. Doing more of the processing and marketing activities involved in the marketing chain takes time, skill, and extra labor.

Some Final Words

Spirituality is not what you do, but how you do it. Our choices and responsibilities also cycle, ever toward becoming more spiritual in purpose. The more we become sovereign within ourselves, the more spiritual we also become. The two are like a metaphor of each other.

Dr. Richard Alan Miller

It does not matter what is about to happen, or when. Rather, it is about the need for a change in lifestyle. Our food and trade should become part of our way of being, integrated into the very nature of our lifestyle. The contents of these newsletters should serve as a guide toward those ends. This should help toward a shift in our paradigms. Everything cycles, and we are now seeking a difference in our relationship to the land.

Dr. Richard Alan Miller

04-01-13

Dr. Richard Alan Miller

Dr. Richard Alan Miller: Agricultural Biography

Dr. Miller left the miltary in 1972, and announced to the world he was going into herb farming. Henry Barth (5th richest man in the world) heard of this, and flew over from Nuremberg to hire him to do agricultural studies for his farms in the US.

The next 5 years he worked with Haas Botanicals Washington (DC), conducting farm experiments on 28 of Mr. Barth's farms, 300 acres each, in 4 states (WA, OR, ID, and MT). That is where, "I learned how to farm, and use innovative machinery concepts from old bone-yard equipment." More than 90 crops were studied during his contract with Mr Barth. The herb farm series, now compiled into over 360 PDFs, are based on that original work.

Dr. Miller also formed *The Beltane Corporation* (Seattle) in that same year. Starting as sole proprietor he retailed books and herbs. By 1980, he had a staff of 12 employees, with the company wholesaling herbs, spices and teas to the six Western states. The company also imported spices for their milling and herb tea line (*Safeway*-Oakland District).

In 1980 *The Beltane Herb Company, Inc.* expanded with Dr. Miller becoming a limited partner in a reorganization, then functioning as "Agricultural Scientist" and "Buyer" for *Western Herb Farms* (Seattle) and *Country Spice Tea* (Portland). He also moved to eastern Washington to establish and develop extensive farm and forage plans for the mass tea market and export.

During that same period, two additional corporations were formed: *West Coast Dehydrators, Inc.* (Carlton) and *Methow Valley Herb Growers Association* (Twisp). The first corporation designed and built an experimental prototype dehydrator for herb and spice farming (USDA Grant Proposal 8306074 *A Commercial Portable Dehydrator*

for Alternative Small-Farm Agricultural Crops.). The second corporation was a profit-sharing marketing cooperative.

Dr. Miller moved to Grants Pass, OR in 1983. His book, *The Potential Of Herbs As A Cash Crop* (Acres, USA) was developed from several courses he taught at *Rogue Community College* (Grants Pass/Medford). The courses were very popular and led to the formation of *The Southern Oregon Herb Gatherers' Association, Inc.* (Grants Pass), a profit-sharing marketing cooperative.

In 1985, Mr. Miller began publishing a national newsletter for the herb farmer and forager. After ten years of publication, *The Herb Market Report* is still considered one of the best resources on the subject. He now writes columns in numerous national magazines, URL responses for several national corporations, and feature stories and interviews. Recent book titles include *Native Plants Of Commercial Importance* (Acres, USA), *The Magical And Ritual Use Of Herbs* (Destiny), *The Magical And Ritual Use Of Perfumes* (Destiny), *Forest Farming* (in press), *Computers On The Farm* (OAK), and *Successful Farm Ventures* (in press). He is also contributing editor to *Acres, USA* (Kansas City).

Dr. Miller received a grant (USDA Grant Proposal 8600849 *A Centralized Processing Facility for Botanical Alternatives as Cash Crops*) in 1986, and a year later formed *Northwest Botanicals, Inc.* to broker the growing number of new domestic farmers and foragers producing herbs and spices. He has been approached by numerous businesses to develop similar farming and processing facilities. Grants received in 1994 include projects in *Forest Farming* (FEDA), *Specialized Harvesters* (OEDD), and *Preservation of Salal Greens* (USDA).

Dr. Miller has been retained as a special consultant to such firms as *Botanicals International, Inc.* (Long Beach, CA) and *John I Haas, Inc.* (Yakima, WA/Wash D.C./Munich, Germany). His primary emphasis is toward new crops development in both the foraging and farming of herbs and spices. Extensive networks of producers in more than 40 States and 4 Provinces in Canada have been created as a direct result of his writings and workshops. Dr. Miller is now considered a world authority in the marketing of these crops.

Dr. Richard Alan Miller

A number of cottage industries have emerged because of his activities with these various corporations. These include *Golden Eagle Herbal Chew* (Grants Pass) and *Frozen Pesto* (Ashland), both now into the mass markets. Many networks, in such diverse regions as South Dakota, Northern California, Montana, and the Spokane Indians, have received grants as a direct result of his work. He has been listed in *Who's Who of the West* since 1992, and was named to *Who's Who in the World* in 1996, and has been written about in various articles such as the *Wall Street Journal* and *National Geographic.*

His present work includes another USDA-SBIR grant (Agreement Number 94-33610-0107), titled *Salal Preservation: A Forest Farming Venture.* Two other proposals include a BBS for *TeleMarketing* floral products (Florals, NW), and an auction house on the BBS for late remainders and large bulk sales. He is retained by *Richters* of Canada as an outside consultant, and is on regular lecture-tours throughout North America.

Dr. Richard Alan Miller

Dedication

The Herb Market Report is dedicated to our children, and their brave new world.

Dr. Richard Alan Miller

Vol.1

Nos. 1-12

Book 1 *Table of Contents*

Forage | Culture | Harvesting | Market Analysis |

Book 1 *Table of Contents*

| Forage | Culture | Harvesting | Market Analysis |

Dr. Richard Alan Miller,

THE HERB MARKET REPORT

for the herb farmer and forager

Vol. 1   No. 1   Feb. 1985

NEW!

The response to our work in the forage of non-timber forest-floor crops and other noxious weeds in Southern Oregon has been overwhelming. The need for a newsletter for the herb farmer and forager is quite apparent, especially one directed toward market trends and resources. Each month, the newsletter will feature 2 herbs, one on small farm alternatives and the other on a forage crop. Each will include a farm/forage plan, harvest and drying techniques, processing and storage requirements, and marketing options. A cottage industry section will also be featured. Our goal is to develop models for other parts of the country to access their natural resources.

Foragers Turn Weeds into Cash Crops

A new industry for Oregon has taken root in the Rogue River area. Mention the term "forest products," and most people naturally think of trees and lumber products. But the members of the newly formed Southern Oregon Herb Gatherers' Association, a foraging cooperative, are learning that there is more than one way to earn money in the woods of Oregon and Washington.

The collection of specific medicinal plants for the crude drug markets provides a number of jobs in the rural communities each year. From the days of early settlers, numerous native plants have been credited with medicinal properties, eventually leading to their use as home remedies. Many since have become official pharmaceutical products. For many of these plants there is little commercial demand, but a growing number are consumed in substantial tonnages.

Wild plants have been with us long before cultivated crops. They have been our food and medicines for centuries. This form of agriculture is the backbone of the pharmaceutical industry. Among the plants that furnish products for the crude drug trade are common weeds, popular wild flowers, and important forest products. Some of these botanicals have even been exported for over 100 years from North America.

Such botanicals as Sassafras rootbark and Golden Seal root are typical products from the Southeast, while Cascara Segrada bark (a laxative) has been an export for over 40 years from Washington and Oregon.

Many new markets are now available, due in part to the preference of extraction over synthetic production of the pharmaceutical houses and the health-food boom of the 1970's. Once these natural resources have been recognized and marketing identified, they can provide meaningful employment to those who need to suppliment their rural incomes.

At the urging of my students, we decided to put some of my classroom teachings from Rogue Community College into practice. Our first venture took place in the Siskiyou mountains, part of the Cascade Range of Southern Oregon. It was a one-day event, with more than 70 students turning out to learn how to properly harvest Prince's Pine herb (Chimaphila umbellata). Also known as Pipsissewa, this herb is currently used as the primary flavoring agent in the manufacture of root beer.

Of first concern to all was a reforestation program, a plan to assure the crop's continuance for next year's harvest. In the case of Pipsissewa, the plant grows from a rhizome. The act of harvesting the root only propagates the plant into further growth. Known as "copusing," the harvest of Prince's Pine caused the plant to grow more quickly than if it were left to grow naturally. We were, in a sense, creating a gardening program for the forest floor.

Most of the Prince's Pine herb now used by manufacturers is imported, although some is now available from several Appalachian communities. It grows everywhere in the Northwest, primarily in mountainous country with altitudes over 2,500 feet. With more than $3,000 worth of this herb harvested in that one day, this was the start of our foragers' cooperative. Our structure was to be like that of a local Grange, a neighborhood-based profit-sharing cooperative.

This allowed individuals and small groups to work on specific projects, with a centralized warehouse for marketing (and eventual processing). By broadening the number of crops available and increasing the total quantity of each, marketing was not a problem. Soon, a number of larger pharmaceutical houses were submitting requests for specific botanicals, native to our region of the country. Since our first venture, other crops have been harvested, with gross sales of more than $34,000 in the first three months of the cooperative's existence.

These crops include Oregon Grape root, a chemical substitute to Golden Seal. Last month, the cooperative sold more than 10,000 pounds of this root to a firm in Southern California. Other crop harvests included Aspen leaf (used in cough preparations), Catnip herb (a tea ingredient), Chicory root (a coffee substitute), False Hellebore root (important heart drug), Horsetail herb (high in silica), St. John's Wort (hypericum red dye), Thistle (vermouth flavoring), and Yerba Santa (expectorant and flavoring agent). A number of floral products were also sold, including Sugar Pine cones and Teasel.

The concept of foraging is well-suited to those who have chosen a rural style of living, but must also have continual sources of income. A cooperative, organized similarly to the local neighborhood Grange, seems to be an excellent way for a community to develop its economy by creating rural jobs. A number of the foraged products are also well-suited to cottage industries. Dried floral arrangements are an excellent example during holiday seasons.

With proper management, the community and social benefits are more far-reaching than simple economic development. For example, take the case of Mullein (Verbascum thapsus). This herb is considered a noxious weed and grows abundantly throughout most of North America. It is also an import from Yugoslavia. Last year, more than 400 ton was imported into New York by just one brokerage house. It can be cut, conditioned and laid into a windrow, and then baled when dry. In this form, most processors will pay more than $700 per ton ($0.35 per pound). If it is further processed into a "cut" form

and sacked, it begins marketing at $1,300 per ton ($0.65 per pound)!

In August, a feasibility study was conducted in the Chiloquin District of Southern Oregon with a harvest of this crop. A number of years back, this district had a major forest fire. Reseeding programs proved almost futile in the poor, pumice soils. Only after a sixth reseeding were they able to get a plantation started. Unfortunately, one year after the successful reseeding, the trees were intercropped with solid stands of Mullein. Herbicides had been banned several years prior, so the forest district assumed that they would loose their plantation. Mullein grows to 6 feet, while the new treelings were only 12 inches tall.

A number of members from the Southern Oregon Herb Gatherers' Association went in and cut the Mullein herb with machettes. The herb was then trucked to lower fields for drying and eventual baling. Not only did the forest district save their new plantation, they actually made a small amount of money from the brush permits issued. And, most important, a number of rural jobs were created .....producing a product that was previously imported. It also provided a strong argument for alternative methods in weed control.

These herbs are just a few examples of the opportunities available for those seeking supplimental rural incomes. There is a growing need for more domestic sources of supply. With trends toward exporting rather than importing, it may be possible for a number of rural communities to actually improve their quality of lifestyle. Not only does exporting bring new money into the community, it also lowers domestic prices and provides alternatives to herbicides in the control of "noxious weeds."

The future of foraging as a source of supplimenting one's rural income lies with our ability to recognize natural resources. Each region of North America contains similar stories. The forest can become more than just a source for timber. It can also now be seen as "farm ground," perfectly suited for specific botanicals with already existing markets. As one Silviculturist once said about foraging: "For the first time, I now can see a way I can do what I went to College to study: forest management rather than timber management!"

"Subscribe."
(see back page for details)

The Cottage Industry

The original concept of a cottage industry was one of a manufacturer in a rural setting, probably working from their home. Their advantage to the community was seen on several levels. Not only did they broaden the marketing of local products, they also brought new money into the community because their marketing was primarily export. As the community grew, so did these private, home industries. Today, these local entrepreneurs are considered critical to the health and growth of a rural community.

The diversity of marketing available to those interested in herbs and spices is unbelievable. For the small farmer who chooses not to market either by direct or bulk marketing channels still has a number of alternatives. By forming a series of cottage industries around your crops, the profit-margins available can increase by more than 400% in some situations. While these profit-margins are necessary for most producer-manufacturer-distributor-customer structures of marketing, a number of other important benefits for the rural community also emerge.

Each month, a special column will be devoted to exploring some of these options. Next month will feature "Frozen Pesto for the Italian Food Markets."

The Herb and Spice Markets

The herb and spice industry in North America is a young and rapidly expanding business, with most of the more successful companies in the field starting since 1970. The market is divided into several main categories. They are

1. Foods: These include flavorings, additives, and condiments which are used by the food, spice and natural food manufacturers. There is, at present, a large and growing demand from the food manufacturers and spice companies, with the major food suppliers now entering the marketplace with these products. These suppliers, representing more than 45,000 stores, represent a yearly wholesale business of more than 25 billion dollars.

2. Pharmaceuticals: The drug and pharmaceutical manufacturers have all found that, whenever possible, the use of natural ingredients is much more cost-effective than those made synthetically. Since this is the original source of most of our traditional medicines, more and more mainstream doctors are prescribing these medicinal herbs over synthetic alternatives. The market is quite broad. For example, the bio-flavinoid markets currently use more than 2,000 ton per month of Rose Hip in the manufacture of Vitamin C.

3. Cosmetics: Almost all major manufacturers of cosmetics now use a variety of herbs (and spices) in their formula preparations. These include facials and creams, hair rinses and shampoos, salves and lip balms, and many more applications. The perfume industries would be lost without these ingredients and fixatives. Some of the cosmetic products might overlap with medicinal uses, but a distinction is usually made between the marketing aspects.

4. Florals: The dried flower markets have always been part of the herb and spice markets. Such things as Baby's Breath and Mosses are quite important to the florist. Seed-cone and other wildcraft seed also fall into this category of marketing. While this market is more limited than the other three, more people in North America currently earn their living from the market of these crops.

The present problem with these markets is that there are no companies with a supply base large enough to handle even token orders for those diverse markets. In fact, a major blended herb tea company, who actually did more than 12 million dollars in wholesale business last year, was unable to accept new accounts. The newness of the industry in North America has created a significant problem for sources of supply. Only in Europe, the Middle East and Asia, where the herb business is hundreds, even thousands of years old is there the agricultural knowledge and production of many of these key herbs.

Within the framework of the herb and spice markets, there are three distinct forms of wholesale buyer. They are

1. 500 pound minimum buyer: These are usually the regional wholesalers and cooperatives. Each State or Province will have several dozen of this type of wholesale buyer. These would include some of the chain food stores, small manufacturers or local marketers, and most buying clubs and cooperatives. They each may need more than 500 pounds of a given herb or spice over a year period, but are usually not in a position

to inventory larger quantities. The standard method of purchase is from either spot buying (on specials) or on contract, where the farmer/forager ships on monthly or bi-monthly basis.

2. 5,000 pound minimum buyer: These also include regional wholesalers who include processing as part of their services to other manufacturers. Some of the larger manufacturers will use these wholesalers to process their products for interfacing such things as tea bagging machinery. Again, while most of the larger manufacturers and wholesalers use more than 20 to 50 tons of a given product, they most often prefer to buy 5,000 to 10,000 pound quantities on a monthly or bi-monthly basis to stablize their cash-flow and requirements.

3. Import/Export houses: These are the large wholesale houses in each country. They often are oriented toward trade agreements, where they are involved in both the import and export of natural resources. Most of these are in cities with major Ports of entry, where crops are bought by the truckload. A typical wholesale house in this category might buy more than 200 ton of a given crop, although they might also buy smaller quantities when opening new markets.

With these perspectives, the small farmer who grows herbs and spices has a number of alternative markets from which to choose. Regardless of the marketing method available to the small farmer, other factors determine which alternatives a producer can actually use. Marketing is the critical factor, particularly to those having limitations upon land, capital and management. Farmers with these kinds of limitations are operating with large risks. An adequate job of marketing can help reduce and/or eliminate those risks.

Foraging is altogether another matter. It is very well-suited for those with limited resources and incomes. And, because many of the markets for foraged crops are the same as those farmed, it is a perfect way to underwrite a farm venture while establishing a relationship with your buyers.

The Herb Market Report
1305 Vista Drive • Grants Pass, OR 97527

The Herb Market Report is a newsletter published monthly and distributed by The Southern Oregon Herb Gatherers' Association, Inc.

Oak Publishing
1212 SW 5th Street,
Grants Pass, OR 97526
Phone: 541-426-5588

(INTRODUCTORY FIRST ISSUE)

THE HERB MARKET REPORT

for the herb farmer and forager   Vol. 1 No. 2 Mar. 1985

Catnip Herb as a Prime Mint Example

With 3,500 species, the mints represent roughly 1.5% of the flowering plant kingdom. When you look at a list of herbs, condiments and spices, you will find that close to 25% of the listed species are mints. Those current-ly imported into North America in significant tonnages include anise-hyssop, apple-mint, lemon balm, bergamont, catnip, clary sage, horehound, hyssop, lavender, marjoram, oregano, rosemary, white sage, savory and thyme.

I think you get the idea! The potential for "making a mint" in mint farming is great. The farming of catnip for commercial markets was chosen as representative of how most mint crops might be cultivated and harvested for the herb and spice trade. As an alternative crop for the small farmer, it is ideal. It also demonstrates the opportunities available in herb and spice farming.

Before the use of tea from China, English peasants were in the habit of brewing catnip as a stimulant. The leaves and young shoots are still used in France as a seasoning, and is regularly grown for that purpose. Tradi-tional uses for catnip include chewing the leaves to alleviate toothaches. It has been used by inhabitants of the Southern Appalachian regions as a cold remedy since the eighteenth century. Catnip oil, obtained from steam distillation, is used in small quantities as a scent in trapping bobcats and mountainlions even today.

The flowering tops of catnip yield up to 1.0% volatile oil, 78% being nepetalactone (the main attractant to cats). Also present in this oil are citronellal, geraniol, citral, carvacrol and pulegone – all excellent na-tural insecticides. Thymol, principly extracted from thyme, is also extrac-ted from catnip as a fungicide. Thymol has beneficial antiseptic uses on the skin and in the nasal and pharyngeal passages. It can be found in most antiseptic solutions and aromatic sprays. Menthol, an alcohol found in most mints, can be prepared synthetically by the hydrogenation of thymol.

The Farming of Catnip for Commercial Markets

Catnip may be propagated from seed or root division. The seed (3,500 per ounce) should drilled in rows late in the fall and covered lightly. Early spring seed should be germinated before sowing. This is done by soak-the seed in water for 24 hours to soften the casing, mixing in equal amounts

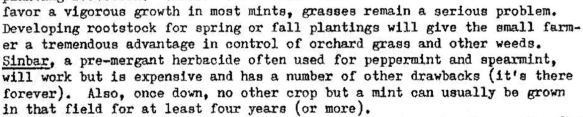

of sand, and then storing the mixture in the
refrigerator for 10 days. The seed is much
too small to drill with normal grain drills,
so a spinner-type broadcaster can be used.
The seed should then be covered immediately
with 1/4 inches of dirt and rolled with a
cultipacktor or roller. The recommended
amount of seed is 10 pounds per acre.

Catnip needs liberal amounts of calcium,
phosphorus and potassium. Manuring at the
rate of 6 to 12 ton per acre is not uncommon,
although manure is low in phosphorus. Sour
soils need to be balanced with lime and brought
to a pH of 6.5. If the soil is boron-deficient,
borax should be added at the rate of 20 to 40
pounds per acre. N.B. borax can damage seed
and should only be applied as a top dressing
on established fields or worked into the soil
at least one week before seeding. All of this
soil preparation, needless to say, must be done
on the basis of adequate soil testing and well
before planting.

Usually sowing is not as satisfactory as
planting rootstock. Shallow cultivation will
favor a vigorous growth in most mints, grasses remain a serious problem.
Developing rootstock for spring or fall plantings will give the small farmer a tremendous advantage in control of orchard grass and other weeds.
Sinbar, a pre-mergant herbacide often used for peppermint and spearmint,
will work but is expensive and has a number of other drawbacks (it's there
forever). Also, once down, no other crop but a mint can usually be grown
in that field for at least four years (or more).

Initial rootstock must be developed either by transplanting self-sown
seedlings or by nursery cultivation. After the third year, a few fleshy,
thick-rooted catnip plants sprout several shoots from the top of their roots.
Propagation can be carried out by slicing these roots in pieces, so that
each has some of the fleshy root and a bud. These pieces are then buried
just below the surface of the soil (like strawberries) and kept well watered.

The best time to propagate by this method is in the spring, as soon as
new growth starts. Seedlings from nursery stock can be planted in the fall,
to give it a jump over weed growth. If leaf growth has become heavy, remove most of it before replanting, leaving only a small center leaf. Row
cropping these new plants seems to give the best control of grasses through
cultivation. Only after the rootstock has had three years of growth can the
field be converted from rows into a general field crop.

Many mints which do well in full sun can also be grown in partial
shade. Most will survive well in situations where they get only 4 to 6

TABLE 1 — Estimated Production Costs for Catnip During Establishment Year, Side-Roll Irrigation, (A).

SCHEDULE OF OPERATIONS AND SELECTED COSTS/ACRE   CATNIP HERB

OPERATION	TOOLING	MONTH	MACH. HOURS	LABOR HOURS	MACH. FIXED COST	VARIABLE COSTS FUEL,OIL LUBE, REPAIRS ($)	LABOR ($)	SERVICE ($)	MATERIAL ($)	TOTALS ($)	TOTAL COST ($)
Irrigation (10x)	Sideroll Irr.,20ac.in.	Apr-Oct	0.0	2.95	51.80	22.80	17.70	30.00	0.0	70.50	122.30
Disc(2x)	120hp,12' Offset Disc	Nov	1.00	1.25	17.99	14.66	7.50	0.0	0.0	22.16	40.15
Plow	135hp,4-Btm Plow	Nov	0.50	0.63	8.94	8.37	3.75	0.0	0.0	12.12	21.06
Fertilize	Custom Fert. App.	Mar	0.0	0.0	0.0	0.0	0.0	4.50	47.90	52.40	52.40
Roll-Harrow(2x)	120hp,12' Roller-Harrow	Mar	1.00	1.25	16.10	14.47	7.50	0.0	0.0	21.97	38.07
Float	120hp,12' Float	Mar	0.50	0.62	6.93	7.07	3.75	0.0	0.0	10.82	17.75
Plant	Custom Plant	Mar	0.0	0.0	0.0	0.0	0.0	100.00	150.00	250.00	250.00
Rotary Hoe	60hp,10' Rotary Hoe	Mar	0.35	0.44	12.34	2.53	2.63	0.0	0.0	5.16	17.50
Harrow(2x)	60hp,15' Drag Harrow	Apr	0.70	0.87	23.40	4.86	5.25	0.0	0.0	10.11	33.51
Apply Herb.	120hp,27' Sprayer	Apr	0.06	0.08	0.77	0.94	0.47	0.0	27.38	28.79	29.56
Rotary Hoe(2x)	60hp,10' Rotary Hoe	May	0.70	0.88	24.66	5.07	5.25	0.0	0.0	10.32	35.00
Fertilize	Custom Aerial	June	0.20	0.25	1.69	2.75	1.50	7.50	32.00	43.75	45.44
Harvest & Proc.	Custom Harv.&Proc.	Sept	0.0	0.0	0.0	0.0	0.0	60.00	0.0	60.00	60.00
Residue Disp.	Custom Disposal	Sept	0.0	0.0	0.0	0.0	0.0	10.00	0.0	10.00	10.00
Misc Use	3/4 Ton Pickup		1.00	1.25	5.87	7.50	0.0	0.0	0.0	15.98	21.85
TOTAL COST/ACRE			6.01	10.47	170.51	92.02	55.30	212.00	257.28	624.08	794.59

TABLE 2 — Estimated Production Costs for Catnip During Establishment Year, Side-Roll Irrigation, (B).

	Unit	Cost/Unit	Quantity	Cost
VARIABLE COSTS				
Preharvest				
Custom Fert.	Acre	4.50	1.00	4.50
Nitrogen	Lbs.	0.32	200.00	64.00
Phosphate	Lbs.	0.33	30.00	9.99
Zinc	Lbs.	1.20	5.00	6.00
Custom Planting	Acre	100.00	1.00	100.00
Catnip Plants	Lbs.	150.00	1.00	150.00
Sinbar	Acre	18.25	1.50	27.36
Custom Aerial	Acre	7.50	1.00	7.50
Irrig. Charge	Dol.	30.00	1.00	30.00
Overhead Cost	Acre	0.05	780.12	39.01
Machinery	Acre	10.88	1.00	10.88
Tractors	Acre	58.33	1.00	58.33
Irrig. Machinery	Acre	22.80	1.00	22.80
Labor (Tractor & Machinery)	Hour	6.00	7.52	45.09
Labor (Irrig.)	Hour	6.00	2.95	17.70
Interest on Op. Cap.	Dol.	0.14	266.32	57.28
Subtotal, Preharvest				$ 630.37
Harvest				
Custom Harvest & Proc.	Acre	60.00	1.00	60.00
Custom Residue Disposal	Acre	10.00	1.00	10.00
Subtotal, Harvest				$ 70.00
Total Variable Cost				$ 700.37
FIXED COSTS				
Machinery	Acre	33.94	1.00	33.94
Tractors	Acre	84.77	1.00	84.77
Irrigation Machinery	Acre	51.80	1.00	51.80
Taxes (Land)	Acre	22.00	1.00	22.00
Land (Net Rent)	Acre	100.00	1.00	100.00
Total Fixed Cost				$ 292.52
TOTAL COSTS				$ 992.89

hours of full midday sun. The higher the clay content of the soil the more likely the mint will suffer from waterlogging or disease during excessively wet seasons. As a rule, the brighter and drier the habitat, the higher the oil-content of mints. Disease can wipe out mint monocultures, especially in heavy soils. With high profits available to the small farmer, he can afford to rotate his rootstock often enough to avoid most of these proble___.

Most mints prefer a 6 to 10 day irrigation schedule. This means that the crop receives 12 hours of irrigation water (usually from side-roll systems) every 6 to 10 days. Catnip prefers a slightly drier set of about 10 days, while such mints as lemon balm prefer 6 days. It is recommended that your water lines be moved every 12 hours with most mints. Irrigation should be discontinued at least 10 days before harvest. This allows the oils to move further up into the plant, while making the stem easier to dry at a more uniform rate with the leaf.

The flowering tops are harvested when the plants are in full bloom. The climate of most areas allow two cuttings a year, once in July and again in September. When grown on a commercial scale, catnip may be cut with a side-bar cutter mower, set at a height of 10 inches. After one day of cutting, the crop needs to be turned into a windrow. This raking is usually done with a side-throw delivery rake, in the same direction that the field was cut. To prevent leaf-shatter, subsequent rakings or teddings to fluff the crop (for more uniform drying) should be kept at a minimum. If catnip is cut with a rotary mower, with a good condition on the stem, it only requires two turns.

Gathering catnip, when the stem contains less than 15% moisture, can be done with a standard baler. Suitable dryness is easily determined when the crop is dry to the touch, and the stem "cracks" when bent. Most farmers leave the bales in the field approximately three days to further dry the stem, turning them in the field each day. If the herbage is to be used for oil distillation, it may be dried to only 60% moisture (usually 2 days of sun-cure) and then taken directly to the distillery via a flail-chopper/piggy-back system of wagons.

Yields of up to 3 ton per acre can be expected from good, irrigated fields after the third year of production. Each cut usually produces about 1.5 ton dry-weight yields in bale-form. Crude catnip, when sold in baled form, begins marketing at $800 per ton ($0.40 per pound). With processing into a cut-and-sift (C/S) form, high quality catnip begins marketing at $0.85 per pound ($1,700 per ton). With further processing, catnip powders (80 mesh U.S.S.) can sell for $1.20 per pound, with 100-pound quantities of C/S selling for $1.80 per pound. For the same farm costs growing hay, a small farmer can realize a minimum of over $2,000 per acre gross incomes.

Most medium regional wholesalers use about 2,000 pounds annually in a C/S, with a gross national market somewhere around 800 tons. Most of this is imported now from Germany. These consumption figures do not account for oil markets and their futures. Both markets will expand with availability. As an example, when one considers the fact that the oils in lemon balm are

TABLE 3   Estimated Production Costs for Catnip, Side-Roll Irrigation. (A).

SCHEDULE OF OPERATIONS AND SELECTED COSTS/ACRE   CATNIP HERB

OPERATION	TOOLING	MONTH	MACH. HOURS	LABOR HOURS	MACH. FIXED COST	VARIABLE COSTS FUEL,OIL LUBE,REPAIRS	LABOR	SERVICE	MATERIAL	TOTALS	TOTAL COSTS
					$	$	$	$	$	$	$
Irrigation (12x)	Sideroll Irr.,24mo.in.	Apr-Oct	0.0	3.50	52.08	23.52	21.00	30.00	0.0	74.52	126.60
Apply Herb.	Custom Spraying	Nov	0.0	0.0	0.0	0.0	0.0	5.25	27.38	32.63	32.63
Fertilize	Custom Fert. App.	Mar	0.0	0.0	0.0	0.0	0.0	4.50	82.70	87.20	87.20
Weeding	Hand Weeding	Apr	0.0	0.0	3.70	0.0	16.28	0.0	0.0	16.28	19.98
Apply Herb.	120hp,27'Sprayer	Apr	0.06	0.08	0.77	0.94	0.47	0.0	15.00	16.41	17.18
Apply Insect.*	Custom Aerial	May	0.0	0.0	0.0	0.0	0.0	2.50	7.00	9.50	9.50
Harvest & Proc.	Custom Harv.& Proc.	July	0.0	0.0	0.0	0.0	0.0	60.00	0.0	60.00	60.00
Fertilize	Custom Fert. App.	July	0.0	0.0	0.0	0.0	0.0	4.50	43.75	48.25	48.25
Harvest & Proc.	Custom Harv.& Proc.	Sept	0.0	0.0	0.0	0.0	0.0	60.00	0.0	60.00	60.00
Residue Disp.	Custom Disposal	Oct	0.0	0.0	0.0	0.0	0.0	20.00	0.0	20.00	20.00
Misc Use	3/4 Ton Pickup		1.0	1.25	5.87	8.48	7.50	0.0	0.0	15.98	21.85
TOTAL COST/ACRE			1.06	4.83	62.42	32.94	45.25	186.75	175.83	440.77	503.19

* Insecticide applied once every three years

TABLE 4   Estimated Production Costs for Catnip, Side-Roll Irrigation. (B).

	Unit	Cost/Unit	Quantity	Cost
VARIABLE COSTS				
Preharvest				
Custom Spraying	Acre	5.25	1.00	5.25
Simbar	Lbs.	18.25	1.50	27.38
Custom Fert.	Acre	4.50	2.00	9.00
Nitrogen	Lbs.	0.32	200.00	64.00
Phosphate	Lbs.	0.33	30.00	9.90
Zinc	Lbs.	1.20	5.00	6.00
Sulfer	Lbs.	0.07	40.00	2.80
Hand Hoeing	Hr.	4.40	3.70	16.28
Herbicide	Acre	15.00	1.00	15.00
Custom Aerial*	Acre	2.50	1.00	2.50
Insecticide*	Acre	7.00	1.00	7.00
Overhead Cost	Dol.	0.05	729.50	36.47
Urea	Lbs.	0.35	125.00	43.75
Irrig. Charge	Acre	30.00	1.00	30.00
Machinery	Acre	8.57	1.00	8.57
Tractors	Acre	0.86	1.00	0.86
Irrigation Machinery	Acre	23.52	1.00	23.52
Labor (Tractor & Machinery)	Hour	6.00	1.33	7.97
Labor (Irrigation)	Hour	6.00	3.50	21.00
Interest on Op. Cap.	Dol.	0.14	135.79	18.73
Subtotal, Preharvest				$ 355.98
Harvest				
Custom Harvest & Proc.	Acre	60.00	1.00	60.00
Custom Residue Disposal	Acre	10.00	2.00	40.00
Subtotal, Harvest				$ 100.00
Total Variable Cost				$ 455.98
FIXED COSTS				
Machinery	Acre	6.10	1.00	6.10
Tractors	Acre	0.53	1.00	0.53
Irrigation Machinery	Acre	52.08	1.00	52.08
Taxes (Land)	Acre	22.00	1.00	22.00
Prorated Estab. Cost	Acre	589.14	0.33	194.00
Land (Net Rent)	Acre	100.00	1.00	100.00
Total Fixed Cost				$ 374.71
TOTAL COSTS				$ 830.69

* Insecticide applied once every three years

TABLE 5

Summary of Receipts, Costs, and Returns to Land and Management for Catnip Herb, with Side-Roll Irrigation.

	Unit	Cost/Unit	Quantity	Cost
GROSS RECEIPTS FROM PRODUCTION				
Catnip Herb (July)	Lbs.	0.65	3,000	$ 1,950.00
Catnip Herb (Sept)	Lbs.	0.65	3,000	1,950.00
1. Total Receipts				$ 3,900.00
Less: Total Variable Cost				$ 455.98
2. Returns Over Variable Cost				$ 3,444.02
Less: Machinery Fixed Cost				$ 62.42
Prorated Estab. Cost				$ 294.00
Real Estate Taxes				$ 22.00
3. Returns to Land and Management				$ 3,065.60

TABLE 6

Hourly Cost Summaries for Implements and Power Units, (approximate).

Machine	Hours of Annual Use	Purchase Price	Depreciation per Hour	Interest per Hour	Insurance per Hour	Taxes per Hour	Total Fixed Cost per Hour	Repair Cost per Hour	Fuel Cost per Hour
Wheel Tractor, 120 HP	800	41,623	3.252	4.553	0.195	0.468	8.468	3.64	8.80
Wheel Tractor, 135 HP	800	46,638	3.644	5.101	0.219	0.525	9.488	4.08	11.00
Wheel Tractor, 60 HP	100	19,885	12.428	17.400	0.746	1.790	32.363	0.50	5.50
Pickup, 3/4 Ton	300	8,500	3.015	2.489	0.107	0.255	5.866	1.01	6.50
V Ditcher	50	2,400	2.893	3.683	0.158	0.432	7.165	1.62	0.
Slicker Ditcher, 12 ft.	300	1,200	0.539	0.371	0.016	0.036	0.963	0.28	0.0
Offset Disc, 12 ft.	150	6,900	4.895	4.041	0.173	0.414	9.524	0.90	0.0
Plow, 4 BTM	150	5,593	5.327	2.610	0.112	0.336	8.384	0.0	0.0
Roller-Harrow, 12 ft.	150	5,433	4.137	3.044	0.130	0.326	7.637	0.71	0.0
Float, 12 ft.	75	2,715	2.275	2.679	0.115	0.326	5.395	0.37	0.0
Rotary Hoe, 10 ft.	150	2,100	1.490	1.230	0.053	0.126	2.898	0.42	0.0
Drag Harrow, 15 ft.	100	716	0.450	0.530	0.023	0.064	1.067	0.12	0.0
PTO Sprayer	250	4,600	1.958	1.617	0.069	0.166	3.809	1.34	0.0
Corrugator, 4 Row	200	4,500	2.394	1.977	0.085	0.202	4.658	1.13	0.0

Note: TABLES have been adapted from the work of Herbert R. Hinman (Extension Economist, Cooperative Extension, Washington State University, Pullman) and James H. Griffin (Extension Area Agent, Yakima County) on Spearmint in Washington State.

similar to those in lemon grass (a major imported tea flavoring), the actual potential in any of these mints becomes significant.

The ratio of mint oils imported into the United States and Canada each year is more than ten times their export, with literally millions of dollars ~ving these countries on crops easily grown domestically. The dried leaf ~oducts are even higher, as these different mint-spices are used in almost every form of manufacturing. These marketing perspectives only touch the "tip of the iceberg." With a better understanding of the contents or physical chemistry of each plant, marketing becomes wide open for the small farmer.

The tables used in this article present a series of schedules or operations and costs per acre which need to be compiled before beginning any small farm agricultural venture. They are critical to the success (or failure) of any project in farming. Even the alfalfa farmer would have these costs squarely in front of him, or should, to remain in business. While they are only representative for a 40 acre field of catnip, they can be used as a model for any number of other herbs or spices.

The Cottage Industry: Frozen Pesto

Most of us now realize that the Italian foods require a fresh basil, rather than one which has been dehydrated and powdered. There is no comparison in flavor when using a fresh basil from the garden in preparing pasta dishes. Most of the more exclusive Italian restaurants have a big problem during winter months, when fresh basil is only available from indoor-grown facilities. Not only are these crops ou^te expensive, they seem to lack the oils ..d in those grown in a field. The question is how to package basil so that it retains its important flavoring for winter use. The solution to this question could be a major cottage industry for most all rural communities near large cities.

One suggestion offered is the manufacture of pesto, a combination of basil with other spices and oil. This preparation can be frozen, and has almost the same flavoring as a fresh basil when mixed with pastas. It can be packaged in either a 12-oz (net) plastic or cardboard container and frozen for storage. Most major supermarket chains are equiped to warehouse this as a frozen product, and would welcome it over the currently prepared canned spinach, also now marketed as pesto.

The following recipe comes from an excellent Italian homemaker, Margaret Sansone (Beavercreek, OR). She has successfully frozen this product, and the best culinary experts can not tell the difference between this frozen product and one made from garden-fresh produce:

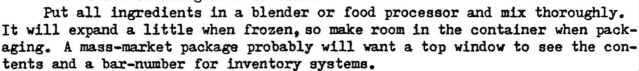

> 2 cups fresh basil leaves
> 1 cup fresh parsley (Italian)
> 1/2 cup pine nuts or walnuts
> 1/2 cup parmesan or romano cheese
> 1.2 - 2.3 cup olive oil
> 2 cloves and garlic sections

Put all ingredients in a blender or food processor and mix thoroughly. It will expand a little when frozen, so make room in the container when packaging. A mass-market package probably will want a top window to see the contents and a bar-number for inventory systems.

THE POTENTIAL OF HERBS AS A CASH-CROP by Richard Alan Miller will be available next month in both paperback and hardback. Copies can be ordered directly from Acres, U.S.A., P.O.Box 9547, Kansas City, MO   64133.

The Herb Market Report
1305 Vista Drive • Grants Pass, OR 97527

The Herb Market Report is a newsletter published monthly and distributed by The Southern Oregon Herb Gatherers' Association, Inc.

Oak Publishing
1212 SW 5th Street,
Grants Pass, OR 97526
Phone: 541-426-5588

Copyright 1986-2013 © Dr. Richard Alan Miller

Address Correction Requested

BULK RATE
U.S. Postage Paid
Grants Pass, OR
Permit No. 66

"Subscribe."

THE HERB MARKET REPORT

for the herb farmer and forager   Vol. 1 No. 3   Apr. 1985

The Forage of Cascara Segrada Bark

Cascara segrada (Rhammus purshiana) is a tree from the West Coast whose bark is commercially important. It was chosen as a forage example as representative on how buying stations are formed for other local forest products in different regions of the country.

Also known as shittam and buckthorn, cascara is a deciduous perennial tree growing from 15 to 30 feet in height. It grows in Oregon, Washington, California, Idaho, Montana, Colorado, and Arizona. Cascara prefers canyon walls, rich bottomlands, mountain ridges, usually in with conifers.

It is most easily recognized by its distinctive leaf, appearing oval and ridged. The leaves are 2 to 6 inches long, and 1 to 3 inches wide. The flowers have short stems with small greenish-yellow petals. The fruit is globular, black, and approximately one-quarter inch across.

Cascara is consider the most widely used cathartic in the world. An unknown Spanish priest found the Indians using it and was so impressed with its mildness and efficacy that he called it by its Spanish name meaning "sacred bark." Its Eurasian relative Rhammus catartica was used even before the Norman Conquest.

It was incorporated into western medicine from traditional Indian use at about the time wild cherry, slippery elm, and sassafras also became wildly used. It was first marketed in the United States by the Park, Davis & Co. in 1877. Its current markets are very well established, primarily in Europe.

The primary active ingredients are anthracenes (6-9% antraquinone glycosides),

based on emodins (similar to aloin) including barbaloin and deoxybarbaloin, emodin, oxanthrone, aloe-emodin, and chrysophanol. The bark contains a glucoside which yields crysophanic acid on hydrolysis. It also contains cascarosides known as cascarin and purshianin.

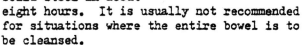

The anthraquinone glycosides are strong stimulant cathartics. The action is due primarily to increased perisalsis of the colon, although large doses may affect the upper bowels in the same manner. Cascara induces a solid or semi-solid stool in about eight hours. It is usually not recommended for situations where the entire bowel is to be cleansed.

Excessive amounts may produce extensive diarrhea, accompanied by nausea and vomiting. Sever cramping may also be present. Emodin can cause dermatitis. The chronic diarrhea us due to excessive losses of potassium.

Collection of the bark is made during the summer beginning at the end of May and continuing until the rain ends in the region. Hotter weather draws the sap from the bark and forces it into the inner tree. It is properly harvest by first cutting the tree down so that a new tree will grow from its roots. If the tree is left standing and the bark is stripped from some part of the tree, it will die and no new tree will grow.

We would like to encourage informative events, articles, and other resources. We will share these via the newsletter and our computer database. Your participation will help us both grow toward the viability of alternative small-farm agriculture.

Article submissions are most welcome, as well. They should range from 200-800 words and be double-spaced (typed). Technical information on cultivation is always appreciated, as well as marketing alternatives. Again, thank you for your help.

Once the tree is down, the bark is easily stripped by making longitudinal incisions and peeling off sections which tend to roll into large "quills." The bark is then laid out on tarps in the sun to dry, being turned every day. The inner bark is protected from the sun by the curving of the bark inward. This "red" color is what determines the market-quality. The bark is then chipped into one inch pieces and packed into 20 to 80 pound burlap sacks for shipping.

Since the tree is part of the Buckthorn family, it grows from rootstock. This means that if the tree is semi-harvested, it will "bleed" to death. By chopping the entire tree down, the rootstock will send up further shoots which eventually make the tree larger (several trees now exist where there was once only one).

Commercial cultivation of cascara segrada is under way in Oregon, Washington and British Columbia. However, there remains abundant supplies of naturally growing trees which exceed even future export demands. It is easily grown from seedlings within its natural range.

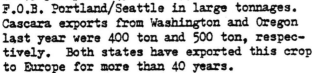

Current suppliers such as Pacific Coast Cascara Bark Co., I.P. Callisons, and Penik Corp (aka Western Crud) sell a chipped bark, packaged in burlap sacks at $0.54 per pound (current year-new) and $0.75 per pound (year-old), F.O.B. Portland/Seattle in large tonnages. Cascara exports from Washington and Oregon last year were 400 ton and 500 ton, respectively. Both states have exported this crop to Europe for more than 40 years.

The average forager of cascara bark can usually peel more than 300 pounds in one day, presuming availability of trees which are close to each other. The key is to locate a good stand along the coastline. Most Forest Services and Railroad lands are available and well-documented, with free brush permits for this crop. Sometimes a timber company might cut the tree when clearing land for a logging venture.

Green bark (wet) is usually sold to collection sites at $0.12 to $0.20 per pound. The bark is then dried and chipped further and sold to collection trucks from the various "buying stations" from $0.35 to $0.48 in burlap sacks. The weight-loss when dry-ing green bark is less than 45%. Watch for mosses and other foreign material.

Most retailers which would like to sell powders, or the larger pharmaceutical houses which want to extract the oils for those markets both prefer to buy year-old bark. Price variations depend on the season, but range from $0.85 per pound in tonnage to more than $1.75 per pound in 100-pound quantities. During the early spring, before the cascara has begun to be harvested, prices for year-old bark (in tonnage) can rise considerably. This year it was up to $1.40 per pound.

While the total global use in 1984 was about 1,000 ton, the world markets could be expanded to more than 2,000 ton. There are shortages now, and a number of states (like Idaho) could consider this a minor cash-crop. Structurally, a cooperative could collect bark from several parts of a state, marketing the product as a wholesale middleman. For those too small for inventory/credit situations, the cooperative could offer a cash-on-the-spot basis, similar to a buying station for some large agri-business.

Larger quantities could be handled even without good weather, where tarp/sun-cure methods have been used. Green bark can be chipped first and then dried via a corn dryer or similar continuous-feed dryer system. Propane heat sources are the cleanest and cheapest. The barks can be dried at slightly higher temperatures, ranging up to 140°F.. A loading hopper and bagging scale works the best for filling sacks, especially if a commercial sewing machine is available to stitch the bag (with a lable). Polypropylene is a prefered sack when working in large quantities.

A Note from the Editor

The response to our work in the forage of non-timber forest-floor crops and other noxious weeds in Southern Oregon has been overwhelming. As a result, a number of 2-day intensive workshops are now being offered. The emphasis is toward marketing. Dates now scheduled are

April 13th (one-day), Gold Beach, OR. Contact Marge Johnson (503) 347-9389.

April 20/21st (2-day), Portland, OR. Contact Monti McHone (503) 760-2996.

June 22/23rd (2-day), Portland, OR. Contact Scott Browder at The Western Forestry Center (503) 228-1367. Field-hikes/Camp.

THE POTENTIAL OF HERBS AS A CASH-CROP, by Richard Alan Miller will be available next month. Write Acres, U.S.A., P.O.Box 9547, Kansas City, MO 64133 for pre-publication price and tapes of previous workshops.

Organization for the Advancement of Knowledge

LECTURES, WRITING, RESEARCH

The following questionnaire has been developed to assist in the formation of local networks. It will answer such questions as "What crops grow best on my land?" and "What weeds are commercially important from my region?"

Your participation is critical as a starting point, or beginning. <u>Please type or print this form</u>, and return it to our O.A.K. address. It will help us produce a better and more useful newsletter, as well. Thanks for your help.

Name: _____   Telephone: ( ) _____

Address: _____

_____   County: _____

Acreage: _____

Soil Types: _____

Soil Descriptions: _____

_____

Past Crops (10 years): _____

_____

Water Availability: _____

Growing Season: _____

High/Low Temperatures: _____   Rainfall: _____

Local Commercial Crops: _____

_____

Local Native and Introduced Wild Herbs: _____

_____

_____ (include Latin)

Available Farm Machinery: _____

_____

_____

(Please Print or Type)

Farm/Forage Experience: _____

_____

_____

Are you   a) _____   already in the herb/spice business?

          b) _____   interested in starting an herb/spice business?

          c) _____   other? _____

What kind of herb/spice business are you presently engaged? (check all applicable)

_____ Gardener   _____ Farmer   _____ Fresh cut   _____ Manufacturer

_____ Retail   _____ Wholesale   _____ Writer/Lecturer

_____ Mail Order   _____ Shop Owner   _____ Forager   _____ Other

_____

_____ (brief overview)

Where do you want to be with herbs/spices in 5 years? _____

_____

_____

What other resources do you have which might help establish a local network? _____

_____

_____

What other kinds of resource information would be helpful to your business? _____

_____

_____

_____

We would like to encourage informative events, articles, and other resources. We will share these via the newsletter and our computer database. Your participation will help us both grow toward the viability of alternative small-farm agriculture.

Article submissions are most welcome, as well. They should range from 200-800 words and be double-spaced (typed). Technical information on cultivation is always appreciated, as well as marketing alternatives. Again, thank you for your help.

Organization for the Advancement of Knowledge

LECTURES. WRITING. RESEARCH

The following questionnaire has been developed to assist in the formation of local networks. It will answer such questions as "What crops grow best on my land?" and "What weeds are commercially important from my region?"

Your participation is critical as a starting point, or beginning. <u>Please type or print this form</u>, and return it to our O.A.K. address. It will help us produce a better and more useful newsletter, as well. Thanks for your help.

Name: _____   Telephone: ( ) _____

Address: _____

_____   County: _____

Acreage: _____

Soil Types: _____

Soil Descriptions: _____

_____

Past Crops (10 years): _____

_____

Water Availability: _____

Growing Season: _____

High/Low Temperatures: _____   Rainfall: _____

Local Commercial Crops: _____

_____

Local Native and Introduced Wild Herbs: _____

_____

(include Latin)

Available Farm Machinery: _____

_____

_____

The Cottage Industry: Everlasting Flowers

Everlasting flowers are those varieties of flowers which hold their shape and color when dried. Their primary market is to the wholesale and retail florist. The actual market is quite large, and more extensive than most might realize. Last year, for example, one rural county in Eastern Washington actually exported more than 400 ton of Baby's Breath as a foraged crop. This amounted to more than 600 partial summer jobs for that rural community. Most of those involved in the actual forage and marketing were not even from that county, representing tremendous losses in revenues for that community.

The list of diverse products which could be marketed in this area is rapidly expanding. Not only can individuals market directly to local wholesalers and retail stores, export opportunities continue to expand as well. As a cottage industry, the potentials for supplimenting rural incomes are excellent. Not only can these various products be sold in bulk, but manufactured "arrangements" offer even greater profits for the small farmer who wishes to deal with smaller quantities in marketing.

The book PODS, WILDFLOWERS AND WEEDS IN THEIR FINAL BEAUTY by Jane Embertson is an excellent guide for beginning a venture in this form of cottage industries. It is a visual guide to more than 150 species of wildflower pods and weed pods, with 450 full-color photographs that show the flower in bloom, its pod, and a dried arrangement. It is a guide to help identify the pods in the wild, when to pick them, and how to use them creatively. The book retails for $13.95 and is available from Charles Scribner's Sons in New York.

Yellow dock flower-stalks are a typical example. While most forager harvest the root in early fall with the first rains, the flower-stalk could be harvested more than two months earlier, with prices ranging about $1.20 for bundles of 12. It can be fixed with glycerin for better storage and higher incomes.

The Herb Market Report

1305 Vista Drive • Grants Pass, OR 97527

The Herb Market Report is a newsletter published monthly and distributed by The Southern Oregon Herb Gatherers' Association, Inc.

Oak Publishing
1212 SW 5th Street,
Grants Pass, OR 97526
Phone: 541-426-5588

Address Correction Requested

Vol. 1 No. 3

THE HERB MARKET REPORT

for the herb farmer and forager   Vol. 1 No. 4 May, 1985

Licorice Root, An Alternative "Sugar" Crop

Licorice (<u>Glycyrrhiza glabra</u> L.) is a temperate-zone perennial herb which is grown for the roots. It is native from southern Europe to Pakistan and northern India. It has a long history of cultivation in England, Belgium, France, Germany, Spain, Italy, Greece, Turkey, Russia, Egypt, Syria, Iraq and in recent years, China and northern India. It has been grown in the United States only as experimental, not commercially.

The rootstock is long, cylindrical, branched, flexible, and burrowing, with horizontal, creeping, underground stems (also known as stolons). It is these stolons which are harvested, sometimes reaching lengths of 5 to 6 feet. They have buds on them which send up stems in the second year. The above-ground foliage grows like a shrub with heights of 3 to 7 feet.

The leaf is alternate, pinnate, with 9 to 17 ovate, yellow-green leafets, one to 2 inches long and viscid on the underside. The flowers are pea-like in erect, axillary, long-stalked spikes and are lavender to purple. Seedpods are maroon and about one inch in length, oblong, pointed, flattened, and contain 2 to 4 kidney-shaped seeds.

Spanish Licorice (<u>G. glabra</u> var. <u>typica</u>) has smooth seedpods. Its rootstock and stolons are 1/4 to 3/4 inches thick, dark-maroon in color, longitudinally wrinkled and sweeter than other types of licorice. Russian Licorice (<u>G. glabra</u> var. <u>glandulifera</u>) is a viscid-hairy plant with spiny seedpods. It has no stolon but multiple, spindle-shaped roots, 2 inches wide, with purplish, scaly bark, which is somewhat bitter and more or less acrid. Persian Licorice (<u>G. glabra</u> var. <u>violacea</u>) has very thick roots, averaging over 3 inches thick.

The plant may be grown from seed, but the usual method is by division of the crown or by root cuttings. The settings in a prepared field (pre-fertilized) is 2 feet apart, with 3 to 4 feet between rows. The plant in the natural state is found in deep, moist soil, as on river banks subject to flooding, but where the late summer is hot and dry. When cultivated, irrigation is necessary from the very beginning of planting. After establishment, however, the crop requires little other attention apart from weed control.

Growth is slow during the first two years. The Glycyrrhizin content (the main chemistry of importance) increases as the plant develops and does not vary with the season. When the plants are three to four years old and before they have borne fruit, they should be taken up in the autumn and the tops cut off and set aside for compost (being high in nitrogen). Remnants of roots in the soil generate a new crop which can be augmented by the planting of roots cuttings.

The harvested roots and runners are cut into sections. The roots of the Russian type and some of the other are peeled at this point before shade drying. In overseas productions, this may take four to six months, reducing moisture contents from 50 to 10% The average yield of roots and runners is 4 to 5 ton per acre.

The chief property of licorice is the saponin-like glycoside glycyrrhizin (glycyrrhizic acid), $C_{42}H_{62}O_{16}$. This occurs in amounts varying from 5 to 20%. Spanish Licorice averages 6 to 8%, Russian Licorice averages 10 to 14%. Glycyrrhizin is fifty times sweeter than sucrose, but the addition of one pound glycyrrhizin will double the sweetness of 100 lbs. of sugar.

Licorice also contains 20% starch, 3.8% glucose, 2.4 to 6.5% sucrose, 2 to 4% asparagine, 0.8% fat, resins, mannitol, and bitter agents. Other properties reported are the coumarin derivatives herniarin and umbelliferone, and the flavonones liquiritin, liquiritigen, isoliquiritin and isoliquiritigenin (responsible for the yellow coloring), and the glycosides liquiritoside and isoliquiritoside. These two are credited with licorice's anti-ulcer activity.

Extracts of the above-ground parts of the licorice plant have produced estrogenic activity in experimental animals and the phenolic glycestrone has been shown to have about 1/500 the potency of estrone.

Licorice was once rationed to desert troops to prevent extreme thirst with low water intake. Glycyrrhizin increases extracellular fluid and plasma volumes, inducing sodium relation and loss of potassium. Decoctions of the peeled , dried root were also given to relieve coughs, catarrh, bronchitis, sorethroats, laryngitis, urinary irritation and the pain of diarrhea.

Today licorice is used primarily as an extract, made from crushing or shredding the fresh roots, decocting under low steam pressure and evaporation. This forms a dark brown paste which is formed into sticks or rolls for marketing. The glycyrrhizin content of this extract can vary from 1.2 to 24%. Licorice powder is either the pulverized extract or the dried root, ground into a fine powder. If it is brownish-yellow, it is the unpeeled roots, pale-yellow if peeled.

Licorice is a common ingredient in cough sirups and cough drops, primarily for its flavor as well as its demulcent, expectorant and anti-inflammatory properties. It is often added to bitter laxative preparations like cascara segrada bark (newsletter no. 3) to improve the flavor and because it sensitizes the intestines and potentiates the action.

A thick sirup of the powdered extract and water (or commercially prepared N-glycyrrhetinoyl amino acid derivites) may be prescribed in cases of gastric and duodenal ulcers. Though relief is achieved, some patients develope edema and hypertension or cardiac asthma on account of the increased venous and systolic arterial pressure and pulse pressure. Licorice (or glycyrrhetinic acid) may be beneficial in Addison's disease and rheumatoid arthritis, and the treatment of dermatitis. In India, licorice powder is mixed with fat and honey and applied to cuts and wounds.

Dried pieces of licorice root (6 inch) are quite popular as chewsticks in Italy,

Spain and most parts of the West Indies. In the Netherlands these sticks are called "palu dushi" or sweet stick. Large quantities of licorice are employed in chewing gum and confectionery candies. Glycyrrhizin potentiates the flavor of cocoa, replacing 25% of cocoa in manufactured products.

Licorice is increasingly utilized in soft drinks, liqueurs, ice cream, puddings, bakery products, soy sauce and soybean-protein meat substitutes. It is added to beer to enhance the "head" and aroma, and to porter and stout to provide more body and a darker hue. It also is used in mouthwashes, breath "purifiers" and toothpaste, and has even been used for flavoring tobacco.

The pulp residue from the preparation of ammonium glycyrrhizin is extracted with a solution of dilute caustic soda, the product being used as a foam stabilizer in fire extinquishers. The spent pulp is usable as a culture media for food yeasts and mushroom cultivation. It serves as a fertilizer or mulch, and has even been used as composition board and insulation panels.

Last year the United States imported more than 27,000 tons of licorice root and more than 150 tons of licorice extract. The market is also expanding at more than 10% per year. Licorice root entered the country at about $900 per ton in 20-ton quantities, with markets soaring to $1,700 per ton in 1,000 pound quantities, ($0.85 per pound). It is difficult to mill, having a tendency to shred. Because of this, it is either sold as a powder or "square-cut" form of C/S. These prices begin at $1.00 per pound.

If you have an average annual temperature ranging from 43°F. to 66°F. and a well-drained, light sandy soil, licorice might be worth considering as an excellent alternative cash-crop with good market futures.

The Herb Market Review: Selected Imports for 1984

The following tables were taken from "Chemical Marketing Reporter," a bi-weekly newspaper on chemical imports into New York each week. While these tables are incomplete, they do give some perspective on selected crops which might want to be considered.

This is a new section for the newsletter and will be updated each month with import figures from other cities and countries. These statistics are critical for the small farmer making decisions as to what crops to consider for cultivation.

Seed and Spice Imports: December '84

		Dec. 1984 Volume	Nov. 1984 Volume	Yr-to-Date Volume	Dec. 1983 Volume
Anise seed	lb.	103.035	159,503	2,844,629	200,424
Basil	lb.	366,030	357,517	3,875,514	257,856
Caraway seed	lb.	608,527	831,233	11,390,512	460,415
Cardamom	lb.	9,483	18,796	317,670	7,747
Cassia	lb.	2,965,891	2,949,633	281,688,020	1,860,295
Celery seed	lb.	931,247	573,930	1,505,177	---
Cinnamon, unground	lb.	548,206	391,333	9,279,308	197,042
Cloves	lb.	145,661	210,343	5,099,331	139,717
Coriander	lb.	716,572	1,629,963	20,166,760	678,873
Cumin seed	lb.	738,408	939,819	6,307,233	1,701,616
Dill seed	lb.	75,032	205,671	1,126,836	34
Fennel seed	lb.	350,518	481,145	3,685,806	229,315
Ginger root	lb.	1,348,523	860,151	17,467,588	697,212
Laurel leaves, crude	lb.	216,696	33,000	1,912,329	97,994
Mace	lb.	15,755	39,009	1,176,907	17,663
Marjoram, crude	lb.	39,703	156,578	1,277,547	53,200
Mint leaves, crude	lb.	4,584	78,272	1,157,040	22,226
Mustard seed, whole	lb.	5,590,860	8,554,324	16,118,084	8,155,672
Nutmegs, unground	lb.	313,474	605,458	25,454,999	337,276
Origanum, whole	lb.	1,109,511	799,187	14,252,266	609,065
Paprika	lb.	1,882,740	1,159,669	18,312,032	874,871
Pepper, black, unground	lb.	9,238,898	10,356,817	118,030,643	7,264,015
Pepper, red, capiscum	lb.	845,897	595,711	18,000,350	936,474
Pepper, white, unground	lb.	---	995,137	2,022,904	883,879
Pimento, unground	lb.	105,836	285,065	2,729,943	159,617
Rosemary, crude	lb.	42,255	42,759	3,806,169	154,414
Sage unground	lb.	451,778	256,762	3,832,512	470,345
Tarragon, crude	lb.	20,999	17,316	2,079,362	13,694
Thyme, crude	lb.	80,331	156,456	4,779,718	128,750
Turmeric	lb.	92,674	366,502	3,792,600	108,474
Vanilla beans	lb.	126,042	225,793	5,864,336	191,051

Essential Oil Imports: December 1984

		Dec. 1984	Nov. 1984	Yr. to date	Dec. 1983
Anise	lb.	---	2,646	76,768	110
Bergamot	lb.	2,601	4,240	52,143	5,017
Bitter Almond	lb.	13,746	13,669	261,422	45,193
Camphor	lb.	---	---	104,583	15,542
Caraway	lb.	661	---	23,443	430
Cassia	lb.	26,076	1	189,207	1,764
Cedarleaf	lb.	404	5,069	140,791	10
Cinnamon	lb.	4,480	4,507	52,765	8,248
Citronella	lb.	39,638	53,809	1,270,894	26,830
Clove	lb.	217,235	84,998	1,331,067	146,144
Cornmint	lb.	29,212	62,627	583,919	62,720
Eucalyptus	lb.	17,814	99,824	558,394	59,383
Geranium	lb.	8,809	6,234	111,247z	7,616
Grapefruit	lb.	220	297	76,513	176
Lavenders	lb.	9,515	15,323	175,717	17,792
Lemon	lb.	149,973	32,150	1,190,017	276,336
Lemongrass	lb.	20,000	---	110,282	6,000
Lime	lb.	27,120	70,252	1,153,155	72,487
Linaloe (Bois De Rose)	lb.	30,357	200	223,343	5,268
Neroli	lb.	47	37	1,294	232
Nutmeg	lb.	33,318	15,168	238,130	---
Orange	lb.	709,952	409,646	5,626,336	1,106,730
Origanum	lb.	1,212	---	10,265	882
Orris	lb.	46	45	907	27
Palmarosa	lb.	1,1578	1,887	35,075	375
Patchouli	lb.	40,123	46,929	668,338	19,309
Peppermint	lb.	240	2,793	43,496	155
Petitgrain	lb.	5,136	4,502	205,365	33,694
Pine Needle	lb.	8,856	348,452	941,911	1,600
Rose	lb.	5,831	8,359	56,560	4,033
Rosemary	lb.	2,154	25,587	67,340	24,791
Sandlewood	lb.	8,825	4,939	64,878	4,079
Thyme	lb.	110	3,307	16,326	8,719
Vetivert	lb.	14,071	12,229	81,196	769
Ylang Ylang or Cananga	lb.	2,225	2,790	75,536	2,899

The Forage of Horsetail, Nature's Gold Collector

Horsetail herb (Equisetum arvense L.) can be found virtually in every part of North America. This native creeping rhizome grows from Washington to Florada, as well as Canada and Mexico. There are a number of variations on E. arvense, all being equally marketable with several prefered to floral markets. It has several other common names, including shave-grass, scouring-rush, bottle brush, snake-grass, horse-pipes, meadow pine, and pine grass.

It is commonly found in moist, sandy fields and meadows, along roadsides and railroad tracks, and in fields. Since these plants prefer sandy or gravelly soils, they are frequently found along streams in alluvial deposits.

Horsetail is a perennial. The aboveground stems are jointed, deep-creeping, tuber-bearing rootstock. The jointed stem sections are 1 to 2 inches long and can be pulled apart. These stems are vary brittle and harsh because of the large amounts of silica in the tissues.

The sterile, branched, green plants are 3 to 6 feet high and resemble miniature pine trees. The branches on the sterile form are in whorls and leaves of both forms are small, scale-like, and found at the joints.

The fertile stems are erect without branches, 4 to 10 inches high, and bear a cone of "sporangia" which produces the reproductive spores or "seeds." The fertile shoots appear very early in the spring and then disappear. The sterile shoots appear later and remain until fall. It is the sterile shoots which are harvested, although both are marketable.

Horsetails are nearest allied to the ferns, and include only one genus, Equisetum. The name derives from the Latin word equus (a horse) and seta (a bristle), which might have also earned them their popular names of horsetail and bottle brush. In Japan, the sterile shoots are boiled and eaten. Sometimes they are boiled, salted and kept in vinegar and mixed with soy sauce.

The roots are used as a food by New Mexico Indians. Because of the high silica content, the herb is used for scouring and polishing. Not only is horsetail rich in silica, it also accumulates gold (0.03-0.075 ppm) and silver (0.23 ppm) compared to norms for woody angiosperms of less then 0.00045 ppm for gold and 0.06 ppm for silver. Horsetail may accumulate more gold than any other plant, averaging 125 gm per ton (wet).

It has been used successfully in Guatemala for bone cancer. Horsetail contains 8% silicic acid, 5% equisetonin (a saponin), equisetin ($C_{17}H_{31}N_3O_2$), nicotine, aconitic acid, starch, several fatty acids, and silica.

A decoction of this plant is strongly astringent and is used as a styptic (stops bleeding) and will reduce swelling of eyelids. Externally the decoction will stop bleeding and heal wounds. Studies have shown that fractured bones will heal much faster when horsetail is taken internally. The high silica content is said to render it especially effective in pulmonary consumption.

A fluid extract is prepared from the barren stems of this plant and is used as both an external and internal astringent for treatment of skin sores, diarrhea, dyspepsia, and diuresis.

Thiamase and thiaminaes, a thiamine-destroying substance, is thought to be particularly responsible for the toxic properties of horsetail. Hay that contains 20% or more horsetail produces symptoms of "equisetosis" in horses within 2 to 5 weeks. The animal suffers emaciation, muscular weakness, especially in the hind quarters, and difficulty in turning. In extreme cases, there is high temperature, rapid pulse, paralysis, coma, and then death.

The plant is only toxic in excess. Children have been poisoned by using the stems as blow guns or whistles. Most of these symptoms were reported only after chronic ingestion, however. Thiamine hydrochloride has produced dramatic improvement in horses but is less successful in relieving clinical signs of ruminants.

The sterile shoots are harvested from early June through September. Although a scythe or sickle have been traditionally used, a gas-powered weed-eater/vacuum system can be used for larger stands and greater profits in harvest time. In this manner, the vacuum system blows the shoots into the back end of a truck for future sun-cure drying on tarps. Care must be taken not to include too much grass in with the crop. The plant dries more easily than most and in good sun, will be completely ready for sacking (or baling) within one day.

All forms of Equisetum are marketable. The best stands can be found along marshes and rivers. Smaller stands can be found everywhere on banks of roads, especially against water ditches and irrigation systems. If more than 50 cars pass by the stand per day, it would probably be best not to consider if for harvest. The lead toxicity from the exhaust makes it prohibitive. There are better stands back in the woods, in any case.

As a rule of thumb, toxic levels of lead from automobile exhausts for 200 cars per day is more than 40 feet from the road. This would be an important consideration for other crops like blackberries and other forage crops near large arterials.

The plant has a creeping rhizome, which produces a number of roots at its many joints. It is considered a noxious weed by most County Extension Services and is quite difficult to extirpate from cultivated lands. Since only the sterile shoots are harvested, there is no problem even causing this plant difficulty when harvesting entire sections.

The price variation for horsetail can range from $700 per ton ($0.35 per pound) in small tonnages as a whole (baled) product to more than $1.60 per pound when sold as a C/S in 100 pound quantities. Most manufacturers are currently importing this herb from Germany and India at more than $0.65 per pound. It is a perfect crop to harvest right after coltsfoot (Tussilago farfara), both intercropping with different seasons.

An average forager can harvest as much as 400 pounds of wet product in one day, resulting in over 200 pounds of dry product within two days. This can vary markedly with the size of the stand and the harvest techniques used.

Several have considered this crop as a means to extract molecular gold out of tailings from old gold mines. It is not uncommon to find small nuggets in the root systems of horsetail growing long river banks, as well.

"CHINESE TOOTHBRUSH"

Licorice sticks have been sold for centuries as a "candy" in most European countries. As indicated in the farming section, licorice stolons can range up to 5 feet when cultivated, with diameters ranging from 1/4 inch to 3/4 inch. To make a marketable product, these roots are bundled (20 to a bundle) with wire and cut with a bandsaw to 6 inch lengths for ease in packaging.

China has used licorice root in this form for centuries as a toothbrush. The ends tend to frey when moistened, and forms a wonderful "brush" at the end which is soft to irritated gums. A scouring motion actually cleans plack better than most other types of toothbrush while not irritating the gums like most brushing action currently used in North America.

A cottage industry potential would be to package individual 6-inch roots in a special plastic container or cellophane bag for a "tree"-type display near a cash register. If packaging advertisement was attractive and an "oriental" theme used, the impulse buying for this product in a large supermarket could be excellent.

Considering that the packaging, a cello bag and label, cost less than $0.05, and the ingredient about the same, the primary costs would be in the labor of marketing. A good rule of thumb is that to market a product successfully in most mass market chains, your cost-of-goods produced should be 1/4 the retail selling price. This means that if you have $0.15 into manufacturing this product, it should retail for $0.60 (minimum).

This 400% gross profit margin allows you to consider a distributor or warehousing. For example, if the item cost $0.15 to manufacture (including labor and overhead), you should sell it to the supermarket warehouse for $0.25 in gross quantities. They, in turn, would sell it to individual stores at $0.30 and then the store would retail it for $0.49 to $0.59 per unit. You would also be required to supply the tree (stand) and want to inspect displays randomly in different stores every so often.

For perspective, most warehouses deliver to about 200 stores in a district. If each store took a tree, holding 48 units, the sale would be for more than 60 gross. This is more than $2,000.00 in gross sales, with reorders probably occuring every 2 to 4 weeks. Health food stores are another direction for marketing, usually with even better profit margins.

A BOOK YOU WILL NOT WANT TO MISS!

THE POTENTIAL OF HERBS AS A CASH-CROP

by Richard Alan Miller, ©1985, Acres U.S.A., P.O. Box 9547, Kansas City, Missouri, 64133.

The author, Richard Alan Miller, has marketed herbs and spices for over ten years. As a regional wholesaler, he saw the need for developing domestic sources of supply. Over the last four years, specific farm plans and marketing have been developed, both by his firms and the USDA. As the need for commerical dehydration became more apparent, a Portable Dehydrator prototype was built and tested. As a result, commercial production of herbs and spices is now feasible.

His work and this book are critical for the survival of small farm agriculture. Alternative crops such as herbs and spices offer the small farm those necessary yields in cash-sales to assure a future for the small farmer. The goal is to export currently imported products.

This is a first book, in a series, on alternative agriculture for the small farmer. Richard Alan Miller may be contacted in writing to: O.A.K., Inc., 1305 Vista Drive, Grants Pass, Oregon 97527.

This book is in press and will be ready in a few weeks. We are offering a special pre-publication price. Advance orders are being taken as this is a limited printing and reserved copies will be shipped before the completed edition is announced in Acres, U.S.A.

Table-Of-Contents:

Special Pre-publication price is as follows:

Softcover $13.00 includes shipping

Name _____

Address _____

City _____ State _____ Zip _____

Mail coupon to: Acres U.S.A., P.O. Box 9547, Kansas City, MO 64133

The Herb Market Report

1305 Vista Drive • Grants Pass, OR 97527

The Herb Market Report is a newsletter published monthly and distributed by The Southern Oregon Herb Gatherers' Association, Inc.

Oak Publishing
1212 SW 5th Street,
Grants Pass, OR 97526
Phone: 541-426-5588

Copyright 1986-2013 © Dr. Richard Alan Miller

Address Correction Requested

Vol. 1 No. 4

BULK RATE
U.S. Postage Paid
Grants Pass, OR
Permit No. 66

THE HERB MARKET REPORT

for the herb farmer and forager   Vol. 1 No. 5   Jun. 1985

The Elusive Oregano and Origanum Chemotypes

During the past few years there has been a marked increase in the interest shown in the herbal spices. One of the most popular of the spices is oregano, used to enhance many kinds of foods. Two kinds of oregano, namely European and Mexican, are the most common on the world spice market today.

European oregano is derived from plants of the genus Origanum (Labiatae), while Mexican oregano (yerba dulce) is generally prepared from Lippia spp. (Verbenaceace). European oregano is considered to be superior in quality to the Mexican types, commanding prices of more than three times that of the Mexican crops on the world market. The best European oregano is produced in Greece, where it grows wild and is collected by shepherds.

Literary descriptions of spice plants usually refer to the botanical name and plant morphological characteristics. Oregano, although known and used for centuries, is still the subject of great confusion in its taxonomy. Most texts dealing with the uses of spices and their growth in gardens, usually refer to Origanum vulgare L. (common or wild marjoram) as a source of oregano. Based on this assumption, several attempts were made to prepare condiments from O. vulgare L. originating from Europe and North America. The spices obtained, however, were lacking completely in both aroma and taste found in commercial oregano.

While investigating these discrepancies, Calpouzos ("Botanical Aspects of Oregano" in Economic Botany, Vol.8, No.3, 1954) compared the leaf anatomy of O. vulgare L. collected in Europe, Asia, and North America, with that of commercial oregano. Only Origanum hirtum (a form of O. vulgare L.) had the leaf anatomy which corresponded to that of commercially marketed European oregano.

Thus, Calpouzos decided that not all individual plants of O. vulgare are automatically oregano, and conversely, not all oregano is necessarily prepared from Origanum spp. His review showed that at least 39 species in 16 genera are used throughout the world as condiments or medicines and are called "oregano". He concluded that "The condiment name oregano should be understood to refer not to any one species but to a particular spice flavor furnished by plants of several genera in different parts of the world."

It is commonly known that the presence of essential oils and their composition determine the specific aroma of plants and the flavor of the condiment. Thus, the chemical composition of essential oils is the most important criteron for spice identification and quality.

A high carvacrol content in essential oil is the key to the concept of "oregano" spice and is a prerequisite determining a plant's suitability for the preparation of this condiment. Origanum heracleoticum L., THE MAIN SOURCE OF Greek oregano, is a chemically non-uniform species. Within its wild population there are at least three chemovarieties which, although similar in their external appearance, differ in their odors.

On the basis of their flavors and essential oil compositions, these varieties could be defined as marjoram, thyme and oregano-types. The latter, which contains mainly carvacrol, is traditionally, and most exclusively, collected for oregano spice preparation on the basis of its odor.

The different types of plants cannot be distinguished by their external appearance. The choice is by odor and taste, and is made not by botanists or chemists, but by shepherds. This means that the preference granted to the carvacrol-type of Origanum is traditional. The origin of this tradition will be covered in another newsletter.

Distinguishing marjoram from oregano is fairly easy during later stages of growth. Origanum has the conventional more or less tubular calyx terminated by five teeth or lobes. In Majorana the calyx is split down one side and flares out, resembling a bract.

There are other more superficial differences, notably that in Majorana the flowers are generally arranged in tightly congested globos to spike-like heads, whereas in Origanum they are more loosely disposed.

Origanum onites, also known as pot marjoram, has the shell-like formation of the calyx and is thus distinguished from wild marjoram. To separate it from sweet marjoram, now called Origanum majorana, there are 20-to 24-inch stems and unstalked or sessile leaves on Origanum onites, or pot marjoram. The leaves have reddish dotlike glands on calyx and corolla. These features must be observed with a magnifying glass. The scent of "Rigani," as pot marjoram is called on Crete, is brighter and sharper than either oregano or sweet marjoram.

Plants for sale in the spring are not usually in flower, so how can the gardener determine at that season which is sweet marjoram and which is oregano? It is not easy unless you have felt, smelled and watched sweet marjoram produce its curious fat buds, which gave rise to the Elizabethan name of "knotted marjoram." They are composed of overlapping bracts which are rounded and split at the calyx to allow small white tubular flowers to protrude just a bit. The texture of the leaves is more velvety than those of Origanum vulgare, or oregano. You can lightly brush the leaves and recognize the scent that you know from a jar of dried sweet marjoram. If there are blooms, look for the characteristics of branching spikelets of pink or white flowers of Origanum species and varieties.

It might frustrate you to know that there are several other genera of herbs with the same "oregano" scent and essential oils. One is Coleus amboinicus, native to tropical regions. Another is a species of Monarda, resembling M. fistulosa, sold as dried oregano in the southwestern United States and Mexico. The most readily available to herb gardeners in the North is a hardy, roundish-leaved species of thyme, one of several plants called Spanish thyme, Thymus nummularius. Its taste and smell are stronger than those of any member of the genus Origanum. The dried foliage is often used as a pizza flavoring in smaller quantities.

The genus Origanum also includes several other species grown for oregano flavor - O. virens)Spanish oregano), O. sipyleum from Turkey, and the numerous variations of Greek oregano, O. heracleoticum.

Oregano can be started either from seed or by cuttings. Good drainage and tilth are essential, although the soil fertility is minimal. Water is also minimal, although some

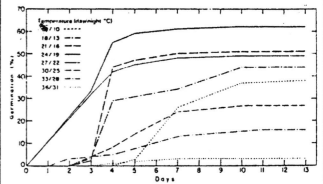

Effects of temperature
on germination of oregano.

irrigation is recommended. Cuttings planted in rows, 12 inches apart, is recommended since weed control is very important. Mulching the plants help keep them clean from grasses and other problems.

As soon as the flowers appear, oregano is ready for harvest. It should be trimmed about 6 weeks after planting, cutting off all shoots to within one inch from the growing center. This practice stimulates dense, bushy growth. Although it can in some situations be dried in the sun, it is best to dehydrate this product for higher oil retension. Oregano is then usually rubbed through a fine screen to prepare it for culinary use.

Last year more than 7,100 tons of oregano herb was imported into the United States, with more than 5 ton of oil. Mexican oregano begins to be available in March while the more desired Greek and Italian products become available in June. In some situations, a special hybredization can be seen in flower stages even in December. The better grades of oregano begin their pricing at $0.90 per pound, with a processed cut beginning at more than $1.45 per pound.

Oregano is used extensively as a major flavoring ingredient in pizza and other foods. The Mexican variety (Lippia graveolens) is more spicy and is used in prepared foods such as chili and relishes. Although mainly used as a spice, China has used this herb to treat fever, vomiting, and other disorders. The thymol and carvacrol phenols in oregano have strong fungicidal properties, although the Greek oregano with significant quantities of thymol is rare.

Contributors welcome

THE POTENTIAL OF HERBS AS A CASH-CROP
will be availabale in July

MAJOR MARKETS:
The United States of America

The USA is the world's largest importer and consumer of herbs and spices. Consumption of herbs and spices per capita (including celery seed) increased from 18 grams in 1960 to 32 grams in 1972, while total consumption increased from 3,000 ton to 6,000 ton during the same period. From 1971 through 1975 imports of herbs and spices into the USA averaged almost 13,500 ton per year, with a value at nearly 5.75 million dollars.

The trend of consumption and imports has risen, with unit values increasing more rapidly than volume. Last year the dollar value was more than 23 million, and this only reflects specific spices monitored from the Port of New York. This reflects less than 75 percent of imports. While most US requirements are met through imports, some spices are now produced domestically in commercial quantities, particularly basil, dill, parsley and celery. In smaller quantities, mint leaves, tarragon, sage, marjoram and thyme are also grown domestically, primarily California. The consumption of herbs is increasing

at best. Most reports only include specific spices and condiments entering the Port of New York (representing only 75 per cent of the total imports for those crops). Within the USA there are regional and ethnic variations in herb and spice consumption. Esti-

End-Use Patterns for Herbs in the Major Markets	Percentage		
	Retail	*Institutional*	*Industrial*
USA	50–60	15–20	25–30
Japan	25	10	65
Federal Republic of Germany	30	10–15	55–60
France	60	20	20
United Kingdom	40	20	40
Netherlands	20	20	60
Switzerland	50–60	10–20	30–40

mates of usage between various sectors differ, but the general consensus is that 50 to 60 per cent is used in the retail sector, and 40 to 50 per cent in the industrial and food service sectors. The food service sector appears to be the fastest growing area of use, reflecting the growing popularity of convenience foods and the increasing number of people eating away from home. The industrial sector is

ANNUAL HERB CONSUMPTION (ESTIMATED), 1979

Tonnes

	USA	Federal Republic of Germany	UK	Netherlands	Switzerland	Belgium	Japan
Basil	600–700	100–150	10–20	10–20	5	10	10
Bay (Laurel) leaves	300–400	200–250	75–100	60–70	5–10	30	200–300
Celery seed	1500–2000	100	200	75–100	...	20	150–200
Chervil	5–15	5–20	--	5–10	—	—	--
Dill herb	—	200	5	5–10	5	5	5
Dill seed	500–700	30	—	—	...	...	50
Marjoram	300–400	500–1000	50–75	150	10–29	10–20	10–20
Mint	250	200–2000	300–350	100	...	...	...
Oregano	2000–2500	200	10–20	50–60	...	10–20	20
Rosemary	200–300	200–300	25	30–50	5	5	25
Sage	1500	50–75	250–300	20–30	5	5	20–30
Savory	70–90	150–200	10–15	15–25	2–3	2–3	...
Tarragon	40–50	10–80	10	25	2	10–15	2
Thyme	500	200–300	200	50	10–20	10–40	40–60

Source: Trade estimates

Notes: These data must be regarded as orders of magnitude rather than precise estimates. A major difficulty is the proportion of production consumed domestically, and because of this some major consumers, especially France and Italy, have not been included in the above table as the margin of error in estimation is considered to be too great. For similar reasons celery herb (leaf) and parsley have not been included.
—nil or negligible
... not available.

a rate faster than that of spices. The growth in annual consumption for herbs is now estimated at about 10 per cent.

The USA is the only country that provides statistical information on herb and spice imports, and even that information is sketchy

the second fastest growing area of use. The food manufacturers prefer buying from grinders and processors rather than importing. This ensures a close quality control over shipments and blending to manufacturers' specifications, known as "quality assurance."

The Forage and Cultivation of Baby's Breath

Baby's Breath (<u>Gypsophila paniculata</u> L.) has been grown for many years both for fresh and dried cut flowers. Its importance as a filler in flower arrangements has grown in the past few years. The most important growing-centers of <u>Gypsophila</u> in the world are Florida, California, Holland, Israel and Columbia. Cultivation methods differ in the different countries. In some areas, growing is done outdoors while in others it is in controlled greenhouses.

Natural flowering in Europe and Northern America is from late spring to autumn, during which period there may be 2 to 3 flowering flushes. In Europe, <u>Gypsophila</u> has been grown for many years as a perennial crop. In California, <u>Gypsophila</u> is grown mainly as a summer-flowering perennial field crop. In order to obtain winter-spring flowering in Florida, root clumps and "crowns" are planted during September to February. In summer, the clumps are dug out and stored at low temperature. Repeated planting of stored plants in this system promotes disease problems of which the most serious is crown gall.

In 1973, more than 330 acres of baby's breath was cultivated in open fields in Florida with a value at $4.5 million. Production of this crop has expanded at enormous rates, due to demand and shortages. During the first 6 weeks after setting plants, <u>Gypsophila</u> produces several branches, but remains low growing and compact. Most of the plant mass during that time is comprised of lanceolate leaves ca 3 in. x 0.5 in. After that period, the leafy side-shoots rapidly elongate upward into flower bearing panicles having few leaves. Leaves that do grow on the panicles usually are much smaller than the other leaves produced by the plant. A plant produces flower panicles over a period of 2 months or more. Individual panicles, however, develop and mature over a much shorter period.

In Israel there has been a vast increase in <u>Gypsophila</u> cultivation over the past few years as well, growing from about half a hectare of outdoor growing in 1975 to ca 200 hectares of greenhouse-grown plants in 1981. As with most of countries under cultivation, these figures have grown exponetially to attempt meeting world demands. Flowering is controlled to coincide with the flower-exporting period of October to May. Expansion of this crop in Israel as a winter cut flower may be related to two major advances: (a) the production of disease-free plants of uniform clonal material by tissue culture; (b) the development of growth and flowering-control procedures by determination of planting and pruning-time and by photoperiodic lighting.

Most <u>Gypsophilas</u> in Israel are grown in unheated plastic houses, but a few growers now use heated greenhouses during mid-winter to promote the spring flush of flowering. The most common cultivar in Israel is 'Bristol Fairy', originally developed in Connecticut in 1935. The main cultivation problem in Israel is the spreading of flowering over the whole winter period. <u>Gypsophila</u> tends to bloom in flushes. At the end of each flush, the plants are pruned to ground level and new growth starts from buds in the crown region of the plant.

The temperature conditions in autumn in the period after planting or pruning have a decisive influence on flowering. This is expressed by the time of flowering, flower production, the length of flowering and harvesting period, and therefore also the date of pruning for the next flowering flush and the flowering thereof. <u>Gypsophila paniculata</u> is a long-day plant. The longer the photoperic the greater the promotion of flowering. Light throughout the night promotes flowering by 4 weeks in comparison to a 4-hour night break. 4 hours light at the end of the day is less effective in advancing flowering when compared to the same hours of light given as a night-break or at the end of the night. Supplimenting light sources should contain both red and far-red. Cool-White fluorescent lamps, which mit poorly in the far-red region, do not promote flowering of Gypsophila and the plants will tend to remain in the vegetative rosette phase.

This influence of temperature on the response of the plants to the inductive long day is well documented. The higher the temperature, the greater the promotive effect of the long photoperiod.

Gibberellin is known to promote flowering of long-day plants, and sometimes even to substitute for the photoperiodic requirement. In several experiments, plants grown under natural winter days were sprayed with GA_3 at concentrations of up to 500 mg/l for a varying number of times (up to 10). In one experiment, plants were sprayed weekly for 3 months with 100 mg/l GA_3 or GA_{4+7}. In a few cases some stem elongation and "blind" bolting was observed, but in no case was flowering promoted in natural short days by gibberellin treatment.

In another study, it was concluded that an optimum propagation scheme for G. paniculata 'Bristol Fairy' should involve base-dipping terminal cuttings from young stock plants into 3,000-10,000 mg indolebutyric acid (IBA)/liter 45% ethanol and inserting cuttings directly into rooting units. There was little difference between the 5 second and 30 second dip.

Baby's Breath Harvest

The entire herb is cut about 3 inches from the ground and bundled into one-pound 'bunches' (wet) by tying the stems at one end. The bunch is then 'bundled' into 10 to 20 bunches so that the flower-heads are at each end of the bundle. These bundles are then stacked into the back end of a truck with the flower-heads against the walls. They can be stored in this manner for up to 3 days before they must be hung to dry. Most foragers build their truck wall up to an additional 6 feet to stack more bundles in the back end.

The actual time for harvest is usually quite small, sometimes where most of the harvest is lost to rain. There is about a 2 to 3 week window where the flower opens and remains so until seeds form. This varies from ne year to the next but is close to the second week of July. As a foraged crop, the land should be secured in February with a deposit. Flower harvests lost to rain can be harvested for seed in August and September.

The bunches should be hung upside down in a dark shed, away from the sunlight. They take about 3 weeks to dry in this manner, losing about 50 per cent of their weight. The bunches are then retied (or not) into 6-ounce units and sold in this fashion. Suitable cardboard boxes might be useful, holding up to 20 bunches. Flowers can be dyed before drying simply by placing them in buckets of dye, stem-side down for several hours before hanging. Glycerin is sometimes used to also "cure" the flower-heads, preventing shatter and handling problems.

Baby's breath is a perennial and as such, has a healthy root system. It is always best, however, to leave several standing flowers to reseed the area after harvest. Harvesting only seems to spread future crops. Irrigation is not necessary, the plant prefering a more hostile environment. In fact, it will dominate most other noxious weeds. It is, in fact, considered a noxious weed in most states.

Baby's breath likes to grow where rattle snakes also like to habitat. This can be a real problem. Most foragers have found that wearing small bells in their boots distracts the snakes, causing them to leave your near vacinity. They respond to sound and are easily disturbed with this technique. It is especially useful for small children who like to run through tall grass. Bells on their shoes is especially protective for them.

Preliminary research at several Universities indicate that the seed is best germinated by burning the hillsides in the late fall and early spring. With a burning, the plant seems to double it's intercrop ratio. As a hardy perennial, the seed should also be frozen for several days before drilling.

The plant is sold to all nursery and floral shops, both wholesale and retail alike. Last year some 400 tons of baby's breath was removed from Okanogan County in Washington. A similar tonnage was taken from the Pasco-Kenewick area. California currently farms larger flower-head varieties (G. perfecta) which commands a lower price.

For example, G.perfecta sells for $3.25 per 8-ounce bunch while G. paniculata sells for $5.50 per 8-ounce bunch. In large quantities, most wholesale florists will pay $3.00 per 8-ounce bunch. If the product has been dyed and fixed, then it can sell for more than $6.00 per bunch with packaging.

An average forager can pick up to 600 pounds in a given day. Sold to a wholesaler at the edge of a field green, he receives $0.25 to $0.35 per pound. An additional $0.05 is paid to the owner of the field, usually with a wight-ticket from an advance.

TEST YOUR FARM MANAGEMENT SKILLS

David Lins, University of Illinois ag economist, has developed the following self-exam to help you analyze your management skills.

A. Interest expenses are _____ 25% of my total farm receipts.
1. less than; 2. about equal to; 3. more than; 4. don't know.

B. My current assets are _____ my current liabilities.
1. more than; 2. about equal to; 3. less than; 4. don't know.

C. My total debt is _____ my net worth.
1. less than; 2. about equal to; 3. more than; 4. don't know.

D. I _____ bankruptcy.
1. have not considered declaring; 2. have considered declaring; 3. have declared.

E. For the past two years my annual income has been _____ .
1. positive both years; 2. positive one year and negative one year; 3. negative both years; 4. don't know.

F. Within the last year, my lender has rejected _____ my loan request.
1. no portion of; 2. part of; 3. all of.

G. I keep _____ enterprise accounts for my farming operation.
1. complete; 2. partial; 3. no.

H. In three of the past five years, my crop yields have been _____ the average for my county.
1. above; 2. about equal to; 3. less than; 4. don't know.

I. In three of the past five years, the prices I've received for my production have been _____ compared to the state average.
1. above; 2. about equal to; 3. less than; 4. don't know.

J. I've prepared _____ cash flow projection for my farming operation.
1. a detailed; 2. a rough or quick; 3. no.

K. My level of operating credit has _____ the size of my operation in the past three years.
1. decreased in relation to; 2. kept up to; 3. increased more rapidly than; 4. don't know.

L. My bills are _____ .
1. paid on time; 2. arriving faster than I can pay them; 3. increasingly hard to pay and my unpaid bills are half again what they were last year; 4. don't know the status of my bills.

Scoring:

12-13 points — You've got things well under control.

14-16 points — You probably have some skills you need to improve.

17-24 points — Prioritize skills that need work, then tackle one or more immediately.

25-44 points — You've indicated many areas that need improvement. Help from a lender, financial adviser or extension specialist could speed your improvement.

from "Farming" magazine, May/June, 1985

The Herb Market Report
1305 Vista Drive • Grants Pass, OR 97527

The Herb Market Report is a newsletter published monthly and distributed by The Southern Oregon Herb Gatherers' Association, Inc.

Oak Publishing
1212 SW 5th Street,
Grants Pass, OR 97526
Phone: 541-426-5588

Copyright 1986-2013 © Dr. Richard Alan Miller

Address Correction Requested

Vol. 1 No. 5

THE HERB MARKET REPORT

for the herb farmer and forager   Vol. 1 No. 6 July 1985

CULTURE AND HARVEST OF SWORD FERNS

Sword fern (<u>Polystickum munitum</u>) is a large evergreen fern 2 to 4 feet in height. Pointed, narrow, tapered, slightly curved fronds rise from a central stool on the ground in large, compact, circular clusters. The narrow, sharp-pointed, serrated leaflets are shaped somewhat like the frond itself. They are closely, and slightly alternately, arranged along a single upright stem.

Sword fern is a common forest plant in moist forests, ranging from British Columbia through California. It reaches its best development in old-growth timber stands along the Pacific Coast of Oregon and Washington.

Sword fern, unlike huckleberry and salal, reaches its best development on highly productive timber sites. In fact, sword fern is one of the site indicator plants used by foresters to identify the highly productive Site I and Site II timber lands. Conditions that contribute to good sword fern are heavy rainfall and deep, fertile soils.

It is therefore not surprising that fern production is concentrated on the west slopes of the Olympic and Coast Range where these conditions commonly prevail. Sword fern is also picked commercially in lower slopes and valleys between the Coast Range and Cascade Mountains where heavy rainfall occurs with deep fertile forest soils. In drier areas, it is confined largely to moister sites such as wooded ravines and north and eastern slopes.

Sword fern attains its best development under old-growth stands of hemlock, cedar, Sitka spruce, and Douglas fir. Small openings, created where a tree has windthrown or died, are especially productive. However, light requirements are less for ferns than for huckleberry or salal. Sword fern also occurs under stands of alder and maple, but early season harvesting is required to avoid sooty mold discolorations on the fronds. These occur where sugary secretions drip onto the fern leaves from aphids feeding on overhead hardwood leaves.

Forest thinning enhances sword fern production by permitting partial sunlight to the ground and reducing competition for soil moisture. However, complete removal of the overstory timber produces a stiff, rough-textured, V-shaped frond with an off-green color. Ferns are relatively scarce under young, fully stocked stands with dense, unbroken crown canopies. Too little sunlight reaches the ground under these circumstances. Also, ferns have had too little time to become well established under younger stands. In general, the older the stand, the better the fern production.

In a study on sustained yield management, Leo Isaac (Forest Geneticist) concluded from his study that a 25 to 33 percent pick was about right to maintain the fern plant in a continuously productive condition. He further concluded that picking in late winter or spring had less shock effect on a fern plant than the same degree of picking during the fall or early winter. Besides causing a substantial reduction in number of fronds per plant, shock from overpicking also stunts future growth. Fronds under 25 inches in length have no commercial value.

About three million dollars worth annually are produced in Oregon and Washington alone. Florists use it in making wreaths, sprays, and background material. In

making up funeral sprays, a heavy rectan-
gular wire framework is used. Tree moss
is tied to it at both sides. This is called the base. Flowers are then worked into
the base on top of the ferns and other materials. Some of the stems are stiff
enough to go into the moss without difficulty. Others have to be wired. Ferns
also are found in special store window dis-
plays. It is used either in its natural
green or painted to every color imaginable.

So great is the demand for this plant
that it is becoming rare in the vicinity of
large cities. While the destruction of the
forest is in a measure accountable for the
diminishing supply, the collecting of the
leaves is also partly to blame. Some claim
that their harvesting techniques are not
injurious to the plant. But the leaves are
the starch manufacturing organs and when
they are removed, the plant is very apt to
suffer. Good pickers leave at least three
or more leaves to insure the life of the
plant. Even this practice, however, will
set the plant back so that smaller and fewer leaves are produced the following season. The plants will recover if the leaves
are not picked each year.

While the returns from picking sword
ferns can be profitable, it is also a very
exacting business. Ferns which are broken,
or have turned yellow near the tips are not
marketable. This would include imperfect
tips, or damage due to blight (fungus) or
dry rot, and those too immature or too old.
Ferns which grow too much in the open are
too course and stiff. They must be at
least 24 inches long to be useful to the
florist. Lengths more than 28 inches are
not usually marketable due to increased
shipping costs to the buyer.

Heat and moisture cause the fungus
to develop more rapidly. This speckles
the leaves, eventually yellowing and curl-
ing to death. Extreme care must be taken
to pick only healthy leaves. The fungus
has a strong and easily recognizable odor.
It shows as a light colored spot much like
an immature sori, making it difficult for
the beginner to detect. The sori, which are
primitive seed vessels, are found only on
the undersides of the leaves, however.

If the leaf is collected with a little
of this fungus on it and there is any heat
or moisture in the bunch in which it is
packed, the disease will go clear though
the bunch within days. It gathers momen-
tum as it goes. Wherever rain runs down
the leaves, the fungus will follow. Extreme care must be taken when shipping a case.

If there is any fungus present, within 8
days it can destroy an entire case of fifty
bunches.

Ferns are packed fifty lives to the
bunch. Twenty bunches make a roll. Rolls
are wrapped in burlap. It is the picker's
job to strip the basal ends of the stems,
to tie them in bunches, make up the burlap
rolls and deliver them to buyers. Prices
paid depend on demand. It ranges from
$1.00 to $2.50, depending on the economic
conditions, the season and the time of year.
In late spring and early summer, pickers are
paid more because collecting is more difficult.

Incomes can vary markedly with individuals. Some beginners can pick up to
50 bunches in one day, usually averaging
less than 25 bunches. Experienced foragers
have collected more than 250 bunches in
one day, but usually average over 100,
depending on the area and patch harvested.
An average of 100 bunches per day year a-
round is considered an excellent production, and some are able to do this on a
regular basis.

The foraged ferns should be stored in
cool places away from wind and sun. Water,
especially in warm weather, is necessary to
keep them from wilting. The purpose of
packing them in burlap is to keep them from
bruising. Some pickers, as they go through
the woods, make up bunches, drop them on
the ground with the butt ends all laid in
the same direction. On the way out they
follow the rails of bunches they have made
and gather them up as they go. They pick,
strip and tie in bunches all at the same
time. When they get home, they then strip
them, or straighten them and pick out the
bad ones that got into the bunches.

New ferns will hold up for forty-eight
hours, old ones can be stored for a long
time. When they are delivered to the buyer
the rolls are stood on end in tubs of water
and left there for thirty minutes. The
buyer then sorts them out, discarding all
imperfect materials which the forager may
have overlooked. Then they are packed in
corrugated pasteboard cartons containing
50 bunches each and placed in cold storage
to await shipment to wholesale florists.

The picking season on new fern starts
late in May, just as soon as they firm e-
nough to stand up under shipping conditions.
This can be recognized by their glossy appearance. Thereafter, picking can continue until spring. There are a great many
different kinds of ferns growing wild in
the forest. None are more marketable, however, than the sword fern in the market.

MAJOR MARKETS:
France

France is probably the second most important consumer of herbs after the United States. Unfortunately, very little detail on their consumption is published. Although herbs are an essential ingredient in French cooking and large quantities are produced within France, no production data are available. Most sources recognize that over the past 20 years French herb production has diminished as a result of increased production costs, particularly in relation to land and labor, and of the greater returns obtained from competing crops.

On the other hand, most trade sources agree that herb consumption has increased and, therefore, France has had to become increasingly dependent on imported sources. French import statistics do not separate or specify individual herbs, but group them together under the heading 'other spices.' Even if herb imports were separately specified one would still be confronted with a problem in that France is a major producer of essential oils and it is impossible to establish the quantity of herbs used for their manufacture.

Trade sources agree that demand is increasing in all sectors of the industry, with the retail sector consuming approximately two thirds of the total, the remaining being used by the food manufacturing and catering industries (see Vol. 1, No.5).

West Germany

West Germany is the second largest market for culinary herbs in Europe. Despite domestic production of mint, rosemary, tarragon, chervil and parsley, most of the herb market is dependent upon imported supplies. Exports of herbs are of little significance although some processors commented that, despite the small quantities involved, export of processed herbs and seasonings are rising quickly. There is, however, a substantial transit trade in herbs, centered on Hamburg.

Estimates of West German consumption on individual herbs are shown in Vol. 1, No. 5 issue of "The Herb Market Report." All trade sources agree that demand for herbs is growing at a rate of more than 10 percent per year. Although in West Germany most of the herbs listed in this discussion are used almost entirely for culinary purposes, some herbs have important uses in pharmaceuticals and herbal teas, and it is these outlets which are growing the most rapidly now.

West German trading firms have developed close links with Comecon countries, and a large proportion of West German imports come from this source, particularly the German Democratic Republic from which herbs enter West Germany free of any tariffs. Other important sources include France, Hungary and Yugoslavia. In each case few problems arise with regard to reliability and quality.

While Hamburg dominates the import trade in herbs and spices, several dealers in herbs are located in southern Germany. As in the case of the USA, several major processors have a preference for domestic sources of supply despite higher prices, because production is usually of a higher quality and growers or dealers are able to satisfy specific user requirements more easily. Many traders argue that for culinary herbs quality is often of greater importance than price. Quality specifications for the Germany market are becoming more rigorous, especially with regard to the level of contaminants and the use of herbicides and pesticides.

In fact, some purchasers are requesting certificates from producers stating that no contaminants, insecticides or pesticides have been employed, but it is extremely difficult or impossible to comply with such requests. Most herbs imported into Germany are recleaned or further processed, or both.

A Question of BERGAMOT and the Eau de Cologne

Webster's New World Dictionary defines the word bergamot as either "(1) a pear-shaped citrus fruit grown in Southern Europe for its oil (used in perfumery), or (2) any of several aromatic N. American herbs of the mint family."

The economy of citrus oils in general can be clearly depicted by the study of bergamot oil production. Only the expressed oil from the peels of the fruits from the small bergamot tree, Citrus bergamia are of any substantial interest. The pulp is of little value beyond what can be converted into citric acid. The leaves and twigs may be distilled to yield a bergamot-petitgrain oil, but the fruits are not edible.

Bergamot oil is produced by cold expression from the peel of the nearly ripe fruit. The tree grows almost exclusively in a narrow coastal strip in the southern part of Calabria, Italy. Cultivation of bergamot trees in other parts of the world have, for the most part, failed to produce bergamot oils comparable in value and quality to that of the Calabrian oil. There are some exceptions and include Guinea and Morocco, but not in North America as yet.

Bergamot trees are grafted on stubs of bitter orange trees. The fruits are of the size of big oranges and almost lemon-shaped. The annual world production (with 90% Calabrian) fluctuates between 200 and 300 tons, with continual shortages to world demand. The oil is used extensively in perfumery for its sweet freshness, particularly in citrus colognes, body powders, sun-tan lotions. Part of the sweetness and rich bodynote is due to the presence of large amounts of linalyl acetate combined with linalool and traces of methyl anthranilate. Bergamot oil is also used in flavors for its sweet-fru-

ity and refreshing notes. It is quite popular in "hard candy" and as a modifier, along with other citrus oils. It is also used in flavoring of tobacco, particularly in the Continental types of pipe tobacco.

While North America may have difficulty in the cultivation of this specific citrus tree, it does have several chemical analogs growing wild throughout the continent. One, Mentha x piperita var. citrata (Ehr.) is one of the most attractively scented of all herbs. This species of genus Mentha is a rich source of two aroma chemical, namely linalool and linaly acetate. Todd and Murry (Perf. Essent. Oil Rec., 5 (1968), 97) were able to evolve an agronomically superior clone of the species. Using ionizing radiation, Kak and Kaul (Perfumerie und Kosmetic, 59, (1978b), 296) isolated a number of mutant clones having a higher content of linalool and/or linalyl acetate in their oils.

The aroma is, however, somewhat intangible and it is variously described as lemon, orange, bergamot, lavender, and eau de Cologne-mint. Its former botanical name, M. odorata, is therefore rather more accurate than the present one, which suggests only a lemon scent.

Bergamot mint is a very aromatic decumbent, glabrous perennial from 12 to 24 inches tall, on overground leafy stolons. Stems are branched and bear dark green, purple-tinged, smooth, ovate or elliptic, petiolate leaves 1 to 2 inches long. Mauve flowers occur in rounded dense terminal spikes from mid to late autumn. It perfers rich, moist soils with partial shade. While it grows wild, it is best cultivated horticulturally by division of stolons in the spring, planting them 2 inches deep. It can be processed exactly like peppermint oil, although current productions domestically are not used medicinally and only sparingly in tisanes, jellies, cold drinks, and salad preparations. With some appropriate chemical variations, it may be employed in a range of scented and cosmetic articles.

Optimum row spacings for bergamot mint are 15 inches x 15 inches for maximum herbage yields of 100 pounds of oil per acre. Yields will be reduced with wider row spacing of 20 inches x 15 inches and 22 inches x 15 inch spacings. Stem cuttings could be used for large scale cultivation of Mentha citrata Ehrh. At least one leaf is required on the stem cutting for successful rooting of the plant, however. Treating the runners with IAA (500 ppm) for 4 to 6 minutes or IBA (200 ppm) for 6 to 8 minutes increases the percentage of rooting.

Herbage and essential oil yields can be increased further with the application of 50 to 100 kg N/ha over no nitrogen application. Phosphorus application of 60 kg P_2O_5/ha also increases the herbage and essential oil yields. Potassium application seems to have no effect on the yield of bergamot mint. The essential oil content is also not influenced by NPK fertilization.

There is another plant from the mint family (Labiatae) which is known as bergamot, bee balm, and Oswego tea. This is the red bergamot Monarda didyma, widely cultivated as a garden ornamental for its combination of orange scent and attractive flowers. Its scent is very similar to that of bergamot orange. Several varieties now exist of which the best-known is Cambridge-scarlet. Other types include salmon, rose, purple, or white in color. The wild red M. didyma is the most aromatic.

Red bergamot belongs to the Monarda or horsemint genus, named after the sixteenth-century Spanish medical botanist Nicholas de Monardes, and is closely related to wild or purple bergamot (M. fistulosa L.) which is also called Oswego tea. Oswego derives its name from the Oswego River district near Lake Ontario in the United States where the herb grew abundantly in the past. After the Boston Tea Party (1773), a protest against the tea duty imposed on the colonies, Oswego tea replaced Indian tea in many households during that period.

Red bergamot is generally recognized by its red tubular florets arranged in whorls. It is a hardy perennial, and a member of the mint family. It can be a very invasive plant with dense, shallow root systems with many runners. Monarda didyma thrives in moist, somewhat acid soils, while the lavender-flowered species, M. fistulosa, covers the abandoned pastures in limestone areas throughout New England. The lemon bergamot, M. citriodora, grows in the Appalachian mountains. All are native to North America.

Root division is a most reliable method of propagation. Plants from seed are seldom uniform as they tend to cross-pollinate with wild bergamots. Germination of the seed is about 2 weeks in diffused light, with viability falling off sharply with seed over two years old. Expect little or no harvest from the first year of seedlings, taking almost one year to establish. Transplanting is most successful at any time of the year except late fall.

Established plantings should be divided every 3 to 4 years, or they will die out due to rapid spreading habits. The roots are easily pulled apart, with only the outer roots being replanted. The center roots should be discarded. Bergamot requires high moisture and fertile (humis-rich) soils. Care must be taken during cultivation because of the shallow root systems of red bergamot. In autumn the entire plant should be covered with compost 1 inch deep for both winter protection and a source of nutrients the following year.

It is grown extensively throughout Europe as a source for thymol, a crystalline phenol usually obtained from thyme. Both the volatile oil and thymol have antiseptic uses on the skin and in the nasal and pharyngeal passage. In common with other phenols, however, thymol combines chemically with proteins. In large amounts it can produce irritant effects on the mucous membranes of the gastro-intestinal tract.

Then there is horsemint, Monarda punctata. Horsemint's primary principle is known as monarda oil. It is composed of 60% thymol and smaller amounts of cyemene, d-limonene, carvacrol, linalool, and hydrothymoquinone. The primary markets for these mints is primarily as an external and internal fungicide, anthelmintic, and bacteriocide. The mint has an aromatic odor and a warm, bitter taste. The tea is used as a carminative for colic, flatulence, and sick stomach. Winnebago and Dakota Indians used an infusion as a heart stimulant.

COTTAGE INDUSTRY:
Connoisseur's pot-pourri

Mix a wide-mouth jar full of dried rose petals with a handful of salt and let stand for several weeks. Store dried lavender (Lavandula spica), rosemary (Rosmarinus officinalis), rinks (Dianthus plumarius), and Wallflowers (Cheiranthus) in separate containers, together with a little salt or bay salt and some scented leaves.

Prepare wedges of citrus fruit peel by sticking them all over with cloves (Syzygium aromaticum) and allowing them to dry naturally for a few weeks.

When all the ingredients are ready, thoroughly mix the petals with the leaves. Add the citrus fruit and clove whole (or grind them in a blender) and add handfuls to equal the quantity of salt used. Add a teaspoon of cinnamon (Cinnamomum zeylanicum) and another of allspice (Pementa dioica). Mix well and leave overnight. Then add a few drops of essential oils: lavender (Lavandula spica), bergamot (Monarda didyma), and geranium (Palargonium spp). Store in a closed container for eight to ten weeks.

When properly packaged in glass or clay, a perfect cottage industry exists.

The Herb Market Report
1305 Vista Drive • Grants Pass, OR 97527

The Herb Market Report is a newsletter published monthly and distributed by The Southern Oregon Herb Gatherers' Association, Inc.

Oak Publishing
1212 SW 5th Street,
Grants Pass, OR 97526
Phone: 541-426-5588

Address Correction Requested
Vol. 1 No. 6 July 1985

THE HERB MARKET REPORT

for the herb farmer and forager   Vol.1 No.7 August, 1985

The Forage And Market of YELLOW DOCK

Yellow dock (Rumex crispus L.) is part of the Buckwheat Family (Polygoneaceae). Also known as curly or curled dock, garden patience, sour dock, and bitter dock, it is a troublesome weed now found throughout the United States and Canada. Although it is found almost everywhere, it prefers moist pastures and fields. It is most commonly found in waste areas, old building sites, and along roadsides, rocky ground usually not well suited for crops.

In ancient writings both this species and another common weed, the broad-leaved dock (R. obtusifolius L.) have been used for the same medicinal purposes, more recently shown to be similar in chemical constituents. R. obtusifolius was known as Lapathum acutum from the 14th century, while yellow dock was called L. crispum. It was early in the 19th. century with its use in American medicine that it was given the Latin name Rumex. Today Rumex is found in English herbals, and Lapathum in European ones.

Yellow dock is a perennial which grows to five feet in height. The leaves are six to twelve inches long, linear and curly-edged. It produces yellow to green flowers in clusters, and dense spikes of winged triangular seeds. It blooms from June through August and can be seen late in the summer by it's characteristic red pods. Curled dock flower spikes may be picked all summer for its wide range of colors. It is yellow in bloom and gradually turns green, honey-toned, rich red brown, and later very dark brown.

The husky, full look of these spikes is desirable for large arrangements and is especially used as a background in one-sided bouquets. It is best used in this manner with dried goldenrod, aster, rose hips, figwort, whorled milkweed, straw-flowers, and other large dried leaves. While most dried florists will pay up to $0.10/flower-spike in quantities of 1,000, this is not the major use for yellow dock.

Pioneers used yellow dock for treatment of skin diseases and as a laxative and tonic. Crushed leaves were used by the Indians to bring boils and other suppurations to a head. The root contained tannin, used for closing and healing cuts, while the juices of the leaves were used to treat ringworm and other other skin parasites.

The family Polygonaceae contains many anthraquinone drugs: Hydroxyanthraquinone glycosides, based on aloe-emodin, emodin, physcion, as well as astringent compounds of glucogallin, gallic acid, catechin, and chrysophanal. Yellow dock is also rich in tannins and iron. As James Duke puts it in his book HERBALBUM (p36):

> "The MD no doubt would say poppycock;
> You can't cure psoriasis with yellow
> dock!
> But chrysarobin contained
> Can cure skin complaints,
> And becomes a bit cheaper
> than Medical Doc!"

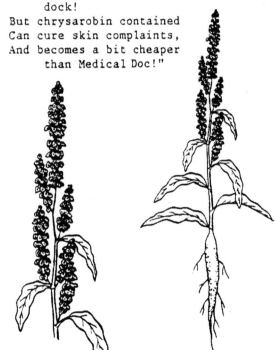

Yellow dock also contains oxalates, usually in the form of potassium oxalate. Oxalate crytals mechanically penetrate the tissue and create wounds. The kidneys are especially susceptible to this mechanical damage since the crytals concentrate there for excretion. The roots are considered a gentle laxative and as an astringent or cholagogue (preventing biliousness).

It is quite popular in homeopathic markets. The dried root may be taken as a powder in capsules or by decoction of 30 to 60 grains. As a liquid extract (1:1 in 25% alcohol) in doses of 1 to 2 ml., with usage not exceeding three times each day. I recommend caution when using this root internally.

Handling the leaves may give dermatitis. Symptoms occurring within 2 to 4 hours after ingestion include nausea, vomiting, diarrhea, and often some oral irritation. If significant amounts are ingested, renal damage may occur. It is recommended that gloves be worn when harvesting large quantities of the root or flower spikes. I also usually wear a mask for the dust and other airborne products.

The roots are best dug in the late autumn, right after the first rains. Yellow dock grows best in rocky soils, ones that become very hard during the summer months. Even with irrigated fields, the softness of the ground becomes a significant factor when considering large stands. The flower spike can be taken earlier, ranging from early April through late August.

Traditional forms of harvest, especially in the Mid West, include a shovel and other tools used in the harvest of potatoes from a large garden. Land in Missouri and Kansas have especially large roots which can range up to 60 pounds, wet, with a good forager averaging up to 2,000 pounds per long day. 1,000 pounds is quite common with larger root fields.

The yellow dock growing along the coastal regions of North America are quite large, but the roots average a wet weight of less than 2 pounds. Because they grow in large stands in level fields, traditional forms of farm machinery used for harvesting potatoes can often be used. If harvested in the manner, the tops should be removed before the root is plowed to the surface. If it is a good field, these flower spikes can be cut by hand as a by-product for the floral markets.

Some dock grows from a rhizome. The chemistry is the same, however, and this can often be marketed with the more traditional "carrot"-like taproots of R. crispus L. It markets for less, of course. Both should be split and then dried in the sun on tarps. The most common forage techniques is to drive over them with your truck on pavement. It should be cut into 2 to 6 inch pieces for best drying. It drys slowly and can lose up to 60 per-

cent weight-loss in drying. Most roots only loose 35 per cent, however.

Yellow dock has not been cultivated as a special crop because it grows wild almost everywhere. It is a deciduous perennial which thrives in varied locations and is usually considered a noxious weed by most states and Provinces. It will spread, even with the roots removed, if the flowers are allowed to seed.

Yellow dock is usually collected at buying stations, like cascara segrada bark. The forager is paid up to $0.15 per pound for the wet root in a split form on the spot. The buyer then sets it out on tarps for a 2-week drying period. Often it needs to be covered for early spring rains. Some artifical rack drying system would also work well for the late fall harvests.

Major botanical houses which buy this crop by the 5,000 pound minimum quantity usually offer $0.65 per pound. On a contract, however, expect $0.55 per pound, with rhizome dock prices at $0.35 per pound. In cut-and-sift/powders, yellow dock begins marketing at $1.30 per pound in 100 pound quantities. Sifted powders sell for $1.80 per pound.

Not only used as a red dye for the wool industries, it is also used as an abrasive dentifrice in some manufacturing of toothpastes. An average forager can harvest more than 800 pounds wet product in one day. This results in more than 300 pounds dry-weight yellow dock for marketing. It is sold in 60 or 100 pound sacks, perferably polypropylene. The key is in finding large enough stands of yellow dock to stay on task.

MAJOR MARKETS: The United Kingdom

The United Kingdom market for herbs and spices is much smaller than those of the United States, France and West Germany. Nevertheless, usage of and interest in both medicinal and culinary herbs have increased enormously during the 1970s. Some of the increased demand has been satisfied by domestic production and home-garden production, but estimates of these volumes and value is impossible to determine since no official monitor exists. There is also a small market for fresh herbs, emanating in the main from restaurants and the catering trade, but this is unlikely to be of interest to non-UK producers.

The United Kingdom has only recently begun to record imports of some specific herbs and spices. The limited trade data available make the estimation of likely future trends difficult, hence the best information comes on estimates from members of the trade. The annual herb consumption estimates for the UK was listed in Vol. 1, No. 5 issue of "The Herb Market Report." These statistics should be regarded as providing orders of magnitude rather than precise measures. The most important herbs used in the UK are mint, parsley and sage, all of which are grown commercially there.

Imports are needed to supplement supplies, probably of the order of 150 tons for mint, 175 tons for sage and 75-100 ton for parsley. No other herbs with the exception of small quantities of tarragon, are grown in commercial quantities in the UK. Most mint consumed in the UK is spearmint (Mentha spicata and M. viridis), peppermint (M. piperita) only being used in small quantities for tea and medicinal purposes.

Within the UK there are two major outlets for culinary herbs. The first is the food manufacturing sector which consumes around 50-60 per cent of herbs, although the percentage is different for each herb. The major use is in stuffings, as well as in sauces and seasoning. Growth in demand is influenced by the growth of the processed and convenience food market, and estimates suggest that annual growth is about 5-6 per cent. Some herbs are used to make essential oil and oleoresins, but this sector is not yet very important, although it is growing. The second outlet is the retail sector, providing small packs for use in the home or bulk-packs for use in institutions and the catering trade. This is the major growth sector, estimated at around 10-15 per cent per annum.

The United Kingdom is probably the second major processor and consumer of herb oleoresins after the USA. Nevertheless the quantities produced and consumed are very small in comparison with spice oleoresins and essential oils. During the late 1960s there was a strong movement amongst all major UK food manufacturing companies away from ground herbs and spices towards oleoresins. However, there has more recently been a marked slowdown in the growth of herb oleoresin consumption and this, combined with the reported excess capacity of oleoresin production in the UK and elsewhere, offers little encouragement for new oleoresin producers.

U. S. D. A.'s FOREIGN AGRICULTURE SERVICE

The United States Department of Agriculture (USDA) has a special branch within their organization to monitor foreign trade with other countries. Known as the Foreign Agricultural Service (FAS), a series of important circulars are prepared each year on "Tea, Spices and Essential Oils" trades. Copies of these bulletins are available for $5.00 by writing directly to FAS, Information Division, Room 4644-S, USDA, Washington, D.C. 20250. (FTEA 1-85/2-85).

While these documents are quite interesting, their information content is somewhat limited in scope and accuracy. Most figures are less than one-half those listed from the "Chemical Marketing Reporter," per Vol.1, No. 4 of "The Herb Market Report." It should be noted that both only monitor the Port of New York, and do not include other major ports of entry such as Chicago, Los Angeles, San Francisco, and some of the Texas ports. The crops listed are also quite limited and do not include most of the botanicals used in pharmaceutical and floral industries.

The following tables are from the 1985 FAS circulars, indicating import quantities and spot price variations for 1983-1985. The U.S. imports of specified condiments, seasonings, and flavorings in 1984 rose to an all-time high of 195,855 tons valued at $271.3 million, an increase of 12 per cent in volume and 18 per cent in value over the previous record high of 1983.

Specified Condiments and Flavoring Materials
Approx. N.Y. spot prices in cents / lb.

	1983	1984	1985
ALLSPICE (PIMENTO):			
Guatemalan	114	130	109
Honduran	114	130	109
Jamaican	117	140	120
Mexican	(1/)	119	(1/)
ANISE:			
Chinese star	155	185	215
Egyptian	79	110	63
Spanish	117	100	70
Turkish	79	55	48
BASIL:			
Egyptian	90	57	60
French	105	105	88
Domestic	375	415	350
CAPSICUM PEPPERS:			
Chinese	75	77	72
Indian	70	68	69
Pakistan	66	61	49
CARAWAY:			
Dutch	56	71	85
Egyptian	50	52	78
CARDAMOM:			
Bleached "A"	1375	2800	2300
Decorticated	355	1250	800
Guatemalan fancy greens	775	1400	(1/)
Guatemalan mixed greens	315	1100	790
CASSIA:			
Chinese, Taiwan	43	43	52
Indonesian Batavia "AA"	135	130	135
Indonesian Korintje "A"	62	62	66
CELERY SEED:			
Indian	43	65	85
CINNAMON:			
Ceylon No. 2	135	85	95
Seychelles	50	(1/)	(1/)
CLOVES:			
Brazilian	445	390	200
Madagascar	470	385	200
CORIANDER:			
Moroccan	37	38	30
Romanian	35	38	30
CUMIN:			
Indian	92	80	64
Turkish	85	63	39
Pakistan	87	(1/)	(1/)
DILL SEED:			
Dewhiskered	36	42	46
FENNEL:			
Egyptian	68	65	37
Indian	86	80	56
FENUGREEK:			
Indian	34	33	33
Moroccan	(1/)	33	33
GINGER:			
Chinese, whole peeled	57	160	155
Chinese, sliced	48	140	120
Indian, cochin	110	155	110
Jamaican No. 3	138	(1/)	(1/)
LAUREL (BAY) LEAVES:			
Turkish	64	50	56
Turkish cutting grade	54	48	48

	1983	1984	1985
MACE:			
East Indian	225	305	325
MARJORAM:			
Egyptian	150	155	58
French	165	190	95
MINT LEAVES:			
Peppermint	240	270	275
Spearmint	225	225	225
MUSTARD SEED:			
Canadian No. 1 yellow	23	56	28
Oriental	21	28	28
NUTMEGS:			
East Indian	80	77	74
West Indian	80	85	85
ORIGANUM:			
Greek 30 mesh	125	100	105
Mexican	108	67	53
Turkish 30 mesh	115	86	80
PAPRIKA:			
Spanish 90 ASTA	95	(1/)	88
Spanish 120 ASTA	98	95	95
Spanish 100 ASTA	92	91	91
PARSLEY:			
Domestic	160	245	245
Imported	75	195	210
PEPPER, BLACK:			
Brazilian	54	92	126
Indonesian, Lampong	64	89	130
Indian, Malabar	64	89	130
PEPPER, WHITE:			
Brazilian	85	150	160
Indonesian, Muntok	85	150	160
POPPY SEED:			
Australian	85	69	38
Dutch	78-88	70-79	39
Turkish	72	68	37
ROSEMARY:			
Portuguese	46	40	37
Spanish	46	40	37
SAFFRON:			
Spanish	29000	28500	26500
SAGE:			
Albanian	112	91	126
Dalmatian No. 1	160	160	170
Turkish	72	69	87
SAVORY:			
Albanian	(1/)	57	(1/)
Yugoslavian	55	60	67
SESAME SEED:			
Guatemalan natural	68	50	45
Central American hulled	77	60	56
TARRAGON:			
Domestic	900	900	(1/)
THYME:			
French	118	118	95
Spanish	78	78	62
TURMERIC:			
Haitian	34	(1/)	58
Indian, Alleppey	52	115	93
VANILLA BEANS:			
Madagascar, bourbon	3000-3100	3125	3700
Indonesia, Java	2700-3000	2700-3000	2700-3000

1/ Quotations not available.   2/ F.O.B. Los Angeles.

April 1985   Horticultural and Tropical Products Division, FAS/USDA

SOURCE: New York market area spice brokers.

U.S. Imports of Condiments, Seasonings & Flavoring Materials[1]

	1983		1984	
	Metric tons	1,000 dollars	Metric tons	1,000 dollars
Allspice (pimento)	755.9	1,600.4	833.4	1,932.5
(ground)	4.3	12.5	15.2	40.7
Anise seed	652.5	1,156.3	860.0	1,318.5
Basil	1,154.3	1,536.5	1,437.5	1,640.7
(other than crude)	35.0	71.8	26.6	47.9
Capers	685.4	3,304.9	885.9	3,811.2
Capsicum or red peppers:				
Anaheim and ancho	847.9	705.4	839.5	1,036.1
Other	5,950.1	6,915.6	6,702.9	7,879.5
(ground)	463.1	1,015.3	307.7	724.8
Caraway seed	3,339.3	3,522.1	3,972.7	5,302.6
Cardamom seed	87.1	598.2	80.1	1,116.1
Cassia	8,863.9	8,302.3	10,814.3	10,671.2
(ground)	287.0	386.4	312.7	383.7
Celery seed	2,311.2	1,778.0	2,177.4	2,964.5
Cinnamon	952.5	1,711.0	2,744.3	3,822.4
(ground)	106.3	181.2	46.4	106.2
Cloves	663.6	5,622.1	1,054.9	6,667.4
(ground)	7.3	50.2	17.2	35.9
Coriander	4,183.6	1,721.5	6,340.3	2,391.1
Cumin seed	3,192.7	4,837.5	4,399.9	5,329.1
Curry and curry powder	391.7	1,306.1	306.7	1,042.9
Dill seed	597.6	533.1	740.8	621.7
Fennel seed	1,742.0	2,130.4	1,986.2	1,783.9
Garlic (dehydrated)	382.7	571.4	180.0	297.0
Ginger	3,560.5	3,664.1	4,171.5	5,792.8
(ground)	81.1	132.4	36.4	91.9
(sweet)	260.4	395.0	293.6	415.7
(candied)	1,116.9	909.0	290.5	488.2
Laurel (Bay) leaves	437.1	497.8	552.7	506.3
(other than crude)	.5	3.7	15.3	25.2
Mace	276.9	1,001.2	234.3	1,331.6
(ground)	4.5	6.5	—	—
Marjoram	322.7	649.2	499.7	1,067.0
(other than crude)	1.7	5.7	4.2	10.9
Mint leaves	164.4	275.5	144.3	203.5
(manufactured)	134.0	379.1	98.3	317.6
Mustard seed	31,930.6	10,599.9	37,241.8	13,071.7
(ground)	1,575.6	1,985.6	2,727.2	2,886.2
(other)	1,608.0	2,831.1	1,860.8	2,943.9
Nutmegs	2,061.5	2,954.5	1,973.4	2,967.2
(ground)	26.2	59.5	47.5	62.2
Onions (dehydrated)	14.5	26.0	110.5	169.1
Origanum leaves	3,593.1	6,198.3	4,338.1	4,877.0
(other than crude)	32.7	63.9	12.3	19.9
Paprika 3/	5,040.1	7,444.1	6,679.9	8,912.3
Parsley	313.6	264.7	731.8	622.8
(manufactured)	98.2	286.5	68.8	207.3
Pepper, black	28,346.1	29,296.9	34,505.4	56,704.4
Pepper, white	3,129.5	4,514.8	3,642.6	9,240.8
(black and white ground)	166.6	360.3	173.0	510.5
Poppy seed	3,100.8	4,312.1	4,345.9	3,196.9
Rosemary	466.4	272.7	304.6	133.2
(other than crude)	15.4	14.9	12.6	9.8
Sage	1,512.7	3,223.1	1,891.5	3,716.5
(ground or rubbed)	18.6	37.1	5.5	19.1
Savory	96.4	69.8	72.1	67.2
(other than crude)	.2	1.5	.1	.6
Sesame seed	42,789.4	39,962.8	36,759.0	32,986.0
Tarragon	46.4	278.1	55.3	387.0
(other than crude)	20.9	59.5	10.0	40.7
Thyme	893.7	1,297.1	712.0	946.4
(other than crude)	12.2	30.5	4.0	17.8
Turmeric	1,600.1	1,368.6	1,789.1	2,155.0
Vanilla beans	977.4	50,811.6	841.4	49,933.8
Mixed spices	1,338.3	3,270.3	1,515.2	3,290.3
Total	174,842.9	229,385.3	195,854.9	271,313.9

1/ Unground, unless otherwise specified. 2/ 50 kilograms or less. 3/ Ground and unground.

NOTE: All values refer to f.o.b. country of origin.

SOURCE: U.S. Department of Commerce. Horticultural and Tropical Products Division, FAS/USDA　April 1985

BOOK REVIEW: Dr. James A. Duke

This is a new section heading for our newsletter. As subscriptions increase, so will the number of pages and the various topic headings. Book reviews and important contributors to the field of herb and spice farming and foraging are critical for your growing need for information. One such individual to know about is Dr. James A. Duke.

Dr. Duke is one of the United States Department of Agriculture's most knowledgeable herb scientists. He is also Chief of Germplasm Research at the Beltsville Agricultural Research Center in Maryland. He has also written a number of important books on the subject of botanicals. My library overflows with his works.

His best, by far, is the new title HANDBOOK OF MEDICINAL HERBS (CRC Press) as a two volume set from a new series. The most imaginative is his "anthology of varicose verse" HERBALBUM (Herbal Vineyard). This text even has a section on songs with a chapter titled "Verbal Non-Herbals." He has captured the essence of each herb through his poetry and wit. Other books include CULINARY HERBS (Tradco-Medic). This is a pot pourri of cross-references for the various uses of herbs, with artwork from his wife Peggy-Ann.

More important, however, is Duke's access to technical information on specific cultivation requirements, biotic factors, and other details on botanicals and herb crops. He has prepared numerous monographs with excellent detail, and this is where he becomes important to us all. A complete list of his books and their availability can be obtained by writing directly to Herbal Vineyard, Fulton, MD 20759

NOTE FROM THE EDITOR

I would like to expand this newsletter and need your help. We would like to increase circulation, and would like contributions for future issues. If you have found an interesting herbal clipping in your reading, please send it to us and we will attempt to share it with others.

The Herb Market Report
1305 Vista Drive • Grants Pass, OR 97527

The Herb Market Report is a newsletter published monthly and distributed by The Southern Oregon Herb Gatherers' Association, Inc.

Oak Publishing
1212 SW 5th Street,
Grants Pass, OR 97526
Phone: 541-426-5588

Copyright 1986-2013 © Dr. Richard Alan Miller

THE POTENTIAL OF HERBS AS A CASH-CROP is now in print and available. Send $12.00 for an autographed edition.

Address Correction Requested

Vol. 1 No. 7

THE HERB MARKET REPORT
for the herb farmer and forager   Vol. 1 No. 8 Sept., 1985

The Forage and Cultivation of Chicory Root

Chicory, (<u>Cichorium intybus</u> L.), is a a perennial herb which has been naturalized throughout most of North America. As a native to Europe, North Africa, and Western Asia, it is primarily used for its leaves in salads. Current interest in chicory is because it is also used as an additive to coffee. The roots of some varieties are harvested, sliced, roasted, ground, and added to coffee to enhance the flavor.

Also known as blue-sailor, succory, and witloof, this long-time cultivated plant can reach heights of 6 feet and has bright blue flowers. A number of different cultivars of chicory have been developed to meet the different commercial uses of the plant. Centers of chicory production include Belgium, Holland, France, and the United States.

The use of chicory can be traced back to the Egyptians. They, like the Arabians, used the blanched leaves as a salad green. This custom has continued into modern day on a commercial scale in Belgium and horticulturally throughout Europe. Sometimes the blanched winter salad leaves are known as endive, from the Arabic word <u>hendibeh.</u> Dickens in his <u>Household Words</u> described the extensive cultivation of this crop in England for the root which was ground and roasted as a coffee substititue.

Chicory is a deep rooted perennial with spindle-shaped taproots. It has bright blue flowers and cauline hairy leaves (borne on stem) resembling those of dandelion. It can be found growing wild on roadsides, field edges, rocky ground, and on nitrogenous, calcareous and alluvial soils. Appearing from late summer to mid-autumn, the flower-heads close by midday.

We seldom think of the wild herb as being the same species as the expensive 'endive' or "chicons" which appears in the market as pale, pointed, slightly bitter but delicious salad ingredient. Curly chicory (<u>Cichorium endiva</u> L.), commonly called endive, is cultivated as a salad green.

It forms broad heads of crisped or widely ruffled leaves.

Chicory culture is similar to that of endive and leaf lettuce. It is a cool season crop which may be planted in the spring or early summer. The reported life zone of chicory ranges from 40° to 80°F., 12 to 156 inches of annual precipitation, and a soil pH of 4.5 to 8.3. The plant does best in cool weather and calcareous soils. It is seeded in rows 15 to 18 inches for ease in cultivation requirements. Plants within the row should be spaced 4 to 5 inches apart.

Witloof chicory can also be planted in the greenhouse or in a hot frame in late April, transplanted into the field in late May, or directly seeded into the field in mid to late May. Leaves grow rapidly and can be harvested as needed for salad markets.

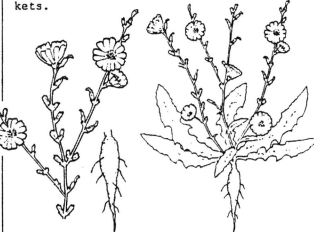

Witloof chicory plants can also be harvested in late fall by pulling the entire plant out of the ground with the roots intact. Only roots larger than 3/4-inch diameter should be saved. The plants are pulled and placed in storage as they are needed for forcing. The tops are then cut off, leaving stubs about 1 to 2 inches long. The roots are placed in trays or planted in bushel containers in moist soil.

The crown of the plant is covered with 4 inches of dry or sandy soil. Dry sawdust may also be suitable. Heat is needed to initiate forcing, 68° to 70°F. is optimum. Air humidity should be 95 to 100%. The containers are examined in about three weeks and the heads are harvested when 4 to 5 inches long. These can be sold directly to produce markets for use in salads and gourmet cooking.

Root chicory or the Magdeburg type, is harvested in late summer or early fall, when the ground becomes soft again. Roots will contain a large amount of dry matter, taking longer to dry in the sun. These roots can be harvested as a row crop, like potatoes. The roots are then sliced or chipped and dried in the sun on tarps. Manufacturers usually then put this form of chicory into a smaller cut, like a granule cut, and then roast it slowly at 300° to 350°F. in an oven or coffeeroaster.

Chicory is a source for the natural taste modifier maltol, known to intensify the flavor of sugar. The crop is also a potential source of fructose for the flavor industry and related markets. The fresh roots also contain large amounts of inulin, vitamins A and C, chicoric acid, esculitin, esculin, chichociim, and several other bitter compounds .

Cultivars of chicory developed for use as a coffee substitute have large, thickened roots that are externally yellow and internally white. When roasted properly, they impart a strong, bitter flavor that enhances coffee flavors. Cultivars of chicory developed for use in salads have more and larger leaves than others. Salad leaves are often blanched in the field to reduce possible bitterness. Young and tender roots can be boiled and eaten as a vegetable. Chicory extracts are used in alcoholic and nonalcholic beverages.

Inulin is one of the fructosans, a group of polysaccharides that yield fructose upon hydrolysis. Inulin differs from starch in that the former does not make a paste in water. It is used primarily in culture media as an identifying reagent for certain bacteria, some of which are capable of fermenting it, while others are not. It is also used in special diabetic diets and in kidney-function tests.

Maltol, a pyrone, is also found in larch bark, pine needles, and roasted malt. The mode of action is as a flavoring to breads and cakes, intensifying the flavor of sugar 30 to 300 times. It is also FDA approved.

As a medicinal plant, chicory root has been used as a digestive aid, diuretic, laxative, tonic, and mild sedative. The root has also been used against jaundice, inflammation, warts, tumors, and cancer. It was thought to purify the liver and spleen. Extracts from the roots have been shown to affect heart tissue of toads by marked depression of amplitude and rate.

The following table lists the varieties of chicory by type, and source of seed. Addresses of the listed seed companies are also given for reference:

Sources of Seeds

Asgrow Seed Company,
Kalamazo, MI   49001

Ferry Morse Seed Company,
P.O. Box 100,
Mountain View, CA   94040

Herbst Brothers Seedsmen, Inc.,
1000 North Main Street,
Brewster, NY   10509

Northrup King and Company,
1500 Jackson Street, N.E.,
Minneapolis, MN   55143

W. Atlee Burpee Company,
Box 748,
Riverside, CA   92502

Dessert Seed Compan,
P.O. Box 181,
El Centro, CA   92243

Harris Seeds,
Moreton Farm,
Rochester, NY   14264

Nichols Garden Nursery,
1190 North Pacific Highway,
Albany, OR   97321

Stokes Seeds, Inc.,
737 Main Street,
Buffalo, NY   14240

Chicory Varieties, Types and Sources

Variety	Type	Days to Maturity	Source of Seed
Witloof (French endive)	Salad (forcing)	140	Harris, Dessert, Asgrow, Northrup King
Witloof Improved	Salad (forcing)	140	Stokes
Cicoria San Pasquale	Salad (all seasons)	70	Stokes, Dessert
Cicoria catalagna	Salad (Asparagus or Radichetta)	70	Stokes, Harris, Herbst, Nichols, Asgrow, Dessert, Ferry Morse, Northrup King
F & P Early Strain	Salad (Asparagus or Radichetta)	70	Dessert
Sugarhat	Salad	70	Burpee
Gebo	Salad (and forcing)	70	Herbst
Rogue De Verone	Salad (and forcing)	70	Nichols
Magdeburgh Improved	Root	120	Stokes
Large rooted Magdeburg	Root	120	Dessert, Northrup King

from Dr. W. Mansour, O.S.U. Extension Service, Corvalis, OR

MAJOR MARKETS: Other Countries

There are many other countries that consume sizeable quantities of herbs and spices. Again, very little statistical information is available. For example, the socialist countries of Eastern Europe (members of Comecon) are important producers and consumers of herbs. Herb consumption is thought to be growing in these countries, but industrialization and rising labor costs are holding back herb production, and therefore, the excess available for export.

On the other hand, the shortage of foreign exchange is encouraging the authorities to maintain exports at the highest possible level. As standards of living increase in Comecon countries, it could well be that the increasing demand for herbs will have to be satisfied by imports from outside Comecon countries. Ultimately import levels would largely be a matter of Government policy since State foreign trade organizations are usually responsible for the import and export of herbs from these countries.

Currently the Japanese market for herbs is small, but the potential is 15 per cent per annum. This is faster than the growth in demand for spices. An approximate breakdown of usage is about 25 per cent by the retail sector, and 75 per cent by the industrial and institutional sectors, the latter undergoing the most rapid growth.

The eating habits of the Japanese are changing quickly. Western style food having become more popular, while the development of convenience foods and the food processing industry has increased the demand for a greater range of flavors. Curry powder has become a major product of the food processing sector, and although the major ingredients of curries are spices, herbs such as sage, dill, bay leaves and thyme are also used, though in relatively small quantities.

Another major food processing sector is the manufacturer of ham and sausages, in which some herbs, particularly bay leaves, are employed. Household consumption is also growing quickly, particularly because of the growing westernization but also because of the increased publicity being given to herbs. For example, television cookery shows have highlighted the use of various herbs, such as basil and thyme.

Japan is a producer of a number of spices and herbs, but only a few of the latter are known in the West, and for most of her supplies Japan is dependent on imports. Since the 1970s Japan has established direct trading links with China, and the latter is becoming an important supplier of herbs to the Japanese market, a trend which is likely to continue.

Production of oleoresins in Japan is very small, although their use is increasing in the food processing industry. Although some quality specifications exist in Japan, they are not so strict as those applying in the USA, and they are not as yet rigorously enforced. However, it is though that they will become more stringent in the not too distant future.

Several Western European markets, including the Netherlands, Belgium/Luxembourg, Switzerland and Scandanavian countries consume sizeable quantities of some herbs. Where possible, estimates have been made in Vol. 1, No. 5 issue of "The Herb Market Report," but for a general review of the spice market in these and other countries the report by the International Trade Centre, UNCTAD/GATT, 1977 should be consulted.

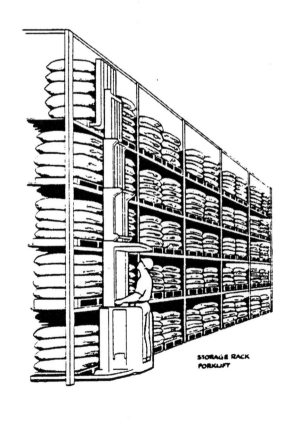

STORAGE RACK
FORKLIFT

Some Important Factors in the Selection of Good Cropland

Reviewing a soil survey report before buying a piece of land could save you headaches in the short-run and money over the long run.

Soil survey maps can be obtained from either the extension office for your County or from the Soil Conservation Service. They should include an aerial photo of the land in question, along with a number of tables giving you detailed information on the cropland in question.

Of all the diverse sets of information in these reports, the are four soil properties which should take up your first attention:
1. Natural drainage;
2. Percent of slope on land;
3. Subsoil texture; and
4. Subsoil depth.

The figures for natural drainage tell you about soil saturation. This gives you an idea of whether or not you'll have to invest in future tillage. Poorly drained soils become saturated with less water, and as a consequence, require additional drainage.

Percentage measurements for slope indicate the amount of fall in each 100 feet of distance. Land referred to as "nearly level" has less than 1-foot (1%) of fall in each 100 feet. By comparison, "steep" land has 8 to 12 feet (8% to 12%) of fall in each 100 feet.

Slope is a good indicator of erosion on a particular piece of cropland. When you get over 10% slopes, you've got a concern about row crops, from an erosion standpoint. In an 80-acre field, then you need to look at what percentage is less than 10% slope and what percentage is greater than 10%.

Arriving at an acceptable amount of slope is a management decison you need to make before investing in a new cropland. If you want to grow chamomiles or mints and more than a quarter of that land has more than 10% slope, you will have some erosion. There is no way around it. If it's 80% at

6% to 8% slope you're going to have erosion problems as well.

The next factor to look at in cropland selection is subsoil texture. There are four key terms used for classifying subsoils: sand, silt, clay, and loam. Loam, a combination of the first three, is considered the most optimum. Most prime cropland is comprised of loam soils.

Make sure you check these subsoil textures in your report. The surface texture alone does not give you a good projection on the land's production capability. You must also keep in mind the type of soil best suited for your needs varies with the crop grown.

If your looking to grow a mint, sandy soils are best. If you looking to grow basil, you do not want those sandy soils. You will need something more in the loam-clay type that has good water-holding capacity.

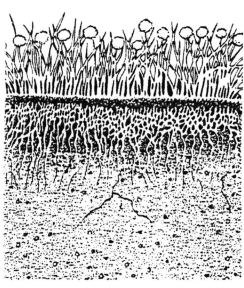

The last factor you need to check in your soil survey is soil depth. You should be wary of any soil less than 40 inches in depth to sand, gravel or rock. Soils shallower than 40 inches sometimes don't provide enough space for full root development. They can also lack enough available water for acceptable plant growth.

Other land factors you might want to look at include location, distance from town, and most importantly, water availability.

1985 Fresh Cut Herb Price Survey

Most small farmers should begin their first herb or spice venture with small acreages, perhaps less than 2 acres with each crop. This severely limits the marketing options for the small farmer. The choices generally fall into those markets buying fresh cut herbs and spices. These include the farmer's market, local grocery stores, growers' markets, and restaurants. Surveys are important as a guide for pricing and showing trends of variance from part of the country to the other.

The following table is a summary of an annual survey taken each year by "The Business of Herbs," an important newsletter for the herb and spice farmer. Our thanks to Portia Meares, Editor, for permission to reprint some of her surveys. Interested readers may wish to write directly to her: P.O. Box 559, Madison, VA 22727 for further information. Her newsletter is excellent for the beginning farmer and gardener.

					STATE						
HERB	CA (bunch)	CO	OK	Mid-West	WI	TN	KY	D.C.	MD	PA	NY (bunch)
		(all	prices	by the	ounce,	unless	otherwise	specified)			
Basil, sweet	1.29	1.50	0.70	0.80	0.35	0.65	1.00	0.75	0.80	0.50	0.75
picollo			0.70		0.35		1.00				0.80
opal			0.70	0.80	0.35		1.00	1.00			0.90
Bee balm											
Burnet				1.10	0.80			2.00	1.00		0.75
Caraway								0.60			0.75
Catnip											
Chervil		2.00		1.55			2.97	2.75	0.90	0.65	0.75
Chives	1.00	1.00	2.00	2.10	0.50	0.90	1.53	2.00	1.00	0.50	0.75
Cilantro	0.39	2.00		0.45			1.06	2.00	1.00	0.50	0.75
Dill, weed	0.39	1.00	0.45		0.35		1.00	0.75	0.75	0.50	0.75
baby weed		2.00		0.60	0.50					0.50	0.75
Fennel, leaves			0.45	0.45				0.75		0.65	0.75
French sorrel		0.25	0.75	0.45	0.40	0.60	1.76		0.75	0.38	0.75
Lavender, flowers	2.00										0.90
Lemon Balm					0.35	0.50	1.00		0.80	0.50	0.75
Lemon verbena					1.50					1.00	0.75
Lovage								0.75		0.50	0.80
Marjoram, sweet	1.00	1.50	0.75	1.55	0.75	0.70	1.75	1.50	0.90	1.00	0.75
Mint, apple					0.50	0.75					1.00
orange					0.35	0.75		1.00	0.75	1.00	1.00
peppermint	1.00	1.50	0.45	0.45	0.35		1.00	1.00	0.75	1.00	0.85
pineapple					0.60					1.00	0.75
spearmint			0.45		0.50	0.50	1.25	0.75	0.75	1.00	0.85
Oregano		1.50	0.75	0.80	0.75			1.25	1.00	1.00	0.75
Parsley, curly		0.75			0.25	0.50		0.75	0.75	0.50	0.75
Italian		0.75	0.50	0.45	0.25	0.50		1.00	0.75	0.50	0.75
Rosemary	1.00	1.50	1.50	1.65	1.25	1.00	1.00	2.25	1.00	2.00	1.25
Sage, common	1.00	2.00	0.50	0.55	0.35	0.60	1.00	1.25	0.80	0.50	0.85
pineapple			1.50						1.00		0.85
clary											0.85
Savory, summer					0.75	0.85					0.75
winter	1.00	1.50					1.49		0.90	1.00	0.75
Tarragon	1.00	1.75	1.50	1.65	1.25	1.50	1.80	2.00	2.00	2.00	1.00
Thyme, common	1.00	1.50	1.40	1.55	0.75	0.75	1.65	2.00	1.00	1.00	0.75
lemon	1.00		1.40		1.00			2.25	1.00	1.00	0.90

BOOK REVIEW:
Chemical Marketing Reporter

There are a number of different source directories available which can often help get most small farmers started with their marketing of herbs and spices. One, which is also an excellent source of import data, is the "Chemical Marketing Reporter."

The "Chemical Marketing Reporter" is a weekly tabloid trade journal, published by Schnell Publishing Company, Inc., 100 Church Street, New York, NY 10007. Subscriptions are $60.00 per year, and include the annual OPD Chemical Buyers Directory. Both have been published for 72 years.

The tabloid usually runs more than 50 pages and includes regular sections on "Perfume & Flavoring Materials," "US Imports of Chemical and Related Materials," and features on why various botanicals and spices vary in their price from one week to the next.

The July 22, 1985 issue, for example, had articles on patchouli and clove leaf, orange oil, cassia, fennel, mustard, paprika, pepper, and turmeric. Each weekly issue runs a section titled "Current Prices of Chemical and Related Materials," with a summary of the week's price changes for spices and herbs which advanced or reduced in spot prices.

In the import section last week, for example, 23,148 pounds of marjoram entered the Port of New York. The consignee was International Brokers and the crop came from Alexandia, Egypt on the ship Lash Italia. A review of prices shows that marjoram from Egypt ranges in price from $0.58 to $0.60, with French marjoram beginning at $1.00 per pound.

Included with the annual subscription to "Chemical Marketing Reporter" is the uniquely useful annual, OPD Chemical Buyers Directory. This source gives names, addresses, phone numbers, telex numbers of the hundreds of dealers in the thousands of chemicals, including most botanicals and spices. This is a very important reference.

Note from the Editor

I would like to expand this newsletter and could use some help. If you have found an interesting herbal clipping in your readings, please send it to us and we will attempt to share it with others.

The Herb Market Report
1305 Vista Drive • Grants Pass, OR 97527

The Herb Market Report is a newsletter published monthly and distributed by The Southern Oregon Herb Gatherers' Association, Inc.

Oak Publishing
1212 SW 5th Street,
Grants Pass, OR 97526
Phone: 541-426-5588

THE POTENTIAL OF HERBS AS A CASH-CROP is now in print and available. Send $12.00 for an autographed edition.

Address Correction Requested

Vol. 1 No. 8

THE HERB MARKET REPORT

for the herb farmer and forager
Vol. 1 No. 9   Oct., 1985

A THYME for Cultivation and Harvest

Thyme is a common name given to the many herbs of the Thymus species. More than three hundred species of thyme now exist, including the many hybrids, varieties, and ecotypes. As a result, classifying the different thymes is, at best, difficult.

Common or garden thyme, (Thymus vulgaris L.), is a diminutive perennial herbaceous shrub of the mint family native to the Mediterranian region and Asia Minor. Admirable for ornamental effects in rock gardens and edging paths and lawns, it is also grown as an herb for seasoning foods and for an essential oil that is used extensively in medicine.

T. vulgaris is native to southern Europe, from Spain to Italy and was introduced into England about 1548. It is now commonly cultivated there and in most mild-temperate and subtropical climates. This includes southern and central Europe, including Bulgaria, the southern U.S.S.R., Morocco, Turkey, Syria, Israel, northern India, southern Africa, New England, California, Columbia, Brazil, and the higher elevations of the West Indies.

This thyme is the one found most frequently in the herb garden. It is suberect, with numerous stems 8 to 18 inches high and a woody fibrous root. The tiny grayish-green narrow leaves rarely exceed 1/4 inch in length by about 1/10 in in width. The small lavender flowers are favorites of the honeybee. The seeds are minute and globose. The three principle varieties of this thyme are English, French, and German, and they differ in leaf shape, leaf color, and essential oil composition.

T. zygis is indigenous to Portugal, Spain, and the Balearic Islands. It is a short, erect shrub which is foraged for the production of Spanish thyme oil. Of the two species, var. gracilis is the more important, thriving at low elevations in the Iberian peninsula of Spain. Var. floribunda is an alpine variety of T. zygis.

Wild thyme, Thymus serpyllum L., is a prostrate, small, creeping perennial that has a woody stem at the base. This herb, also known as creeping thyme or "mother-of-thyme," is a native of Europe and used primarily as an ornamental. Lemon thyme, Thymus X citriodorus (P.), is a many-branched, lemon-scented shrub cultivated as a culinary herb. The lemon thyme plant has a semierect stem which is adaptable to mechanical harvest.

Thymus capitatus L. is native to Israel and other Middle Eastern and Mediterranean countries and is used locally as an oregano. Ornamentals include T. nummularius, T. pannonicu, T. praecox, T. pseudolanuginosis, and T. pulegioids. Thymus praecox subsp. arcticus J. is a popular low-growing, creeping thyme, available with many flower colors and is often used as a ground cover.

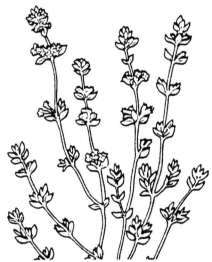

The two most commercially important varieties are the narrow-leaved French Thyme (T. vulgaris) and the variform lemon thyme (T. citriodorus). Both have been successfully grown in California, especially around Dixon. A modified wild-rose cutter is used to harvest several other herbs grown in that area, including chervil, rosemary, tarragon, sage, dillweed, summer savory, and sweet basil.

Thyme may be grown from seed or propagated by division, layering of side shoots or by cuttings taken in early summer. Seedlings are raised in beds and set out when 2 or 3 inches high, or seeds may be drilled directly in the field no more than 1/4 inches deep and at a spacing of 2 or 3 feet. 6 pounds of seed is needed per acre when drilling.

Root cuttings are set out 1 to 1.5 feet apart in rows 2 feet apart. Weeding is performed by hand, but cultivators can be used, and fertilizer is applied in both fall and spring. In cool climates, the plants are usually covered with earth or mulch during the winter.

Most all thymes are long-lived in light, dry, calcareous soils, and short-lived and less aromatic in heavy, wet soils. It thrives in full sun. The reported life zone of thyme ranges from an annual mean temperature of 40°F to 90°F, an annual precipitation variance of 12 to 110 inches of water, and a soil pH ranging from 4.5 to 8.0. It likes a pH of 6.3.

Thyme blooms from June through August, and the flowering tops are harvested in one or two cuttings per season. This can be done with a modified wild-rose cutter, similar to a forage harvester/piggy-back system of wagons. Some leafy stem is also desired when the herbage is shade-dried or dehydrated to preserve the grayish-green color. One may expect a 1,000 to 2,000 pound yield per acre of dried thyme from a well-established field.

To extract the volatile oil, the entire plant is cut, preferably when in full bloom, and subjected to steam distillation without previous drying. Oil is frequently distilled in simple field stills near where large quantities of the plant grow wild in Spain. In Egypt, highest thymol and carvacrol concentrations were detected in the early stage of blooming. An acre will yield 2,000 to 4,000 pounds of fresh thyme, providing 20 to 40 pounds of thyme oil.

The essential oils of thyme are grouped into three main types: thyme oil, which contains 42 to 60 percent phenols and is mainly thymol; origanum oil, which contains 63 to 74 percent phenols and is mainly carvacrol; and lemon thyme oil, which contains citral. Thyme oil is divided into two types, a red, unrectified oil and a white, rectified oil. The oil content of dried plant material is 2 to 5 percent, while fresh plants yield are less. An oleoresin is also now extracted with developed commercial markets.

In 1984, the United States imported more than 2,500 tons of dried thyme and more than 15 ton of thyme oil. While import figures are dropping because of new domestic farm productions, this represented more than $6,000,000 in trade deficits rather than rural farm incomes. For each ton of oil imported, there was more than 100 tons of plant material extracted. This biomass could have been converted into renewable fuels as a wood product.

Thyme is used for flavoring cheeses, soups, stews, stuffings, meats, fish, dressings, sauces, and honey. The essential oil and oleoresin of thyme are also used extensively in the flavor and food industries. The oil is used in the flavoring of toothpastes, mouthwashes, and cough medicines. The oil is also used in the manufacture of perfumes and numerous cosmetics.

Thymol, a white crystalline phenol having antiseptic and fungicidal properties as well as aromatic qualities, occures in thyme oil. Thymol is utilized in pharmaceutical preparations such as gargles, coughdrops, dentifrices, and mouthwashes. It is also used to preserve meat and as a vermifuge to cure hookworm in horses and dogs. Commercially, it is the fungicidal ingredient in many antimildew preparations.

Thyme oil, obtained by water-and-steam distillation, was formerly produced in the south of France and on Cyprus but is now mainly exported from Spain. Thymol for medical and other purposes is derived from thyme oil or synthetically by dehydrogenation of l-piperitone. In Europe, other natural sources are Monarda didyma L. and M. punctata L., the horsemints. In India, thymol is obtained from oil of ajowan (Carum copticum Benth.). Germany is a major buyer in this market.

The name thyme, derived from the Greek, has several counterparts in English, including "courage," "sacrifice," and "to fumigate." Thyme was used as an incense to perfume and purify the temples. The herb was considered to have invigorating qualities and was also a symbol of courage and bravery - a compliment of the highest grade in Greece two thousand years ago was to tell someone he "smelled of thyme."

According to tradition, thyme was in the hay and straw bed of the Virgin Mary and the Christ Child.

"Resubscribe."

Advertise in
The Herb Market Report

CLASSIFIED RATES

Minimum of 20 words for $10.00 per month. ($12.00 for nonsubscribers). 35¢ each additional word. (40¢ for nonsubscribers). Payable in advance.

Copy deadline is 30 days prior to issue date.

DISPLAY ADS

"The Herb Market Report" is published monthly. The publisher reserves the right to reject or cancel any advertising which does not conform to the standards of the publication.

If submitted material is not correctly sized, it will be altered to fit at the discretion of the publishing department.

Artwork, mats and other camera ready ads will be destroyed after 60 days if not otherwise indicated.

A 2% discount is offered for customers on account for payment within 10 days of invoice date.

Prices are for camera-ready ads only. Any extra production expenses will be billed at cost.

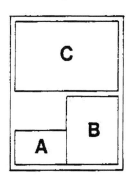

MECHANICAL REQUIREMENTS

	VERTICAL	HORIZONTAL
A. 1/8th page	2-1/2"	3-7/8"
B. 1/4th page	5"	3-7/8"
C. 1/2 page	5"	7-3/4"

DISPLAY AD RATES

	ONE MONTH	THREE MONTHS
A.	$25	$20
B.	$40	$35
C.	$60	$50

ORDER INFORMATION

"The Herb Market Report,"
Advertising Department,
1305 Vista Drive,
Grants Pass, OR   97527
(503) 476-5588

Payment enclosed _____

Please send bill _____

Please reserve _____-page space in the _____ issue(s) of "The Herb Market Report."

Enclosed is $_____ to cover ad rates.

Business name _____

Address _____

_____zip_____

Signed _____

United States: Average Unit Import Values of Specified Essential Oils, 1983 and 1984

Essential Oils	1983	1984
	Dollars per kilogram	
Almond oil (bitter)..............	3.91	4.13
Anise oil........................	9.91	10.94
Bergamot oil.....................	29.30	28.59
Camphor oil......................	2.41	2.93
Caraway oil......................	38.81	38.49
Cassia oil.......................	72.84	69.90
Cedar leaf oil...................	32.95	37.68
Cedarwood oil....................	5.91	5.60
Cinnamon oil.....................	8.17	7.32
Citronella oil...................	4.17	3.89
Citrus oil, other...............	39.60	19.90
Clove oil........................	3.91	4.23
Cornmint oil (Mentha arvensis)....	9.79	10.43
Ecualyptus oil...................	4.70	4.97
Geranium oil.....................	44.99	49.57
Grapefruit oil...................	4.18	4.97
Lavender oil (inc. spike)........	15.92	13.67
Lemon oil........................	10.64	11.96
Lemongrass oil...................	7.41	8.64
Lignaloe (Bois de rose oil).......	17.15	15.20
Lime oil.........................	25.87	26.58
Neroli (Orange flower oil)........	41.16	437.02
Nutmeg oil.......................	14.60	17.56
Onion and garlic oil.............	136.02	92.00
Orange oil.......................	.41	.89
Origanum oil.....................	28.00	31.28
Orris oil........................	109.82	156.96
Palmarosa oil....................	35.46	35.98
Patchouli oil....................	31.39	27.48
Peppermint oil (Mentha piperita)..	17.96	36.18
Petitgrain oil...................	11.17	14.09
Pineneedle oil...................	16.19	18.39
Rose oil (attar of roses)........	2,981.02	1,906.39
Rosemary oil.....................	9.92	8.34
Sandalwood oil...................	83.16	88.69
Sassafras oil....................	3.53	5.66
Spearmint oil....................	12.68	11.97
Thyme oil........................	20.27	21.64
Vetiver oil......................	39.32	43.95
Ylang ylang (Cananga oil).........	41.58	46.09
Other essential oils.............	14.45	15.88

Note: All values refer to f.o.b. country or origin.

SOURCE: U.S. Department of Commerce.   April 1985   Horticultural and Tropical Products Division, FAS/USDA

New Books

The Potential of Herbs as a Cash Crop

Here is an information-filled look at the potential of herb and spice production on small acreages. Alternative crops such as spices and botanicals are feasible but require information not readily available. This book provides that missing information and a perspective on what is involved for the small farmer when considering these alternative crops.

It backgrounds all the considerations, with a heavy emphasis on marketing. The author - Richard Alan Miller - has marketed herbs for over 15 years and sees the need to create domestic sources of supply for products currently imported into the U.S. Not only does this give the small farmer access to some of the economic recovery, it also makes him an important factor in the balance of trade deficits.

Unlike other "living off the land" approaches, this book features tables to help the reader determine needs, qualifications, and required tools to successfully farm herbs and spices. Assets required for successful management are also detailed. Comprehensive, yet simply stated, this book provides a firm foundation for the potential of herbs as a cash crop.

Richard Alan Miller is also the author of the forthcoming companion volume, THE NOMADIC LIFE OF THE PROFESSIONAL FORAGER.

The Magical And Ritual Use of Aphrodisiacs

The quest for a true aphrodisiac is as old as mankind. Whether their effects are physical, psychological, or a combination of the two, those "love foods" that enhance the sexual experience continues to be highly valuable.

Today, more than ever before, our understanding of biochemistry allows for a thorough knowledge of the properties and specific effects of aphrodisiacs. The author - a biochemist, physicist, and herbalist - brings to his new book both scientific expertise and a deep appreciation for the psychological and spiritual element of human sexuality.

To stimulate the imagination and to augment both the biochemical and psychological effects of aphrodisiacs, the author suggests specific contemporary rituals drawn from sources as diverse as Tantic yoga and Western magic. These practices help the couple attune to the deeper implications of sexual union.

Special sections on hormones, foods, pharmaceuticals, and scents give additional insight - both practical and magical - into the vast range and potential of sexual expression.

Richard Alan Miller is also author of this book's companion volume, THE MAGICAL AND RITUAL USE OF HERBS.

Please send me _____ copies of the book
THE POTENTIAL OF HERBS AS A CASH-CROP
$12.00 per book (includes shipping) $ _____

Please send me _____ copies of the book
THE MAGICAL AND RITUAL USE OF APHRODISIACS
$9.00 per book (includes shipping) $ _____

Please send me _____ copies of the book
THE MAGICAL AND RITUAL USE OF HERBS
$7.00 per book (includes shipping) $ _____

Total Enclosed
Please make check payable to OAK $ _____

Please notify me when the forthcoming book
THE NOMADIC LIFE OF THE PROFESSIONAL FORAGER ☐
is available.

Please print

Name _____

Street _____

City _____

State _____ Zip _____

Mail this form to: Organization for the
Advancement of Knowledge
1305 Vista Drive,
Grants Pass, OR   97527

MAJOR MARKETS:
Some Conclusions

Supply difficulties are expected to increase as herb production in the traditional growing areas become increasingly uneconomical using existing techniques. This is due to rising costs of labor and land, and is particularly apparent in relation to the collection of herbs from the wild. The increasing price of herbs and more frequent quality specifications have already encouraged more capital-intensive methods of herb production in some countries, such as the USA, the United Kingdom and West Germany. If prices rise rapidly, and quality requirements in the major American and European markets become more stringent, then new producers may face continued strong competition, especially from producers using capital-intensive techniques in the large producing and consuming countries.

Despite these developments there is certainly scope for potential new producers of culinary herbs, and developing countries could become important suppliers of some herbs. North Africa, particularly Egypt, is supplying an increasing proportion of world supplies, while one German company has recently begun to grow herbs, including dill and parsley, in partnership with the Kenyan Government. Although the level of wages is an important variable, one source suggests that it is the ability to grow herbs all the year round that is a more important consideration.

Produce from the Kenyan project is shipped to the consuming countries by sea rather than the more expensive air-freight, freight costs now being a vital consideration. Other trading companies in the major producing countries have also attempted to develop new sources of supply but have faced economic, technical and political problems which have led in some cases to termination of the operations. Herbs do not always transport well and slight differences in climate and soil can make differences to flavor and odor. It may, therefore, take a few years to produce suitable products. Moreover the harvesting and drying of herbs to a satisfactory standard requires considerable skill and knowledge.

The demand for herbs is growing around 10 per cent per annum, a much faster rate of growth than for most spices. While demand is growing in each sector of the market, namely the household, industrial and food service sectors, it is in the last two that the greatest increase in demand is evident, reflecting the increasing popularity of convenience foods and the growing number of people eating away from home. Herb oleoresins, with the exception of celery seed and sage, are not widely used. Indeed, unless a producer can ensure excellent and consistent quality it is unlikely that he will be able to market herbs that have been processed beyond the initial drying stage, since for several reasons major users prefer to receive their herbs in the unground form.

The major markets' need for clean herbs of good color cannot be overstressed, and a new producer must be aware that quality specifications are almost certain to become more severe. Thus, it should be apparent that the growing of herbs offer little encouragement to inexperienced growers who are looking for large quick returns from a small investment in time and money.

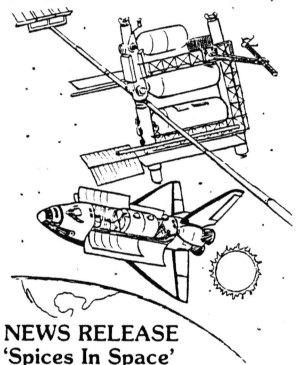

NEWS RELEASE
'Spices In Space'

The following news release was received from the American Society of Aerospace Pilots (ASAP):

"McCormick Schilling Earth Orbiting Research Platform discovers new 'High-Tech Spice.'

"Grants Pass, Oregon;

"While doing research on the growth patterns of truffels in a 0-G environment,

- continued on back page -

United States: Average Unit Import Values of Specified Essential Oils, 1983 and 1984

Essential Oils	1983	1984
	Dollars per kilogram	
Almond oil (bitter)..............	3.91	4.13
Anise oil.......................	9.91	10.94
Bergamot oil....................	29.30	28.59
Camphor oil.....................	2.41	2.93
Caraway oil.....................	38.81	38.49
Cassia oil.....................	72.84	69.90
Cedar leaf oil..................	32.95	37.68
Cedarwood oil..................	5.91	5.60
Cinnamon oil...................	8.17	7.32
Citronella oil.................	4.17	3.89
Citrus oil, other..............	39.60	19.90
Clove oil.....................	3.91	4.23
Cornmint oil (Mentha arvensis)....	9.79	10.43
Ecualyptus oil.................	4.70	4.97
Geranium oil...................	44.99	49.57
Grapefruit oil.................	4.18	4.97
Lavender oil (inc. spike)........	15.92	13.67
Lemon oil.....................	10.64	11.96
Lemongrass oil.................	7.41	8.64
Lignaloe (Bois de rose oil).......	17.15	15.20
Lime oil......................	25.87	26.58
Neroli (Orange flower oil)........	41.16	437.02
Nutmeg oil....................	14.60	17.56
Onion and garlic oil.............	136.02	92.00
Orange oil....................	.41	.89
Origanum oil..................	28.00	31.28
Orris oil.....................	109.82	156.96
Palmarosa oil.................	35.46	35.98
Patchouli oil.................	31.39	27.48
Peppermint oil (Mentha piperita)..	17.96	36.18
Petitgrain oil.................	11.17	14.09
Pineneedle oil.................	16.19	18.39
Rose oil (attar of roses).........	2,981.02	1,906.39
Rosemary oil..................	9.92	8.34
Sandalwood oil.................	83.16	88.69
Sassafras oil.................	3.53	5.66
Spearmint oil.................	12.68	11.97
Thyme oil....................	20.27	21.64
Vetiver oil...................	39.32	43.95
Ylang ylang (Cananga oil).........	41.58	46.09
Other essential oils............	14.45	15.88

Note: All values refer to f.o.b. country or origin.

SOURCE: U.S. Department of Commerce. April 1985 Horticultural and Tropical Products Division, FAS/USDA

4

- continued from page 3 -

minute parasites were discovered forming nodes on the roots of the plants.

"These nodes, now being cultivated on the orbiting research platform Spice Aerospace McCor-Schill (SAMS), have been found to grow only in a non-gravity environment. They require a complete vacuum to continue their life and certain qualities of the root must be maintained. These qualities are now a closely guarded secret.

"The new 'High-Tech Spice,' named Orbiton truffelon, is produced under a very exacting procedure which requires the platform environment to remain absolutely and instantly temperature-controlled for drying of the nodes. It creates one of the most pleasing sensations known to the palate of man: a sensation practically indescribable, but akin to a combination of garlic, onion, clove and vanilla with a hint of cooling freshness.

The new spice is so much in demand (not only because of the incredible flavor it gives to meats, salads and vegetables but also because of it's exotic origin), that it presently sells for $2,500 per oz. It is in high demand among the haute cuisine restaurants of the world and a list is currently being created for selection of future recipients of the delicacy. Although the cost seems exorbitant at this time, it should be noted that due the potency of the trufellic, only minute quantities are needed in food preparation.

"McCorSchill estimates that first year revenues will exceed $3,000,000 and triple every year thereafter as platform production increases. Considering McCorSchill's initial concept of a $125,000,000 research and development write-off for the EArth Orbiting Research Platform, it would appear that the platform will have paid for itself within 4.5 years.

"Estimates at this time indicate that McCorSchill, with planned platform expansion and association increases, will be producing in excess of 30,000 ounces per year."

Note from the Editor

I would like to expand this newsletter and could use some help. If you have found an interesting herbal clipping in your readings, please send it to us and we will attempt to share it with others.

The Herb Market Report

1305 Vista Drive • Grants Pass, OR 97527

The Herb Market Report is a newsletter published monthly and distributed by The Southern Oregon Herb Gatherers' Association, Inc.

Oak Publishing
1212 SW 5th Street,
Grants Pass, OR 97526
Phone: 541-426-5588

Copyright 1986-2013 © Dr. Richard Alan Miller

THE POTENTIAL OF HERBS AS A CASH-CROP is now in print and available. Send $12.00 for an autographed edition.

Address Correction Requested

Vol. 1 No.

THE HERB MARKET REPORT
for the herb farmer and forager   Vol. 1 No. 10 Nov., 1985

The Collection and Handling of Seeds from Forest Trees

More than 50 million acres in the continental United States need immediate planting to trees. This figure does not even include either Alaska or Canada. There are numerous reasons why. They include areas which are not restocking naturally with desirable forest trees, erosion, barriers for protecting livestock and fields, and, most important, the United States needs all the timber it can grow.

This mammoth undertaking will require more than 25 thousand tons of seeds from various forest trees. Although more than 600 species of woody plants are useful for conservation planting, less than 130 species make up the bulk of the seed trade in this area. Further, some 25 species, mostly conifers, account for about 90 percent of the areas which need planting and seeding.

The collection of forest tree seeds in the United States is largely from wild stands. Increasing quantities, however, are now being gathered from plantations. More and more of the collected seed comes from selected superior trees, genetically developed for heavy production.

Much of the supply in the United States is collected by private individuals, most of whom are independent operators. The greater users of the seeds in this country, however, are the public forestry agencies, although there is a growing use by forest industries and commercial seed dealers. Both the public and industrial agencies usually buy unextracted cones or fruits from the small private collectors.

The progressive collector of seeds of forest trees will scout out desirable collection areas in advance. He can get some early estimates at the time of spring flowering, but he should check the crops in the summer after the fruits are well developed, keeping in mind the following points:

1. Confine collection wherever possible to trees above average in one or more of these qualities: Growth rate, stem form, crown and branching habit, resistance to damage, and seed production. Stands with a high proportion of superior trees are especially desirable for seed collections. Where areas of seed production or seed orchards are available, collect from them.

2. Obtain written permission of landowners before making any collection on their land.

3. Where available, utilize the regional tree seed-crop reporting services to locate collecting areas. In any event, estimate production from actual counts of fruits on representative trees or small sample plots well distributed over the collecting area.

4. Test for soundness of seeds in each locality and on individual trees before collection.

5. Label each sack, before it leaves the collecting ground, to show species; exact locality of collection (including elevation); day, month, and year of collection; and any special merits of the parent stand (such as "seed production area," superior stand, or "seed orchard").

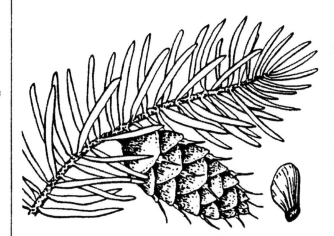

Chances are best for getting seeds high in germ rates and quality if they are collected when they are ripe and before they have suffered deterioration on the tree or on the ground.

Experienced collectors judge the ripeness of fruits by their fullness, size, color, degree of "milkiness" of the seeds, hardness of the seedcoat, their attractiveness to animals, or some combination of these factors. More precise indicies are desireable, of course.

For some pines and spruces, ripeness can be determined more accurately by the floatability of freshly picked cones in suitable test liquids, some of which are linseed oil for eastern white pine and blue spruce; SAE 20 motor oil for loblolly, longleaf, and slash pines; turpentine for white spruce; half linseed oil and half kerosene for Jeffrey and ponderosa pines; kerosene for red and sugar pines.

For many tree species, the best time to collect is when the first seeds begin to fall natually. Large-scale operations must begin sooner than that, however, to avoid substantial losses of good seed. The best time for seed gathering varies for each species from season to season and place to place. As a guide, the general season is known for a great many species including some that can be collected in two seasons, as follows:

Spring: Aspens, cottonwoods, most elms, red maple, silver maple, poplars, and the willows.

Summer: Cherries, chockcherries, Douglas-firs, red maple, mulberries, Siberian pea-tree, and the plums.

Fall: Most ashes, beeches, most birches, boxelder, catalpas, cherries, Douglas-firs, firs, hickories, junipers, most larches, black locust, maples (except red and silver), Osage-orange, pecan, most pines, plums, spruces, sweetgum, sycamores, walnuts, white-cedars, and yellow-poplar.

Winter: Some ashes, yellow birch, boxelder, catalpas, Osage-orange, black spruce, Norway spruce, sycamores, and walnuts.

Any season: Jack pine (except in the southern part of its range), lodgepole pine (except on the eastern side of the Cascades), Monterey pine, and sand pine.

Collection Techniques

Seed can be collected in several ways. None of these ways are usually satisfactory from either a forest conservation or ease of harvest perspective. Experience makes the difference. As a result, special classes are usually offered to employees working with large collection ventures. Small businesses only hire experienced cone foragers.

The most desired method of harvest is to locate a stand of trees growing at uniform heights, especially in an open field. The limbs of these trees can be drawn to the ground with a hook. Cones can then be taken from the ground or by climbing up tall step ladders. Unfortunately, this method does not permit the collector to reach the top of the tree where the crop is heaviest.

Douglas-fir can have excellent crops of cone and only be six or seven feet in height. Such trees are rare however, and usually abundant crops will not be found on this fir with specimens less than fifty or sixty feet high. The best cone crops are found on trees more than one hundred feet in height. The top fifteen to twenty feet will bear the greater part of this crop. The cones grow on or near the ends of the limbs and the side branches. None are ever found next to the trunk.

Thus, the best way of collection is to climb the trees with spurs and safety belt. The collector goes to the tops of trees where the branches are shorter and the cones more abundant. A pole with a hook is used to bend branches inward. When the branch is brought in far enough, the pole is held between the legs so that the limb can be kept within reach. Then the cones can be picked with both hands and put into the burlap sack which hangs from the forager's safety belt.

OREGON AND WASHINGTON
Commercial Seed Cone Production Estimates
During Recent Periodic Seed Years

| Species | Price per Bushel | | Number of Bushels | | |
	Average	Range	Oregon	Washington	Total Ore. & Wash.
Douglas-fir	$2.50	$1.50 -$3.00	300,000	125,000	425,000
Ponderosa Pine	1.50	1.00 - 2.00	7,000	4,000	11,000
Sugar Pine	1.00	.75 - 1.50	3,000		2,000
Noble Fir	1.50	1.40 - 2.50	8,000	4,000	12,000
Grand Fir	1.50	1.00 - 2.50	3,000	5,000	8,000
Concolor Fir	1.50	1.00 - 2.50	2,000		2,000
Sitka Spruce	1.50	1.00 - 2.50	2,000	4,000	6,000
Engelmann Spruce	2.50	2.00 - 3.00	100	100	200
Western Hemlock	7.50	6.00 -10.00	100	200	300
Total			325,200	142,300	466,500

from "Special Forest Products: 1969 Harvesting Report", USDA Forest Service, Pacific Northwest Region. 1970.

A forager, inexperienced in the use of tree climbers, will swear he is going to die from exhaustion before the day has even begun. A few days practice will take care of most of the difficulty, and an experienced forager can go up a tree as easily as an ordinary person might climb a ladder. Working in a tree a hundred feed high can be exhilarating, once you become accustomed to it.

The burlap sack is being filled with Douglas-fir seed cones. Most sacks hold about two bushels.

Some foragers cut the branches from the trees as they climb, prefering to do their harvesting from the ground. Others will top the tree, a techniques often employed in areas where tall trees are considered dangerous around homes or where the limbs interfere with power lines.

Many of the larger logging companies will fall trees with heart rot, too many branches, or faulty trunks, trees which do not make good saw logs. This is primarily for the cones, the contention being that the tree isn't good for anything else. Such a tree will produce from one to two pounds of seed, sufficient for aerial seeding 4 to 8 acres.

The best method of collection, from the forager's point-of-view, is to follow close behind tree fallers in on-going logging operations. He chops the limbs from the fallen trees so the cones can be easily picked. Large sums of money can be made in this situation. The down side to this is that larger trees hit the ground so hard that the cones are scattered in all directions, often spoiling the forager's opportunity.

Many logging firms will not permit foragers to work on their property. Harvesting the seed is a conservation project, but the timber owner does not often take this long range view. If a tree falls on a forager and kills him, which has happened, the logger may find himself in serious difficulties.

Small woodland owners should fall their trees when the cones are ripe, selecting trees with heavy crops. Often the cones will be worth more than the fuel in the trunk of the tree.

Cones are often covered with fresh pitch, making the job of collection a sticky and dirty one. Vaseline, lubricating grease or other similar material helps to keep the hands from becoming too badly gummed. In rainy weather there isn't the trouble, as moisture tends to keep the pitch from sticking.

Most foragers do not bother to grease their hands, and gloves are impractical. Pitch is easily removed at the end of a day with a little solvent. Gas will also work.

Special methods of collection are used on some kinds of trees. Western Hemlock cones, being very small, can be raked off the ends of branches. Port Orford cones and those of the Western Red Cedar can also be taken with a rake. Other methods include a tarp under the tree, climb them and shake the trunks as hard a possible.

Beating the branches with sticks helps also. If done when the seed is ripe and the cones partly open, the seed will fall onto the ground sheets, making the harvest a simple one.

Marketing

Cones are bought both by the pound and bushel, depending upon the buyer. Few dealers care to purchase by the sack. The forager will make more at the beginning of the season by selling by the pound. At this time, the cones are full of moisture and are tightly closed. This requires more to the bushel but less to the pound.

As the cones mature, they become dryer and open their scales. At this stage, they weigh less and occupy more space, making the sale by the bushel more attractive to the forager. A consistent system throughout a season, however, is fair to both the buyer and forager.

Cones are bought by seedmen on the basis of their seed content. Green cones are split longitudinally with a sharp knife. The number of seeds the knife cuts in two determines the value. Douglas Fir cones that "cut" four, five or six seeds are desirable. Some cones will cut only one or two seeds and are not worth harvesting. Worms may damage otherwise good seeds also, reducing the price paid. Cones from one side of the tree may contain more seeds than from the other. A .22 rifle or shotgun is often used by testing crews to shoot down cones for samples.

As a rule of thumb, for every seed cut, you may yield up to one ounce of seed per bushel of cones. If a cone cuts four seeds, you will get four ounces of seed (dry weight) to the bushel of cones. As some trees will bear as much as eight or more bushels, the crop from one such tree will aerial seed eight acres. A quarter of a pound of seed is required for one acre when done by plane.

The seed is often stratified before aerial planting. This is so that germination will take place very soon after it falls upon the ground. This reduces losses from rodents and other seed diets. Mice, chipmunks and squirrels enjoy tree seeds.

There are 43,400 Douglas Fir tree seeds per pound. A quarter pound of seed will contain ten to eleven thousand seeds. If this number resulted in eight hundred trees per acre (8%) this would be excellent. The percentage is usually considerably less. Of course, a good part of the seed harvested is planted in nurseries so that young stock can be hand planted in cut or burned over areas.

Usually these treelings are planted 8 to 12 feet apart. The viability of the seed runs from a very favorable eighty-five percent down to much less than fifty. Most of the conifers can not be grown from cuttings economically and seed planting is the only alternative.

Douglas Fir seed sells for up to twenty dollars a pound some years. Other seasons it will bring as little as six dollars. When crops are poor, the demand is high. There are insects which help wreck the seed crops. An insect larva gets into the cones and eats the seeds. When this damage is high, the viability low, and cone crops small, you can count on high prices.

The amount of seed produced per tree varies widely between species and from year to year. It is influenced also by the age, size, and health of the seed trees. Within any age or size class the dominant, widely spaced or open-grown trees usually produce the most seed if they receive adequate pollination.

In good years a good seed tree may produce the following bushels of cones: Tamarack, 0.75; black spruce and eastern hem-lock, 1; jack pine, ponderosa pine, red pine, and slash pine, 1.5; European larch and white spruce, 2; white pine, 5; and sugar pine, 5 to 7.

Some foragers gather squirrel-cut cones from the ground, but these fruits may not be adequately ripened. 30 and 40 years ago, foragers often collected conifer from squirrel hoards in both the Lake States and the West, but this is rare today, except in the Pacific Northwest.

Fleshy fruits should not be crushed or dried more than superficially. Others should be spread out and dried partly before shipment. The fruits should be processed or extracted as soon as possible after collection.

The Handling of Cones

When the buyers get enough cones on hand they start their plants. The cones are first run over a table which is equipped with an eccentric to jog off the tree needles. Then they are laid on the floor for a week to ten days to give the seeds a chance to absorb the vitality from the green cones - also to dry a little.

The next step is to place them on trays in a dry kiln where they are kept under low heat for two days. This removes the moisture so that the scales will open and free the seed.

A "churn" receives the cones as the next step and is run for five minutes per batch. This process thrashes out the seeds. The cones go into a hopper below and the seeds drop into a pan.

Removal of the wings follows. This is done by putting the seeds in a cylindrical screened barrel equiped with four revolving brushes. A seed cleaning sifter with screening and wind separation completes the job. The finished product is packed into bags for shipment.

Disposal of the empty cones can be a problem. Some buyers burn them, making a very hot fire. A few are sold for ornamentals around Christmas time, such things as the bracts for pot pourri ingredients. With different handling, often the cone can be retained, relatively undamaged. There is a very large market for various cones, especially the larger ones, like sugar pine and white pine.

Most of these are dipped into boiling water for five to ten minutes. Time enough to liquify the pitch and cause it to run over the entire cone, sealing it from outside moisture. Cones treated in this way will last more than 3 years.

Being Led Down the "Primrose Path"

When one considers the numerous and diverse forms of marketing now available to the 20th-Century man, you are given a true picture of just how many options exist when selecting a botanical as a cash crop. The small evening primrose (Oenothera biennis L.) was chosen for discussion as representative of how a botanical often becomes in demand.

The herb is a newcomer to the medical field and is barely noticed by passersby. The yellow flowers it produces twine up the stem and die after a single evening, hence it's common name. After the petals fall, dozens of pods full of tiny seeds remain. The reason for this herb's rise to the heights of medical importance lies in the contents of these seeds.

The rapid rise to fame of evening primrose is intimately linked to the discovery of a family of hormone-like substances known as prostaglandins. These are actually a family of compounds closely related to essential fatty acids. In the 1960s, they were discovered in virtually every cell in the body. In 1971, DR. John R. Vane (Wellcome Research Laboratories - England) discovered that aspirin works by blocking the last step in the body's synthesis of two kinds of PGs.

This led to the belief that PGs somehow were involved in pain, inflammation and fever. Today there are few substances that currently command more widespread interest in the medical sciences than prostaglandins. These important molecules in minute amounts produce a broad spectrum of effects that embrace practically every biological function. The explosion of research papers published on prostaglandins has now reached a level estimated at more than 200 per month!

What seems to be emerging from much of this new research on prostaglandins is the importance of maintaining them in proper balance. The presence of too much or too little of some PGs can induce diseased conditions. The most potent and intensly studied prostaglandins are made from vitamin-like substances called essential fatty acids or EFAs. These compounds are similar to essential amino acids in that they cannot be manufactured by the body, and need to be provided in the diet.

One of the critical EFAs in the making of prostaglandins is cis-linoleic acid, which is converted to gamma-linolenic acid (GLA). Dr. David F. Horrobin (recently Professor of Medicine at the University of Montreal) discovered that because of junk foods, an excess of wrong fats, too much alcohol intake, and the aging process itself - most of us are deficient in the ability to convert linoleic acid into GLA, thereby seriously curtailing the production of one of the most critical prostaglandins, PGE.

Most of the GLA formed in the body rapidly converts into another substance called dihomogammalinolenic acid (DGLA), eventually converted into a number of compounds, most important of which is PGE_1.

PGE_1 has already proved itself to be a miracle molecule. It stops thrombosis and lowers blood pressure. It opens up blood vessels and relieves the pain of angina and slows down the speed at which cholesterol is made. It enables insulin to work more effectively. It prevents inflammation and controls arthritis. It has many actions in the brain, and produces a sense of well-being in humans.

Now it becomes clear why GLA is so critical. Without it the benefits of PGE_1 are either reduced or eliminated, and the results can be critical. With this in mind, how can one increase the amount of GLA or DGLA in one's diet?

The answer is that it is very difficult to increase the amount by eating foods rich in GLA or DGLA. It is also important to know that one cannot just eat PGE_1 (or any postaglandin) because they are destroyed by the digestive process. And GLA and DGLA are found only in tiny amounts in very few foods.

Dr. Horrobin reported only two sources, one for GLA and one for DGLA, which contain substantial amounts. The DGLA source is human milk, and breast-fed infants in their first year consume a large amount every day. Cow's milk contains only a quarter of the amount found in human milk. This has become the most important difference in position between these two foods.

The only substantial source of GLA is the seed oil of evening primrose, as of 2 years ago. It was shown that evening primrose oil, which provides concentrated GLA, can be used as a direct dietary suppliment in patients at risk to cardiovascular conditions. This means the risk of heart attacks could be greatly reduced in patients with heart disease, without radical changes in either lifestyle or dietary habits.

Thus, a market demand was created via this medical research. As a result, several hundred acres of evening primrose were grown last year in Oregon, with similar productions by North Carolina growers. At least two buyers are offering substantial sums for the seed. The primary markets are in cosmetics, with such manufacturers as Jason Natural Cosmetics using it for a line of natural skin and hair care products.

The seeds of the evening primrose contain 15-20 percent oils, with ca 26-29 percent alpha-linoleic-, 28-33 percent beta-linoleic-, 8 percent gamma-linoleic-, 23-25 percent oleic-, and 5 percent palmitic- and 1.6 percent stearic-acids. Current prices to growers is more than $2,000 per ton for the evening primrose seeds.

The evening primrose can thrive in almost any soil or situation, being a hardy biennial. It prefers a good sandy soil with lots of sun. The seeds are sown an inch deep in a shady position out doors in April, transplanting the seedlings when one inch high. They are given 3 inches spacing and kept free of weeds. In September or the following March, they are again transplanted into the flowering positions. As roots strike deep into the ground, care should be taken not to break them when transplanting.

Seeds may be sown in cold frames in autumn for blooming the following year. If the plants are once introduced and the seeds permitted to scatter, there will be a supply of plants without special care the following years.

The seeds which contain the GLA-containing seed oil are tiny and difficult to harvest at present. Unless harvested by hand, much of the crop is lost. Typical productions of evening primrose will yield more than 5 ton of aerial dry biomass per acre. A single plant may produce hundreds of capsules, each with more than 100 seeds, averaging a weight of about 3 mg per seed.

If the seeds contain 2 percent GLA, typical for most productions, eight fruits average about 40 mg GLA. This is the typical dose present in a standard 500-mg capsule of evening primrose oil from the local health food store. This means that the retail costs average about $0.01/mg of GLA. Northern species of evening primrose may contain as much as 6 percent GLA, showing higher percentages in colder climates.

A recent abstract, however, may send a chill through the excited evening primrose growers. Researchers from Nestle in Switzerland have just published some technical information that the black currant (_Ribes nigrum_) contains up to 30.5 percent oils in the seeds, of which up to 19 percent may be GLA. This represents up to 6 percent GLA in the seeds.

Ribes spp. thus constitutes one of the richest natural sources of GLA yet described. These oils appear promising for critically ill patients who seem unable to convert linoleic acid into subsequent EFA (essential fatty acid) fractions. Europeans have had a great interest in the black currant as a health food item. The fruit juice is rich in vitamins A, C, P, and J, and is said to be viricidal and has been used to treat colds and sore throats.

It is now predicted that byproduct currant seeds from Europe will shortly sup-

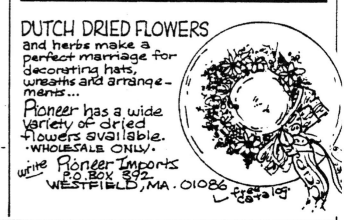

plant evening primrose seeds as a source of GLA. Thus, we come back to our title for this crop: Being led down the "primrose path." As James Duke once wrote: "The flourescent flowers, going from fully closed to open in about 60 seconds, with the days last rays of light are probably better for my psyche than the GLA.

MAJOR MARKETS: Peak Harvest Months

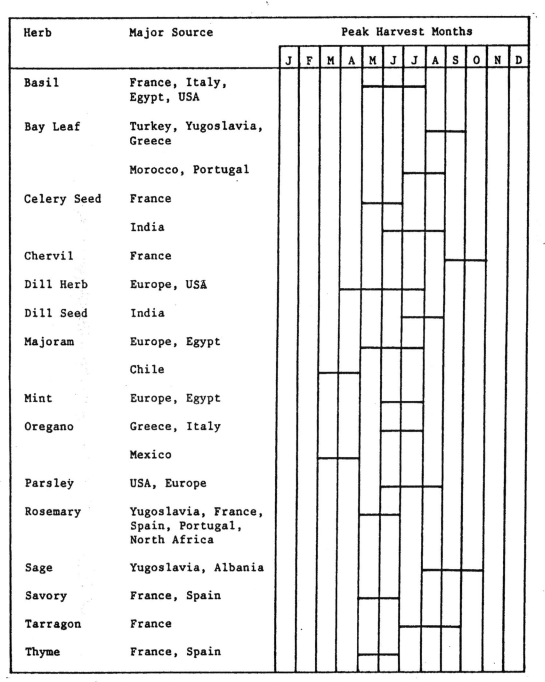

Herb	Major Source	Peak Harvest Months
		J F M A M J J A S O N D
Basil	France, Italy, Egypt, USA	
Bay Leaf	Turkey, Yugoslavia, Greece	
	Morocco, Portugal	
Celery Seed	France	
	India	
Chervil	France	
Dill Herb	Europe, USA	
Dill Seed	India	
Majoram	Europe, Egypt	
	Chile	
Mint	Europe, Egypt	
Oregano	Greece, Italy	
	Mexico	
Parsley	USA, Europe	
Rosemary	Yugoslavia, France, Spain, Portugal, North Africa	
Sage	Yugoslavia, Albania	
Savory	France, Spain	
Tarragon	France	
Thyme	France, Spain	

A study of peak harvest months becomes important in that it is an indicator as to when competitive imports become available to domestic buyers.

BOOK REVIEW:

Encyclopedia of Common Natural Ingredients
Used in Foods, Drugs and Cosmetics.   Albert
Y. Leung. 409pp. John Wiley and Sons,
New York, 1980. $47.00.

There is now available an accurate, up-
to-date encyclopedia for the most important
natural ingredients used in the food, drug,
and cosmetic fields as well as in folk medicine. Each of about 310 natural products
is presented in alphabetical order according
to its most commonly used vernacular name,
fortunately cross-referenced with its binom-
ial in the index.

Information for each plant includes:
general description (distribution, parts
used or derived from, and method of preparation), chemical composition, pharmacologic
or biologic activities, common commercially
available forms, and qualities, uses, and
regulatory status.

Uses are organized by pharmaceutical
and cosmetic, food, folk medicine, and other
categories as applicable. Original as well
as general references are provided for each

product. This is an excellent book for the
potential farmer or forager wanting quick
access to information on economic plants
utilized in the United States. I highly
recommend this text without reservation.

Time to Resubscribe

Almost a year has passed since you
first subscribed to "The Herb Market Report."
Now is the time for you to send us your renewal instructions. You have two more months
remaining on your subscription. An early
response, however, allows us ample time to
do the paper work necessary to process your
renewal. In this way, you'll continue receiving your monthly copy of "The Herb Market
Report" without interruptions.

WORKSHOP

Kansas City, MO - November 23. A one-day farming
workshop, following a four-day farm conference. For
further information, contact Acres, USA - (816)-737-0064

Portland, OR - February 15/16, 1986. A 2-day workshop on foraging. For further information, contact The
Western Forestry Center - (503)-228-1367.

Seattle, WA - No date yet, workshop forming. For
further information, contact Joel Radcliffe - (206)-
324-9792 or P.O.Box 20695, Seattle, WA 98102

The Herb Market Report
1305 Vista Drive • Grants Pass, OR 97527

The Herb Market Report is a newsletter published monthly and distributed by The Southern Oregon Herb Gatherers' Association, Inc.

Oak Publishing
1212 SW 5th Street,
Grants Pass, OR 97526
Phone: 541-426-5588

THE POTENTIAL OF HERBS AS A CASH-CROP is
now in print and available. Send $12.00
for an autographed edition.

Address Correction Requested

Vol. 1 No. 10

THE HERB MARKET REPORT

for the herb farmer and forager   Vol. 1   No. 11   Dec. 1, 1985

ESSENTIAL OILS:
Potential Cash-Crops

The first large-scale production of essential oil in the United States was that of oil of turpentine. The reason for this was the enormous areas covered by pine forests, especially in North and South Carolina, Georgia and Alabama.

Tar, pitch and common turpentine (the oleoresin) were mentioned as products from Virginia in official reports as early as 1610. The production of oil of turpentine in North Carolina and Virginia really began to reach commercial levels in the second half of the eighteenth century.

The production of other essential oils began in the early part of the nineteenth century. The first three again came from local forests: sassafras, American wormseed (Chenopodium anthelminticum L.), and wintergreen. Sweet birch bark was also used to substitute wintergreen, their oils being very similar.

A large-scale production of peppermint oil began even prior to the forest crops, although it was not documented. The oils of turpentine and of peppermint were not only the first essential oils produced in the United States, they are still first today in the quantity produced.

The United States export of essential oils in 1984 totaled more than 11,000 tons with a value of more than $94 million. The primary oils now exported from North America include peppermint and spearmint, the citrus oils (orange, lime, and lemon), cedarwood, and those from imported crops (such as clove and nutmeg).

While it was a record year for lemon and spearmint oil sales, last year's export was almost unchanged from 1983's level. The strong dollar has kept sales of U.S. oils from expanding, and the Florida freeze in January will limit exportable supplies of some of the citrus oils in 1985.

U.S. imports of essential oils, however, showed slight gains from 1983. A review from a previous newsletter (Vol. 1, No. 9) indicates more than $106 million left the country on imports, many of which could have been produced domestically. These include such crops as cornmint, eucalyptus, lavender, and numerous others not even listed.

The United States mint oil supplies in 1984 were good, reflecting rising production. Favorable growing conditions and increased harvested areas have resulted in larger peppermint and spearmint crops and higher returns for producers.

According to the Yearbook of International Trade Statistics, Vol. 2, published by the UN, the total market in terms of exports for 1976 for essential oils and perfumes (SITC No. 551) was 82,584 tons valued at $930.32 million. There has been a 30% increase (approximate) to 1984 figures, averaging more than $40 million increase each year.

A table is given on page 2 listing the leading countries for both exporting and importing essential oils for 1976. You will note that during this time the United States was exporting more than we were importing in total dollars. This is no longer true for 1985, or for the future, from current demands and production schedules.

With this in mind, here are opportunities for the farmer to possibly get access to some of the so-called "economic recovery" and assist in the balancing of trade deficits. The advantages of oil cash-crops include the potential marketability of weedy crops.

For example, if a four-year-old sage field became too woody for leaf/herb harvests, the crop could be harvested for the oil. Another example would be a mint which has become too grassy for leaf/herb production. The crop could be harvested for the oil, and the rootstock replanted for better cultivation.

Leading Countries Exporting and Importing Essential Oils/Resinoids, 1976

Exporters	Qty(tons)	Value ($m)
France	5073	107.3
USA	7189	76.6
China	6440	24.1
Brazil	8940	21.2
Egypt	268	17.4
UK	1742	16.2
Italy	965	13.7
Indonesia	3442	12.4
USSR	173	10.0
Paraguay	na	10.0

Importers		
France	8164	84.5
USA	7162	71.4
UK	5508	51.1
Japan	5708	32.6
Germany	3900	30.0
Switzerland	2033	22.8
Netherlands	2393	17.9
Spain	2498	14.1
Italy	1415	11.7

General Principles

Developed over the course of centuries, this important modern-day industry is based upon principles which vary between two extremes:

(1) In most instances the aromatic plants grow wild or are cultivated as garden or patch crops by natives of the area concerned. The cultivation of the plants and distillation of the oil represents a family industry, usually considered a "side occupation" of the members of the family.

By primitive methods, and limiting themselves generally to one oil, the natives produce small quantities of an oil, which is then sold through a field broker to village buyers. These lots eventually reach exporters in the shipping ports.

The price of these oils depends upon the market, which, in turn, is influenced by supply and demand. The natives are us-ually well aware of prevailing quotations, and prefer stocking up their output to selling it at unattractive prices.

This primitive form of industry is at a very definite advantage because the native operators never value very highly the work done by themselves or their families.. Modern methods of production involve specialized and highly priced labors, in contrast. This old-fashioned method of essential oil production is characterized by dispersion rather than by concentration.

The stills, usually small and portable, are low priced and easy to operate, have to be scattered over the regions concerned. They follow the plant material. Such conditions still exist with respect to numerous oils and in many parts of the world. Examples include East India (lemongrass), China (cassia and star anise), and Java (oil of cananga).

(2) Advanced processing methods, based upon modern principles of plant breeding, mechanized agriculture, engineering and mass production, represent the competing counterpart of the primitive methods.

The oils obtained in regular essential oil factories generally possess a quality superior to those produced by natives in backward districts; but the operating expenses are high.

In addition to the higher standard of living wage requirements, the amortization of investment capital, taxes and other general overhead expenses, all go to increase the costs of production. Under these conditions, a modern factory trying to specialize in the production of only one yearly crop could hardly survive.

Such an organization would have to produce oils from plants grown mainly in the vicinity, or from dried plants which could be shipped from afar at low costs. In other words, a factory of this type would have to be located near large plantations, connected by good roads, and would require conditions of soil, climate and altitude necessary for the crops in question.

Only in a few instances has the production of essential oils been placed on a really modern agricultural and technical basis. Previous to World War I, the great essential oil factories in and near New York City, London, Leipzig, and Grasse (Southern France) used to distill essential oils from plant materials which were imported from abroad.

The problem of shipping space for bulky raw materials, which arose during the war, forced local growers in various parts of the world to install their own distillation equipment and to process their own plant materials for oil. As a result, after World War I, the high cost of transporting raw materials prevented extractors in Europe and the United States from competing with native producers abroad.

Hence, the production of essential oils in many instances reverted from a centralized and highly developed system to a primitive and scattered one.

Today only a few essential oils are produced by very modern or "centralized" methods. Among these are the natural flower oils in the Grasse region of Southern France, and the citrus oils of California and Florida. The latter states have succeeded in producing large quantities of high quality oils because they posses a network of good roads and railroads, permitting the trucking or hauling of fruit from distant orchards and sections to centrally located, modern processing plants.

Because of this feature, the United States has become a large producer and exporter of these oils. In fact, it has achieved independence as regards to the production of both orange and lemon oils. In the coming years, a corresponding evolution may take place with other oils which have been previously distilled in far-off corners of the more primitive countries.

The essential oil industry in its present stage is not limited to the production and distribution of essential oils and the improvement of methods. Nor is it limited to the establishment and maintenance of standards of quality alone. It has come more more to be concerned with the development, production and testing of synthetic aromatics and mixtures which today find their way into so many products, especially prepared foods.

Botany, agriculture, pharmacy and chemistry, engineering, a knowledge of world markets, commercial ingenuity and responsibility have all contributed to the develop-

ment of the modern industry of essential oils. It is the maintenance of this combination which will keep up the high standard and the general usefulness of this industry.

Their Uses

Essential oils find an amazingly wide and varied application in may industries for the scenting and flavoring of all kinds of consumers' finished products, some of them luxuries, mose of them necessities in our advanced civilization.

Many of these products contribute directly to our health, happiness and general well being. To underestimate their importance is to disregard entirely the physiological advantage of continuing to have available these accustomed necessities of our daily lives.

Some volatile oils are more or less powerful external or internal antiseptics, others possess and analgesic, haemolytic, or antizymatic action, while others act as sedatives, stimulants and stomachics.

Spices, with their flavor principles (volatile oils), have been used as flavoring materials since recorded history. Yet, not always is it sufficiently realized that they are actually indispensable to man in order to bring about proper digestion of food.

The digestive juices containing digestive enzymes such as pepsin, trypsin, lipase, amylase, etc., are secreted into the stomach and intestines only when stimulated by the smell and taste of pleasantly flavored foods.

The wide use of volatile oils in perfumes, cosmetics and the scenting of soaps hardly needs to be mentioned. Increasingly, volatile oils and their aromatic isolates serve also for the covering of somewhat objectionable odors, like in the case of artificial leathers. Acceptable and useful articles can now be made from raw materials that were formerly discarded or overlooked because of disagreeable odors.

Few people realize that in the course of a single day, we consume a great variety of volatile oils which originate from many corners of the world. While the total yearly turnover may be estimated as amounting to only about $100 million in the United States alone, the turnover of the consumers' finished goods, which requires small additions of essential oils, reaches into many billions of dollars per year.

The following lists will enumerate some of the various industries which use volatile oils, aromatic isolates, or combinations:

ADHESIVES

Glues	Porcelain cements
Paper tapes	Rubber cements
Pastes	Scotch tape

ANIMAL FEEDS

Cat foods	Dog foods
Cattle feeds	

AUTOMOBILE INDUSTRY

Finishing supplies	Polishes
Cleaners	Soaps

BAKED GOODS INDUSTRY

Biscuits	Mince meat
Cakes	Pies
Crackers	Pretzels
Doughnuts	Puddings
Fruit cakes	Sandwich fillings
Icings	

CANNING INDUSTRY

Fish	Sauces
Meats	Soups

CHEWING GUM INDUSTRY

Chewing gums	Coated gums

CONDIMENT INDUSTRY

Catsups	Pickled fish
Celery salts	Relishes
Chili sauces	Salad dressings
Mayonnaises	Table sauces
Mustards	Vinegars

CONFECTIONARY INDUSTRY

Chocolates	Jellies
Fondants	Mints
Gum drops	Panned goods
Hard candies	Soft centered candies

DENTAL PREPARATIONS

Dentist's preparations	Tooth pastes
Mouth washes	Tooth powders

EXTERMINATOR SUPPLIES

Bedbug sprays	Naphthalene blocks
Cattle sprays	Paradichloride blocks
Cockroach powders	Plant sprays
Fly sprays	Rat baits
Mosquito repellents	Rodent odor eliminators

FOOD INDUSTRY (GENERAL)

Cheeses	Pie fillers
Cornstarch puddings	Prepared cake mixes
Dehy soups/meats/veges	Rennet desserts
Gelatin desserts	Sauerkraut
Mince meats	Vegetable oils/fats

HOUSEHOLD PRODUCTS

Bluings	Room sprays
Deodorants	Starches
Furniture polishes	Vacuum cleaner pads
Laundry soaps	

ICE CREAM INDUSTRY

Ice creams	Prepared ice cream mixes
Ices	Sherbets

INSECTICIDE INDUSTRY

Attractants	Repellents
Disinfectants	Sprays
Insecticides	

JANITOR'S SUPPLIES

Detergents	Scrub soaps
Disinfectants	Sink cleaners
Floor polishes	Sweeping compounds
Floor waxes	

MEAT PACKING INDUSTRY

Bolognas	Prepared meats
Frankfurters	Sausages

PAINT INDUSTRY

Bituminous paints	Paint dilutants
Casein paints	Paints
Enamels	Rubber paints
Lacquers	Synthetic coatings
Paint/varnish removers	Varnishes

PAPER/PRINTING INDUSTRY

Carbon papers	Paper bags/wrappers
Crayons	Printing/writing inks
Drinking cups	Printing paper
Industrial tapes	Typewriter ribbons
Inking pads	Writing paper
Labels	

PERFUME/TOILET INDUSTRY

Baby preparations	Lipsticks
Bath preparations	Lotions
Body deodorants	Manicure preparations
Colognes	Powders
Creams	Room sprays
Depilatories	Rouges
Eye shadows	Sachets
Facial masks	Shaving preparations
Hair preparations	Suntan preparations
Handkerchief extracts	Toilet waters
Incenses	

PETROLEUM/CHEMICAL INDUSTRY

Bluing oils	Organic solvents
Fuel oils	Petroleum distillates
Grease deodorants	Polishes
Greases	Sulfonated oils
Lubricating oils	Tar products
Naphtha solvents	Waxes
Neoprene	

PHARMACEUTICAL INDUSTRY

Antiacid tablets	Liniments
Cough drops	Medicinal preparations
Elixirs	Ointments
Germicides	Patent medicines
Hospital sprays	Tonics
Hospital supplies	Vitamin flavorings
Inhalants	Wholesale druggists'
Laxatives	supplies

PICKLE PACKING INDUSTRY

Dill Pickles	Sour pickles
Fancy cut pickles	Sweet pickles

PRESERVE INDUSTRY

Fruit butters	Jellies
Jams	

ALCOHOLIC BEVERAGE INDUSTRY

Bitters	Vermouths
Cordials	Whiskies
Rums	Wines

RUBBER INDUSTRY

Baby pants	Synthetic rubber products
Gloves	Toys
Shower curtins	Water proofing compounds
Surgical supplies	

SOAP INDUSTRY

Cleaning powders	Scrub soaps
Detergents	Shampoos
Household soaps	Sweeping compounds
Laundry soaps	Technical soaps
Liquid hand soaps	Toilet soaps

SOFT DRINK INDUSTRY

Carbonated beverages	Root beers
Cola drinks	Soda fountain supplies
Fountain syrups	Soft drink powders
Ginger ales	Sundae toppings

TEXTILE PROCESSING PRODUCTS

Artificial fabric	Sisal deodorants
Dyes	Textile chemicals
Hosiery sizing	Textile oils
Linoleum	Upholstery materials
Oil cloths	Water proofing materials

TOBACCO INDUSTRY

Chewing tobaccos	Smoking tobaccos
Cigarettes	Snuffs
Cigars	

VETERINARY SUPPLIES

Cattle sprays	Insect powders
Deodorants	Mange ointments
Dog and cat soaps	

DIVERSIFIED INDUSTRIES

Alcohol denaturing compounds	
Embalming fluid deodorants	
Candles	
Ceramics	Optical lenses
Cleaners' products	War gas simulants

THE CHEMICAL USES OF SEAWEEDS

The collection of wild botanicals does not stop at the ocean's edge. The sea is full of a special variety of flora known as algae. At one time, all coastal residents used seaweeds as foods and medicines. Today, most of the seaweeds used in the United States is imported, although there are a number of large domestic sources of production in New Jersey and California. This number could be increased to more than 5x and still not meet current demands.

There are three major classifications of seaweeds by their color. Sometimes they will appear to be one color, but are categorized in another. Don't let it frustrate you. These three classifications are:

Brown Algae - <u>Phaeophyta</u> phylum - The chlorophyll is masked by other pigmentations. The name is Greek for "dusky." They are ancient in the plant world, preferring cool waters and constant submersion in water.

Green Algae - <u>Chlorophytum</u> phylum - These are able to endure strong sunlight, many are found in fresh waters, and some tropical ones are important calcium concentrators.

Red Algae - <u>Rhodophyta</u> phylum - These are the most light-receptive. They are usually found below water, some as many as 200 meters down. That is as far as sunlight goes.

There are a number of diverse kelp and kelp-product markets. These include fertilizers, cattle foods, pharmaceuticals, cosmetics, foods, and numerous other areas, like paint. The chemical markets of kelps include kelp as a specific species (like dulse or irish moss), agar, algin, and carrageenan.

Agar is the dried hydrophilic, coloidal extract of various red algaes. It is extracted from the algae by boiling them in water at a neutral or slightly acidic pH.

The hot liquor is filtered and on cooling, forms a gel which is purified by freezing and thawing, followed by drying.

The major agar producer has always been Japan. Other countries of production include the United States, Spain, Portugal, Morocco, New Zealand, Australia, Argentina, South Africa, China, and Mexico.

Agar is insoluble in cold water but readily soluble up to 5% in boiling water. The solution on cooling to 35 to 40°C forms a firm, resilient gel which does not melt below 85°C.

This ability to gel at a much lower temperature than the melting temperature of the gel, commonly called hysteresis lag, is uniquely long in agar, and many of its uses depend on this property.

Agar gels also have the property of shrinking and exuding water from their surfaces (syneresis), particularly when broken. The gel strength of agar can be increased by addition of dextrose, sucrose, and locust bean gum, while it tends to weaken with gelatin, algin, starch, and karaya gum.

Agar is insoluble in organic solvents, usually being precipitated from aqueous solution by alcohol and tannin. All agars consist of two polysaccharides, neutral agarose and charged agaropectin (simplified). Agarose is the gelling fraction and agaropectin is the nongelling fraction. Both are composed of a linear chain of alternating β-D-galactopyranose and 3,6-anhydro-α-L-galactopyranose residues, with agaropectin having a higher proportion of uronic acid, sulfate, and pyruvic acid residues.

Commercial agar may contain free amino acids (arginine, glutamic acid, aspartic acid, and threonine) and free sugars (galactose and gluonic acid). It may also contain other sugar residues including 4-0-methyl-L-galactose and 6-0-methyl-D-galactose, D-xylose, and 0-methylpentose.

Agar is nontoxic and can be ingested in large doses without much distress. It passes through the intestinal tract mostly unabsorbed. Studies indicate agar to have antiseptic activities in vitro. It also seems to elevate serum or tissue cholesterol levels in rats.

In pharmaceutical and cosmetic markets, it is used as a bulk laxative, especially in chronic constipation; in the manufacture of emulsions, suspension, gels, and hydrophilic suppositories; in dentistry as basic constituent of reversible impressions and duplicating materials.

In foods, agar is used in canned meat and fish products as a gel filler or binder; in baking goods (icing and glazes); and in confectionery, dairy products, processed fruits, sweet sauces, and reconstituted vegetables, and other products. The highest average use level is about 0.4% in baked goods.

Another major use of agar is in culture media for microorganisms. As a commercial preparation, it is available in flakes, strips, and powder; grade and quality vary, with bacteriological grades demanding the most stringent quality. Some high-quality agars from certain commercial sources have higher congealing temperatures than those required by the F.C.C. and U.S.P..

Algin is a collective term for the hydrophilic colloidal substance isolated from specific brown algae, including Macrocyctis and Laminaria. Macrocystis pyrifera (Giant kelp) is the major source of algin in the United States, primarily from the West Coast. Laminaria digitata is used on the East Coast, with Laminaria species used extensively in Japan.

The process for algin manufacture basically involves a prewash of the seaweed whereby undesirable salts are leached out and removed. It is then followed by extraction with a dilute alkaline solution which solubilizes the alginic acid present in the seaweed.

The resulting thick and viscous mass is clarified, and the algin is obtained as free alginic acid on treatment with mineral acids. The alginic acid can then be converted to sodium alginate. Sodium alginate is the major form of algin currently used in the world. Major producers include the United States, United Kingdom, Norway, France, and Japan.

Alginic acid and its calcium salt are insoluble in water, but its ammonium, sodium, potassium, and magnesium salts as well as its propylene glycol ester are readily soluble in cold and hot water to form viscous solutions. The viscosity of these is dependent on various factors, including concentration, pH, degree of polymerization (D.P.), temperature, and presences of polyvalent metal ions.

Viscosity increases with D.P.. It decreases with increase in temperature but will regain its original value on cooling to its initial temperature provided the solutions are not held above 50°C for long periods. Between pH 4 and 10, the viscosity of algin solutions is generally stable.

Algin solutions form gels with calcium ions, due to the formation of insoluble calcium alginate; these gels are not thermally reversable but may be liquefied by calcium sequestrants. Propylene glycol alginate is more acid tolerant than the other alginates. Its solutions are stable below pH 4 (down to pH 2.6).

Alginic acid is a linear polymer consisting of (1-4)-like residues of β-D-mannopyranosyluronic acid and α-L-gulopyranosyluronic acid. These D-mannuronic acid and L-guluronic acid residues are arranged in the polymer chain in blocks. Blocks of mannuronic acid are separated from those of guluronic acid by blocks that are made up of random or alternating units of mannuronic and guluronic acids.

The homogeneous block (those composed of either acid residues alone) are less readily hydrolyzed than the interconnecting heterogeneous blocks.

Alginates from different sources vary in their proportions of blocks or mannuronic and guluronic acid residues; values of mannuronic acid/guluronic acid ratios range from 0.3 to 2.3 for some alginate samples. These values can be readily determined by infrared spectroscopy.

Research on animals show algin (alginic acid and its sodium and calcium salts, and propylene glycol alginate) to be generally nontoxic. Sodium alginate has the ability to reduce strontium absorption, especially when high in guluronic acid. It can also decrease other radioactive divalent metallic ions in rats.

Orally fed alginic acid and sodium alginate depress plasma and/or living cholesterol levels in rats. Only algin with a high D.P. is active. Its cholesterolemic activity is attributed to its ability to inhibit cholesterol absorption from the gut.

Its pharmaceutical and cosmetic uses include sodium alginate being used as a binding and disintegrating agent in tablets and as a binding agent and demulcent in lozenges; as film former in peel-off facial maskes; as suspending and thickening agent in water miscible gels, lotions, and creams; and as a stabilizer for oil-in-water emulsions.

Calcium alginate is used as absorbable hemostatic; potassium alginate (in conjunction with calcium sulfate and sodium phosphate) is used as an irreversible dental impression material.

In foods, it is used in virtually every category of food products, with an average maxium use level of about 1% in such products as candy, gelatins and puddings, condiments, relishes, processing vegetables, fish products, and imitation dairy products.

Other products in which it is used in lower levels include alcoholic and noalcoholic beverages, frozen dairy desserts, baked goods, meat and meat products, milk products, fats and oils, cheese, egg products, soups, snack foods, and others.

A 0.2% sodium alginate spray is also used as an effective fungicide against fungal infection of rice by Pyricularia orysae.

Carrageenan is a seaweed gum (hyrocolloid) obtained from various red algaes, with Chondrus crispus (Irish moss) as the major source (East Coast). In its manufacture, the dried seaweed is first cleaned with cold water and mechanical devices to remove salt and other extraneous materials. It is then extracted with hot water containing calcium or sodium hydroxide.

The extract is clarified by filtration, its pH adjusted to slightly basic, and carrageenan is obtained either by direct drum- or roll-drying of the filtrate or by precipitation with alcohol (eg. ethyl or isopropyl), depending on the type or purity desired. The United States is the worlds largest producer, with Denmark, France and Spain also producing it.

Carrageenan comes in many types with different solubilities and gel characteristics, depending on the process and types of algae used for its manufacture. It has high reactivity with certain proteins, particularly milk protein, to form weak to strong gels.

Carrageenan is a sulfated, straight-chain galactan composed of residues of D-galactose and 3.6-anhydro-D-galactose with a molecular weight usually of 100,000 to 500,000. In generally contains two major fractions, a gelling fraction called k-carrageenan and a nongelling fraction called

λ-carrageenan.

Solutions and gels of carrageenan are degraded rapidly by low pH and high temperatures. Degraded carrageenan (molecular weight 20,000) do not have the viscosity or gelling properties of food-grade carrageenans.

It is reported to exhibit many pharmacological activities in animals, including lowering of blood cholesterol level, reducing gastric secretions and food absorption, and increasing water content of the gut when large doses are ingested.

It has been shown to have anticoagulant, hypotensive, and immunosuppressive activities. Carrageenan has been reported to alleviate peptic and duodenal ulcers in humans. It has inhibitory effects on pepsin activity in vitro. All low and high viscosity forms exhibit antiproteolytic activities in vitro against papain.

It is used extensively as a binder, emulsifier, or stabilizer in toothpastes; also in hand lotions, creams, tablets, and other pharmaceutical and cosmetic preparations. The degraded form is used in preparations for treating peptic ulsers in France.

In foods, carrageenan (or its salts) is used extensively in milk products such as chocolate milk, ice cream, sherbets, cottage cheese, cream cheese, evaporated milk, milk desserts, puddings, yogurts, infant formulas, and others.

It is also used in other foods such as gravies, thickening sauces, bread doughs, meat products, jams, and jellies, among others. Its major functions are as thickening, gelling, and emulsifying, stabilizing and suspending agents, preventing the settling of solids and in the case of ice cream to prevent ice crystal formation.

For use in gel products such as jams and jellies, its use level is usually 0.5 to 1.1%.

TIME FOR RESUBSCRIPTION

Almost a year has passed since you first subscribed to "The Herb Market Report." Now is the time for you to send us your renewal instructions. You have only one more month remaining on your subscription. An early response allows us ample time to process you renewal. In this way, you will continue receiving your monthly copy of "The Herb Market Report" without interruptions.

BOOK REVIEW

Sea Vegetables - Harvesting Guide & Cookbook
Evelyn McConnaughey. 239pp. Naturegraph
Publishers, 1985. $6.95

This book has been in print only about one week, and is an excellent addition to my library on this subject. The book is divided into three sections. Part I contains information needed by the forager, including identification, harvesting techniques, and essentials on foraging and storage.

Part II offers specific recipes for the diverse kelps available off each coast. These include Seaweed Quiche, Tofu Italian Seaweed Rolls, Corn Rollups, and even Cherry Pie. This is an excellent section and will change your perspectives regarding seaweed being "that icky stuff that washes up onto the shore."

Part III concerns itself with such things as the laws governing seaweeds, and their relationship to other markets. This includes fertilizers, animal fodder, and marine algaes in health and pharmacy.

Naturegraph is a most interesting publisher. While they offer a number of good titles on marine life, they have an excellent selection in natural history, American wildlife, and native American cultures. I am particularly impressed with their section of books dealing with living off the land.

I highly recommend a review of their current catalog and offerings. Please write directly to Naturegraph Publishers, P.O.Box 1075, Happy Camp, CA 96039, attn: Gary Kunkle (Sales) for further information and a catalog.

NOTE FROM THE EDITOR

The newsletter is beginning to expand, and we need your help. We would like to begin featuring other writers and would appreciate submissions for review.

In order to expand, we also need to increase circulation and advertising. Please show the newsletter to your friends and encourage them to subscribe. Back issues are still available (limited).

THE POTENTIAL OF HERBS AS A CASH-CROP is now in print and available. Send $12.00 for an autographed edition.

The Herb Market Report

1305 Vista Drive • Grants Pass, OR 97527
The Herb Market Report is a newsletter published monthly and distributed by The Southern Oregon Herb Gatherers' Association, Inc.

Oak Publishing
1212 SW 5th Street,
Grants Pass, OR 97526
Phone: 541-426-5588

Copyright 1986-2013 © Dr. Richard Alan Miller

Address Correction Requested
Vol. 1 No. 11

WORKSHOPS

Kansas City, MO - November 23. A one-day farming workshop, following a four-day farm conference. For further information, contact Acres, USA - (816) 737-0064

Raleigh, NC - January 11. A one-day farming workshop. For further information, contact Acres, USA - (816) 737-0064

Portland, OR - February 15/16. A 2-day workshop on foraging and marketing. For further information, contact The Western Forestry Center - (503) 228-1367

Seattle, WA - No date yet, workshop forming. For further information, contact Joel Radcliffe - (206) 324-9792, or send a SASE to P.O.Box 20695, Seattle, WA 98102

THE HERB MARKET REPORT

for the herb farmer and forager   Vol. 1 No. 12   Dec. 15, 1985

The Question of MARIGOLDS

A number of readers have questioned the description of marigold on page 116 in my new book THE POTENTIAL OF HERBS AS A CASH-CROP. The following review will hopefully put some of those questions into perspective, especially since many of the marigolds have increasingly important markets.

The common term "marigold" embraces a diversity of plants with golden flowers, most of which belong to the family Compositae. Prominent among the marigold are various species of Tagetes, particularly Tagetes glandulifera Schrank. This is an annual herb, considered synonymous with Tagetes minuta L.

Tagetes glandulifera Schrank, the so-called Mexican marigold or "orina," is native to Central America but now grows almost everywhere from Canada to Argentina. The plant was introduced into South Africa during the Boer War of 1900, probably when a large number of horses and fodder were imported from Argentina.

After the war, Australian troops returning from South Africa brought the plant to Australia where it now grows as a weed. During the East African campaign (1914-1918) the marigold was introduced from South Africa to Kenya Colony, where it took root and is still spreading over wide areas.

Locally known as "khaki bush" it thrives along roadsides and on any land that has been plowed up. In Africa it is claimed that the plant acts as a fly and vermin repellent. The natives of East Africa hang tagetes plants in their huts to keep out the swarms of flies which are a real problem in those parts of the world.

It has been demonstrated that common houseflies and blow flies avoid baits scented with tagetes oil, whereas they are attracted by, and readily lay their eggs on, control baits not scented with the oil. Attempts have also been made to develop an effective larvicide that would kill maggots in wounds. An emulsion of water, carbon tetrachloride, some wool fat, five percent of tagetes oil, and a preserving agent was found to be very effective.

The plant contains an essential oil which can be isolated by steam distillation. In order to obtain the maximum of oil, the plant should be harvested and distilled during the period of seed formation, after the full flowering stage. In East Africa natives cut the plant with long bush knives or machetes.

Because of transportation difficulties, only limited quantities of tagetes oil can be produced from the widely scattered, wild growing plants. To obtain larger quantities of oil the plant is now cultivated.

In Kenya Colony distillation is carried out with direct steam, one batch requiring 3 to 4 hours. The yield of oil ranges from 0.3 to 0.4 per cent. Although very little oil of tagetes is produced at present, there is a growing demand for further production. It has been suggested for use as a modifier in hair lotions of the bay rum type, for example.

The perennial marigold, T. lucida, is a substitute for French tarragon in climates where the Artemisias do not winter well (too warm). The anise flavor of this sweet-scented marigold is not really as subtle as tarragon, but the plant is worth growing because of its distinctive odor.

Known as the "cloud plant" in its native mountains of Mexico, the use of the foliage for flavoring herb teas may be as old as the Aztec culture. It is not as tender as the larger flowering marigolds, and a touch of frost does not blacken the glandular leaves.

Used extensively in both cosmetics and foods as a fragrance component and flavoring additive, the tagetes meal and tagetes extract are used in chicken feed to give the characteristic yellow coloring to chicken skin and egg yolks. With larger uses of chicken products and eggs in our diets, this has become a major cash-crop in recent years.

Experiments with the marigolds against nematodes were conducted at the Connecticut Agricultural Experiment Station several years back. Not all kinds worked as well as those used in these studies. They were varieties of tall Tagetes erecta and small Tagetes patula, commonly grown for their double or single flowers.

There is another type of marigolds, known in the herb trade as calendula, also of the Compositae family. This well-known garden plant, Calendula officinalis, is probably one of the most used herb flowers. While it does have medicinal uses, it is primarily sold for use in numerous cosmetic preparations and potpourris.

Used in the Mediterranean region since ancient Greece, it was used by India and Arabic cultures even before those periods. It has a very long flowering period, hence its Latin name calens, meaning "through the months."

As an annual, it is not found in the wild like most of the tagetes species. It tolerates any soil in full sun, although prefering loam. Seed sown in mid-spring usually establishes quickly, and will self-sow itself for following years. All of the marigolds are quite easily cultivated, and seem to have some oil similarities regarding their use as larvicides.

The flowering heads of both Tagetes and Calendula can be raked or separated from the plant using a device similar to a cranberry scoop. Several students have even had some success using a combine-type bean-harvester. Rather than using an auger, this form of combine has a conveyor belt which goes directly to the hopper.

The flowers dry easily on tarps in partial sun, or on drying racks in a home-made dryer. The Tagetes variety yields larger flower quantities per acre, sometimes as much as 1,500 pounds. Prices for both flowerheads to the potpourri and cosmetic markets range from $1.00 to $2.00 per pound. Last year, Yugoslavia alone imported more than 400 ton dried flowerheads into the United States. This could become an important cash-crop and is very easy to grow and cultivate.

PESTICIDE RESISTANCE: Rising Risk

by Michael Dover and Brian Croft

In the euphoria following the early access of DDT, the "miracle" insecticide of the 1940s, some insect-control specialists worried publicly that they might soon have nothing left to control. Others, however, raised warnings, forseeing what has come to pass - that insects and other pests would become resistant to the arsenal of chemicals used against them.

From 1970 to 1980 the number of resistant insect species has nearly doubled to more than 400, and they continue to multiply. Microorganisms that cause plant diseases also have developed resistance. In 1960 there were 20 resistant fungi and bacteria; today there are more than 150. Weeds and rodents developed resistance to herbicides and poisons as well.

Indeed, many of these species have become resistant to a whole range of chemicals, disrupting local and regional pest-control programs for agriculture and public health.

The costs of resistance have only recently begun to be added up. For example: uncontrollable tobacco budworms are primarily responsible for wiping out cotton-growing in northeastern Mexico. Colorado potato beetles are costing Long Island potato farmers as much as $300 an acre to control, while heavy spraying has contaminated ground water. Resistant spider mites on apples cost European growers up to six times as much to control as the more susceptible types.

Pest resistance also threatens human health: 51of the 60 malaria-carrying Anopheles mosquitoes are now resistant to the three most effective pesticides used for malaria control - DDT, lindane and dielarin - and 14 of the 51 also are immune to various replacement chemicals. But many times replacement chemicals, even when they work, are up to 20 times as expensive.

Resistant insects in the United States alone may be costing farmers more than $150 million a year in crop losses and increased chemical applications. The cost of resistance-induced pest control could drive many farmers out of business.

As long as pesticide companies continued to develop new chemicals rapidly, resistance did not seem to be a serious problem. But discovery of new pesticides has become more difficult and much more costly. As one industry researchers put it, "The easy chemistry has been used up."

continued on page 4

THE FARM
Manure Resources

The nutrients contained in most manures can be an important aspect to any fertilization program, adding to the soil's mostureholding ability. There are a number of factors, however, which must first be considered before using manure as a fertilizer.

These include such things as source of the manure, content of the animals' feed (chemicals and drugs used), how the manure was stored and for how long, how much bedding material should be mixed into the manure, the season of the year, and specific soil needs.

Manure produced by farm animals

	Daily (lbs)	Yearly (tons)
Beef	60.0	11.0
Dairy	70.0	13.0
Horse	44.0	8.0
Hog	9.0	1.7
Sheep	4.0	0.7
Laying Hen	0.3	0.05
Turkey	0.8	

The storage of manure can greatly affect its quality. More than forty percent of the fertilizer elements are contained in the liquid portion. Nutrients are lost with seepage, for example. Even when spread on the ground, nutrients can be lost through leaching and exposure until the manure is turned under.

No manure should be spread until you have tested your soil and have a good knowledge of the content and quality of the manure to be spread. The following table gives an average content for the various manures.

The average content of various manures

	% Moisture	% Organic Matter	% N	% P	% K
Goat			3.00	2.00	3.00
Pultry	55-75	45-25	1.50-1.00	1.20-0.80	0.80-0.40
Sheep	66-68	34-32	1.05-0.95	0.35-0.30	0.95-1.00
Horse	74-78	26-22	0.65-0.70	0.25	0.55-0.75
Cow	83	17	0.50-0.60	0.15-0.20	0.35-0.45
Hog	86	14	0.50	0.35	0.40-0.65

There should be no heavy manure applications prior to a new seeding. Manure applied to grass sod should go on during the winter or in early spring. Manure for the garden should be applied in the fall to avoid burning crops.

Steer manure is considerably higher in all nutrients than is dairy cow manure. Hogs can carry parasitic roundworms which can be transmitted to humans. You should wash thoroughly after handling manure. Keep careful records of all manure applications.

Amounts of different manure varieties to apply

	lbs./1,000 square feet
Goat	125
Dairy Cow	600
Steer	450
Horse	600
Hog	500

continued from page 2

The agrochemical industry is focusing much of its research-development effort on only one class of insecticides (the synthetic pyrethroids) and a small number of fungicide types. And, while pyrethroid sales are increasing rapidly, resistance is appearing at an alarming rate. In 1976 six species were resistant; by 1980 the number was 17. Of the 50 pest species predicted as promising targets of pyrethroids in 1978, at least 15 have already shown resistance.

Meanwhile, the cost - $20 million to $45 million, times 8 to 10 years from discovery to marketing - and difficulty of developing new chemicals demand that we manage existing pesticides more carefully.

To preserve our ability to protect crops, livestock and ourselves from the damage and illness brought on by pests, scientists are now approaching and testing "resistance management." This approach seeks to prevent, delay or reverse the evolution of resistance by employing tactics ranging from preserving pests' natural predators to devising complicated spraying schedules.

In the next two decades chemical pesticides will continue as a mainstay of pest-management technologies. Therefore, resistance management may be the key to continuing effective pest control. Its success depends

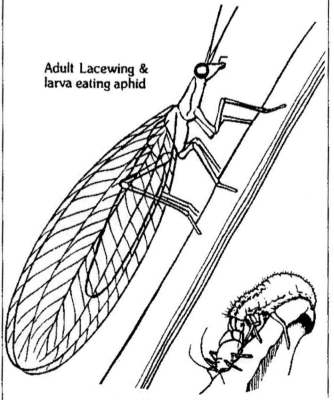

Adult Lacewing &
larva eating aphid

on how we develop, use and regulate pesticides now and in the future. But can research, regulator, educational and economic institution that control pesticide production and use r spond to the challenge of pesticide resistance

In a year-long study of pesticide resistance we talked with industry, government, university and environmental specialists about the wide-range changes needed to make resistance management succeed. Among our recommendations:

- Establish a national resistance-monitoring program involving local, state and federal agencies, chemical companies and private pest-management consultants.
- Incorporate resistance risk into pesticide-registration data requirements
- Establish an independent, industry-sponsored foundation to support research on resistance.
- Impose an end-user tax on pesticides to finance resistance-management programs, phased in over five years to a level of 2 cents per pound.

Today pests and pesticides must be managed within a complex system of political, economic, regulatory, research and educational institutions. Moreover, the institutions involved are well established, with carefully defined interests, power bases and adversarie Change does not come easily. Yet all parti have a stake in a concerted approach to resistance problems.

Whether we like it or not, an effective resistance-management program can succeed only through the cooperation of everyone. The alternative is to continue to lose our ability to control pests, all the while paying greater and greater economic and environmental costs. That is a risk that we cannot afford to take.

Michael Dover is an ecologist and research staff member at World Resource Institute in Washington, D.C.. Brian Croft is professor of entomology at Oregon State University. They wrote the report, "Getting Tough: Public Policy and the Management of Pesticide Resistance," (World Resource Institute).

Copies of the 80-page report are available for $3.50 each from the World Resource Institute, 1735 New York Avenue, N.W., Washington, D.C. 20006.

Special thanks to Allen Garcia of Family Farms in Willows, CA for making us aware of this important work.

Dr. Richard Alan Miller

NORI KELP: The New Fast-Food Tortilla

Last month's article on the chemical markets of seaweeds prompted a number of inquiries for further information, specifically on nori kelp. This interest is a result of the growth of sushi bars, part of a building fast-food wave that is breaking across the United States as Mexican food did some 20 years ago.

Nori is the dark green papery kelp that is rolled around fish and rice to form sushi. It is also a billion-dollar business and the largest near-shore forage crop in Japan. Nori is part of the Porphyra family, a genus which includes more than 75 wild and cultivated species.

Nori is native to cold waters worldwide, growing best in Puget Sound. It grows high on the intertidal zone of the northern Pacific rim, as well as New Zealand, parts of South America. This includes Chile, Europe, and the northwestern and northeastern coasts of the United States.

Dried in sheets, nori is a centuries-old staple of the Japanese and Korean diets where it is used as substrate for rice and fish or crumbled into soups as a seasoning. European whalers ate it to stave off scurvy, Philippine Islanders cook it with other seaweeds as a vegetable, and Welsh miners bake it into bread.

Surprisingly, nori has a higher vitamin C content than oranges and is rich in protein (30-45% by dried weight). Unlike many plant proteins, most of that found in Porphyra can be digested by human systems. It is also an excellent source of A and B vitamines and trace minerals.

Nori has been cultured since 1570 in Japan. The first farmers stuck bamboo brush and oak branches in the shallows and harvested the nori that chanced to grow there. As nori aquaculture evolved, farmers began to string ropes between their poles, then nets to increase their growing substrate.

Eventually, farmers developed the floating surface net (or saku) which allows them to exploit deeper, previously unfarmed waters. The modern saku measures an average of 1.5 by 18 meters.

As a result of new advances in technology, production of nori has soared from 1.4 billion sheets in 1957 (55,000 metric tons) to 10 billion sheets (400,000 metric tons) in the 1983-4 season. A standard sheet of Japanese nori weighs 3 grams and measures 18 by 21 cm.

Similar to agricultural situations in the United States, the number of farms in the Japanese co-op system declined 55% between 1969 and 1979 to about 29,000, while the number of nets at each farm increased 5x to about 300 each. Nori is also grown in Korea, where small farms are still the rule and many of the traditional cultivation techniques are still used.

It is a combination of characteristics peculiar to Porphyra that has allowed the industrialization of nori culture and the resulting boom in production. The first is its reproductive cycle.

Like some other plants, Porphyra passes through two distinct phases. One is the visible nori blade, the other a near-microscopic filament called the conchocelis.

It is at the conchocelis stage that sexual reproduction takes place, producing seed that grows into commercially important nori blades. Conchocelis conveniently bore into oyster and scallop shells, making it easy for the nori farmer to transport seed to his nets.

The discovery that conchocelis was actually a stage in the life of nori and not a separate plant allowed farmers to develop seed cultures in the laboratory, giving them control over exactly when and with what species of nori the farmer would "impregnate" his nets.

Nori's rigously life as an intertidal plant regularly exposed by the tides has also made it suitable for cultivation. Nori can dry until it is brittle to the touch and still survive. It can stand extremes of heat and cold, and possesses a form of cellular anti-freeze system that allows it to be deep-frozen without turning to slush.

As a result, nori farmers can seed nets when conditions are most optimal, hanging some of these seeded nets in cold storage (20°C) for staggered planting later. This technique works well for those interested in crop rotation programs with kelp.

Nori's intertidal habits make it easy for the farmer to "weed" his nets. Regular exposure to air kills most of the competing plants that tend to foul nori nets. Nori grown on poles or in shallows are regularly exposed by the tides. Floating nets are more labor intense for situations requiring intensive weeding.

The best habitats for nori are in waters with a temperature range of 4-15°C, restricting nori growth to a 4-5 month winter season. Seeding usually takes place in September, with growth stagnating in February and March as the water warms.

The tolerance range for nori growth coincides almost exactly with seasonal temperature ranges in Puget Sound. This means that nori cultivation could be a year-round culture for Pacific Northwest aqua-farming.

There are seventeen species of Porphyra native to Puget Sound. Five of these show potential for commercial production. Similar studies have been made for the New England states. Native strains, although slower in growth, is always more hardy and disease-resistant. The Department of Natural Resources in Washington State have even come out with a nori-growing manual, complete with detailed diagrams of nets, floats and seeding tanks.

Nets are stacked five deep in a floating seeding bed for autumn innoculation by conchocelis, then immediately moved into a floating nursery frame. Once the blades reach half an inch in length, the nets are ready to be tethered at the surface or bundled into cold storage for later planting.

Within another 20-60 days, depending on species and conditions, the blades reach 15 to 20 cm in length and are ready for harvest. The plants tend to go to seed if allowed to get any larger.

Each net can be reharvested or "mown" several times at about 2-week intervals before it must be retired for the season. To harvest, nori farmers pull their nets across a device that looks like an upside-down lawn mower.

Nori must be processed immediately after harvest. Originally, the Japanese laid the crop in the sun to dry. Newer techniques use gas jets to produced dried sheets from a slurry of minced, raw nori blades. The process is similar to making paper. Many farmers in the Pacific Northwest prefer nori production as as a part-time, low-tech operation. The reasons, of course, are universal.

The capital required to set up a full-time 200 to 300 net farm is about $250,000. This does not include a $100,000 drying machine, payroll for five to six full-time workers to tend the nets. While that is pocket change for most venture capitalists, most are still cautious toward seaweed farming.

The main problems with nori production is not financing, but the regulations governing shore and tide-use. In Puget Sound, for example, nori farmers must deal with more than 30 state and federal agencies to obtain the necessary permits to begin cultivation. They must contend with land owners who think that nets and buoys will spoil their view.

Once they have secured a relationship to various land owners, then they must obtain permission from the U.S. Coast Guard to install the buoys and a hydraulic permit to anchor the nets. Aquaculture is also under the jurisdiction of the Department of Fish, Game and Agriculture. It can take as much as three years to get the necessary permits to even begin a small operation.

The California variety of nori is rich in Vitamin B_1 and is now harvested for export to China. Another variety, grown in China, contains Vitamin B_2 and 50% more Vitamin C than oranges. The Hawaiian type is rare and is considered a special delicacy. Called Pahe'e, it is kept standing a few hours with salt before eaten with raw fish.

Nori can be bought in folded sheets in the United States in most mass-market food stores. The dark purple are considered better quality than the green, although the purple will turn to green when toasted. Nori is rich in Vitamins A, D, and B_{12}. It is also called purple laver.

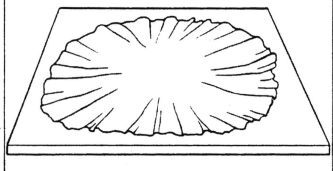

THE SPADING MACHINE

A new development out of Europe is the spading machine. It operates off a PTO shaft from a tractor with primary reduction via a robust gearbox with machine cut gears. The machine more or less spades the soil, and therefore no plow effect is available to smear the soil or develop plowpan barriers. The machine's excellent mixing operation gives good soil structure. A major feature of this tillage system is the minimal tractor power requirement. Also, the machine is low maintenance. Although not readily available in North America, the spading machine is certain to achieve small farm application because of the many designs and working widths being manufactured.

Tools designed especially for small farms are surfacing around the world. The old attitude that machines must be too expensive for small farmers to own or compete against is fading as superfarms find their public policy support eroded.

SPADING MACHINE

NOTE FROM THE EDITOR

The newsletter is beginning to grow and expand, and we need your help. We would like to begin featuring other writers and would appreciate submissions for review.

In order to expand, we also need to increase circulation and advertising. Please show the newsletter to your friends and encourage them to subscribe. Back issues are still available (limited).

THE POTENTIAL OF HERBS AS A CASH-CROP is now in print and available. Send $12.00 for an autographed edition.

"The Herb Market Report" Resources List

For the past year, OAK offices have received numerous requests for seed sources and other resources necessary for the commercial cultivation and forage of herbs. As a result, a computerized resource list has been started, and a print-out is now available.

We have added names and addresses of those who completed the questionnaire in Vol. 1, No.3 of the newsletter. Many of you would like to know neighbors with mutual interests and goals. The purpose is to form local cooperatives for marketing and trucking networks.

If you would like to be included on this list, please send a brief write-up on your activities and interest. Further questionnaires are also available with an SASE. If you object to having your name on this list, please indicate same on your renewal subscription.

If you have a cottage industry or a small business related to herbs, consider in addition to this list placing an ad with us to enhance your market access. We offer personable rates and a special rate card is available.

TIME FOR RESUBSCRIPTION LAST NOTICE

This is your last issue of "The Herb Market Report," unless you have already resubscribed for 1986. Now is the time for you to send us your renewal instructions. An early response allows us ample time to process your renewal. In this way, you will continue to receive your monthly copy of "The Herb Market Report" without interruption.

BOOK REVIEW:

THE HERB GARDENER'S RESOURCE GUIDE - Paula
Oliver. 82pp. Northwind Farm, Route 2,
Box 246, Shevlin, MN 56676. c1985. $7.95.

This is a revised, second edition of
a most popular resource guide. It has been
expanded and is a must for any starting an
herb business. With more than 500 listings,
this book has been beautifully pulled together as a reference, complete with indexing
of products and services.

Whatever you might need in the area of
herbs, this edition will have it. It provides details on related accessories, equipment, publications, programs, tours and
special ordering policies.

Although it is a valuable tool for
those interested in networking with others,
it's primary forcus is toward the gardener.
There is little emphasis on the more commercial aspects of herb farming and foraging.
Future editions might include brokers, buyers, and herb gathering/farming cooperatives.

We highly recommend this text as an important addition to your library, however.
It is extremely helpful for small scale development and cottage industries. Perhaps
when Northwind Farm begins to receive in-
quiry from you, they will become more aware
of the growing interest in the commercial
directions herb farming and foraging.

WORKSHOPS

Austin, TX - January 9, 1986. A one-day farming
workshop. For further information, contact Acres, USA
(816) 737-0064.

Raleigh, NC - January 11, 1986. A one-day farming
workshop. For further information, contact Leo Tew at
(919) 782-9338.

New Orlean, LA - January 14, 1986. A one-day
farming workshop. For further information, contact
Acres, USA at (816) 737-0064.

Kansas City, MO - January 16, 1986. A one-day
farming workshop. For further information, contact
Acres, USA at (816) 737-0064.

Lansing, MI - January 29, 1986. A one-day farming
workshop. For further information, contact Nancy Benn
of National Ag Products at (800)-851-8588.

Portland, OR - February 15/16, 1986. A 2-day workshop on foraging and marketing. For further information,
contact The Western Forestry Center at (503) 228-1367

Seattle, WA - No date yet, workshop forming. For
further information, contact Joel Radcliffe at (206)-
324-9792, or send a SASE to P.O.Box 20695, Seattle, WA
98102

The Herb Market Report
1305 Vista Drive • Grants Pass, OR 97527

The Herb Market Report is a newsletter published monthly and distributed by The Southern Oregon Herb Gatherers' Association. Inc.

Oak Publishing
1212 SW 5th Street,
Grants Pass, OR 97526
Phone: 541-426-5588

Copyright 1986-2013 © Dr. Richard Alan Miller

Vol. 1 No. 12

Vol.2

Nos. 1-12

Book 1 *Table of Contents*

Forage | Culture | Harvesting | Market Analysis |

Dr. Richard Alan Miller

Book 1 *Table of Contents*

| Forage | Culture | Harvesting | Market Analysis |

Dr. Richard Alan Miller,   *Dr. Richard Alan Miller*

THE HERB MARKET REPORT

for the herb farmer and forager   Vol. 2   No. 1   January, 1986

ROSEMARY: A Crop for the Sun Belt States

The Mediterranean countries are the home of numerous plants of the Labiatae family, among which are many perfume plants. Rosemary oil is steam distilled from the flowers, leaves and twigs of the wild-growing Rosmarinus officinalis L. which is found in numerous forms and subvarieties.

The common and generic names are derived from the early Latin ros maris or "dew of the sea," from its habit and preference of growing close to the sea and the dew-like appearance of the blossom at a distance. From earliest times its medicinal virtues were recognized and it has always been a popular aromatic.

The plant grows wild in abundance in Spain, France, Corcica, Italy, Sardinia, Yugoslavia, Russia, the Middle East, Libia, Tunisia, Algeria, and Morocco, and has even been found in East Africa. It is well-suited to the coastal sections of most Sun Belt states, like California, Texas, Louisiana, Alabama, and South Carolina.

Rosemary is an evergreen, perennial shrub which prefers chalky, calcareous hill country. It requires a well-drained soil and warm, wind-sheltered positions in cooler regions. Reaching a height of up to 6 feet, the plant is characterized by linear, narrow leaves whose undersides are matted with thick hair.

The reported life zone for rosemary is 48°F to 82°F with an annual precipitation of 12 to 106 inches and a soil pH of 4.5 to 8.7. The drought tolerant plant can grow in rocky to sandy soils, as long as the drainage is adequate and a minimum soil depth of 8 inches is available.

The pale-blue flowers can develop throughout the growing season, although profuse blooming occurs during late winter and early spring. Rosemary has no serious pests or diseases, but the plant is not cold hardy. It is generally propagated from either stem cuttings or seed.

Fields of rosemary are usually harvested once or twice each year, depending on the geographical area and whether the harvest is for plant material or essential oil. A first cutting can be obtained in the seeding year but is usually delayed until 18 months after seeding.

Plant material can be harvested with a wild rose harvester, similar to a forage harvester with its cutting blades modified. The leaves are dried in the shade or in special dehydrators directly after harvest to maximize retention of color and oil content. Sifters can separate woody stems from the leaves fairly easily when the product is dry. There is some loss of color when leaves are frozen.

The volatile or essential oil of rosemary include cineole, alpha and beta-pinene, camphor, bornylacetate, camphene, linalool, d-limonene, borneol, myrcene, alpha-terpineol, and beta-caryophyllene. The oil is extracted from flowering tops, stems, and leaves by steam distillation or the use of organic solvents. An oleoresin is also marketed commercially in most countries.

Distillation is performed mainly in Spain, Tunisia, Yugoslavia, France and Morocco. Spain supplies by far the bulk of all rosemary oils, but the quality of Spanish oils varies from the very best to the very poorest of all rosemary oils. One or two Spanish distillers specialize in the so-called "rosemary flower oil" which is distilled exclusively from flower material at full inflorescence.

Apart from a very high amount of monoterpenes, rosemary oil contains a significant amount of borneol, a crystalline terpene alcohol. This is also the main oxygenated compound of the oil. Thus, rosemary oil is not very soluble in diluted alcohols below 80%, but finds extensive use in perfumery for citrus colognes, lavender waters, and pine needle fragrances.

It blends well with olibanum and spice oils, making it important for most Oriental perfumes, room-deodorants, household sprays, insecticides, and numerous disinfectants. As a low-boiling and fresh-smelling oil, it has good effect as a masking agent, particularly for phenolic or tar-like odors.

Rosemary oil blends well with lavandin, lavender, citronella oils, origanum or thyme, pine needle oil, coumarin, labdanum, olibanum, elemi, terpinyl propinonate, isobornyl propionate, cedarwood oils and derivatives, methyl ionones, petitgrain oil and nitromusks.

Occasionally a so-called terpeneless rosemary oil is perferred for colognes and lotions. Terpeneless rosemary oil would be four to five times concentrated if truly deterpenized, but it is customary to "top off" 50% or slightly more in order to produce an oil of greater tenacity and better solubility in diluted alcohol.

Rosemary oil is occasionally adulterated with camphor oil (white) or with head fractions from the rectification of Spanish eucalyptus oil. Yugoslavian rosemary oils are often contaminated with oil from the plant Salvia lavandeulaefolia L. which is also known as Spanish sage. This oil contains large amounts of cineole (or eucalyptol).

Dried rosemary leaves, whole or ground, are used as seasonings for soups, stews, sausages, meat, fish, and poultry. Rosemary is also used in numerous nonalcoholic beverages. The plant and extracts have antibacterial and antioxidant activity and can be used to preserve fats and meats.

More than 4,000,000 pounds of dried leaves were imported into the U.S. last year for domestic use, 30% from Soviet Bloc countries. This represents as much as 2,500 acres of cultivated lands. Including the oil imports, more than 30,000 acres were need to meet current import uses for rosemary oil and leaves.

These figues do not even include the numeous species grown form ornamental and hedgerows uses. Often, these plants are used for embankments because of their beauty and deep root system. This helps stabilize the soil and allows the plant to withstand hot, dry periods. The plant is considered a good source of nectar for bees, having blossoms that appear when few other plants are blooming.

Tunisian oil is very uniform and of high quality. Only flowers and leaves are distilled in Tunisia, twigs are never included. This indicates that all plant materials are harvested by hand, and is why Tunis produces less than 50 metric tons of rosemary oil last year.

Yugoslavian oils, distilled from flowers and leaves only, are not quite as outstanding as they were in the years between the two wars. French oils are generally of excellent quality, superior to most other rosemary oils, or at least equal to the select material from Spain or Tunis. In fact, many "French" rosemary oils are merely select oils from Tunis or Spain.

The total world production of rosemary oils is considerably over 250 metric tons per year. Last year, for example, more than 180,000 pounds of rosemary oil was imported into the United States. The primary supplier was Spain, with France, Netherlands, Tunisia and the U.K. being secondary sources. This represents more than 36,000,000 pounds of leaf material for the oil distillation.... and this is just for U.S. consumption alone.

Rosemary oil is a pale yellow or almost colorless, mobile liquid of strong, fresh, woody-herbaceous, somewhat minty-forestlike odor. The "high" fresh notes vanish quickly, yielding to a clean, woody-balsamic bodynote which tones out in a dry-herbaceous, but very pleasant and tenacious bitter-sweet note.

There is considerable difference in the odor of the various types of rosemary oil. The above description is based upon average commercial lots of Tunisian oils and select lots of Spanish oils. Unfortunately, about 60 to 80% of the Spanish production is of a much lower grade. Characteristic of poorer oils is the pronounced camphoraceous-cineolic note which is different from the herbaceous.

Index to Articles in Volume I (1985)

The following is a summary of articles from our 1985 "The Herb Market Report." Back issues are available for $1.50 each, or $15.00 per set of twelve (full year). Current subscriptions is $12.00 for 12 issues.

News Release:

The following article was printed in the LA Times on 12-4-85. titled "Spice hot items:"

"U.S. retail sales of condiments reached a level of almost $3 billion in 1984, registering average annual gains of approximately 7 percent since 1980, a study from Packaged Facts, a market research firm, disclosed.

"The condiments market includes sauces, such as ketchup, mustard and barbecue; dry condiments, including salt, pepper, spices and vegetable seasonings; and extracts and flavorings, such as vanilla and fruit flavorings.

"The fastest-growing category is hot sauces, followed by Mexican sauces and barbecue sauces, the study showed. From 1980 to 1984, hot sauces registered a 29 percent average annual growth in pound volume, and more than 40 percent average annual growth in dollar sales.

"The best-selling condiments sauce is ketchup, totaling more than an estimated $620 million in 1984."

Note from the Editor

Please help us with our catalog search. If you publish a catalog on herbs or related cottage industries, please send us one and put our name on your mailing list.

If you receive or know of a favorite catalog, please send us one or send us the complete mailing address so that we can enjoy it, too. Thanks for the exchange.

THE POTENTIAL OF HERBS AS A CASH-CROP is now in print and available. Send $12.00 for an autographed edition.

Devil's Club Root: A New Northwest Panax Ginseng

Many regions of the United States have local plants which are variants from well-established crops. The purpose of this article is to describe such a plant and how one would begin to develop marketing for such a new crop. This discussion is meant to serve as an example for new crops development.

Ginsengs are some of the most commercially important herbs in the world. The Chinese have been facinated by the "man plant" for more than 5,000 years, now using it as one of their exchanges as a money standard in the Singapore Stock Exchange.

Like mandrake, the most potent ginseng roots are said to be shaped like a man's body. There are even superstitious myths that the best roots are obtained when the root is dug up at midnight during a full moon.

Oriental men have consumed this root daily for over 5,000 years to retain their virility. An ancient medicinal manuscript of India says of ginseng that it "bestows on men both young and old the power of a bull." (Atherva Veda).

Indian tribes of the United States have a tradition with ginseng use as well. The first recorded uses are in the sixteenth century. Entire tribes would harvest the abundant Panax quinquefolium, the North American species of this root crop. The Meskwakis Indians, for example, were known to concoct a special love potion with these harvests, combining it with mica, snake meat, gelatin, and some wild columbine herb. A young girl of the tribe would use the mixture to find a husband by feeding it to an unsuspecting male.

There seems to be no other herbal which energizes the body and clears one's perception to the extent that ginseng does. The Anglicize word "ginseng" is actually used today to include a variety of herbs. The Chinese reserved the man-root characteristic as important to the wild Tung Pei roots. All other Chinese ginsengs are cultivated to a greater or lesser extent and all have their own specific characteristics.

There are a number of variations within the ginseng family, Araliacelae, most being marketed as ginsengs because of their similarity in medicinal action. These include Korean ginseng, Japanese ginseng, wild American ginseng and cultivated American ginseng.

In 1952, the Soviet Acadamy of Sciences in Vladivostok hailed the discovery of a new ginseng, known as Eleutherococcus senticocus or Siberian ginseng. It was shown to be a heartier, sub-arctic variety, which grows in the uncultivated soils of the Siberian taiga. As it found use in the training regimen of Cosmonauts and Olympic atheletes, it also became a commercially important cash crop.

Again, the original discovery of the plant came from centuries of Russian folk tradition. From there, a number of chemical and biological studies were made. According to the Cyclopedia Dictionary of Medical Botany of the USSR by G. S. Ogolovec (1955), this ginseng also gives off minute amounts of a unique type of ultraviolet radiation (bioluminescence) which stimulates the healthy growth of tissue, especially in the endocrine system. This subtle radioactive quality is known as "mitogenic radiation."

Devil's club root, Oplopanax horridum (Smith) Miq., is part of the Araliacelae or ginseng family, and closely resembles Siberian ginseng. Furthermore, it has a long history of herbal use among Indians of Northwest, especially along the coastal regions. Other plants in this family include English ivy and Virginia sarsaparilla.

The first songs about devil's club root originate from an almost forgotten era of the unrecorded past when a Tlingit of the Kake tribe observed two bears attempting to soothe their battle wounds by chewing the root. Since that time, this plant has been extensively used from Yakutat, Alaska to Neah Bay, Washington.

Although devil's club is not found in many places, it is quite abundant in those areas which favor its growth. As the scientific name implies, the plant is something on the order of horrible and has been the bane of woodsmen who must cross steep, damp stream banksit calls home. The stalk, stems, and leaves carry long yellow thorns that are barbed and very sharp.

A devil's club thorn, if untended, can work its way through a finger and emerge - after much pain and infection - on the side opposite its entry. Many loggers and travelers have received painful wounds from grasping the heavy stalk as they slipped on the mossy rocks of its typical habitat.

It is a flowering shrub that grows abundantly in the rain forests of the Pacific Northwest, British Columbia and S.E. Alaska. Known as Alaskan ginseng, the stalks may be as large as 2 inches in diameter and reach a height of twelve feet.

The light brown stems rise from the moss in crooks and twists and are covered with long yellow spines. Several smaller annual stems support the large maple-shaped leaves, flower clusters, and berries. All above-ground parts of the plant except the flowers and berries are spiny and dangerous. The leaves are up to 18 inches across and are coarsely lobed and finely toothed.

From above, the pale green leaves closely resemble a large maple, but below, the many evil spines protruding from the veins make the distinction quite clear. The overall covering of spines and the oddly twisted, often horizontal trunk are the best keys to identification. It also bears large clusters of bright red berries in the fall months, but are not edible.

Historically, some Indians in Puget Sound drank a brew made from devil's club, peeling off bark and thorns, to ward off a cold or ease the effects of rheumatism. The powder of dried bark may have been used as a deodorant, as well as for a baby talc. Some Indians have even combined devil's club root with prince's pine herb and cascara bark, drinking the resulting brew for tuberculosis.

The Skagit Indians drank devil's club tea to reestablish regular menstrual flow after childbirth. The Lummi cut the thorns off and lay the bark on a woman's breast to stop excessive flow of milk. The superstition surrounding this root has become almost magical with most tribes today.

The Klalam Indians of Puget Sound, considered to be very accomplished fishermen, had a unique use of devil's club. They would cut a peeled stick of the plant into small pieces and then in some manner wrap their fishing lines about them, throw in their weighted lines, and when the line reached bottom and went slack, the bright little bits of peeled devil's club would go spinning towards the surface - and the fish would follow.

The modern medical world has been interested in devil's club root sind the midthirties due to the discovery of the presence of an insulin-like substance in the plant. Some doctors announced surprising results in treatment of diabetes with extractions of devil's club roots. This extract seems to have potent hypoglycemic properties, per "Alaska Medicine," Vo.8, No.2; June, 1966.

The most common method of preparing the extract today is to fill a three gallon pot to the brim with either dried roots or stems, or both. Add water to the brim. The contents are maintained just below the boiling point for three to four hours. The extract is next filtered, cooled, and stored in air tight glass bottles. The plant can be used at any time of the year, but the Tlingit believe it is strongest in the spring.

Despite the fact that devil's club is a difficult, dangerous plant to handle, collecting the roots and shoots is easy. Near the bottom of the stalk or just below the moss surface, the spines disappear. Tug upward on the root and it will tear through the moss for several feet, exposing the unguarded portion and the several young shoots.

These shoots are easy to snap off the main root. The shoots remain edible until the first traces of the yellow spines appear. Lightly boil them in salted water and they will retain a tender yet crisp character. Peel the tough, brownish-yellow skin from the roots, which can be chewed for their flavor.

Developing Markets for Devil's Club Root

As it stands today, there are very few buyers for devil's club root. The options on how to approach developing this market are quite broad, however. As a new crop, it has similar opportunities as the new Brazilian herb pau d'arco (Tabebuia altissima).

The first questions to be asked is where should one begin? One should begin by determining what form of marketing you wish to enter. This could include bulk wholesale, retail (processed), or as a cottage industry. A cottage industry would be where a tincture or some other form of manufactured item is created, including packaging for regional distributors.

As a bulk wholesale commodity, a technical flier needs to be created. The slant should be toward the fact that this is a new panax ginseng from the Pacific Northwest, suitable as an ingredient on those products which would like to advertise the fact that they contain "ginseng."

The point might be stressed that this crop is an "industrial," less expensive form of panax ginseng, perfect for manufacturers who are cost-conscious. This flier should be sent to any and all manufacturers who might use a ginseng as an ingredient. These would include herbal tobaccos, herbal soft drinks (like Corrs), tablet and capsule pharmaceutical houses, and such tea blend users as Select Teas, Lipton, and others.

The flier should be short, simple, and to the point. If you could afford a laboratory analysis to verify chemistries and cost-of-constituent comparisons of such things as panax acid in devil's club root to that in American ginseng, now you have something to really help market your product. You will note that while pau d'arco is really a hot item, there still is no verifying chemistry on how and why it "works," a presumed truth.

You have similar "truths" about the traditional Indian myths and uses for devil's club root. Chemical information only broadens marketing, opens closed doors, and allows a faster development of the new crop. A comparison of currently developed chemistries and their costs, like other ginsengs, is the most important single aspect to market entry.

The bulk mailing of this flier should then be followed up with a personal telephone call to the more important and potential customers. This requires both time and money, sometimes not available for the marketing of a new product. Samples for review will also often be requested, ranging from less than one ounce to one pound. A budget for these overhead costs needs to be available and anticipated.

It often takes more than a full year to "convince" a manufacturer to use a new ingredient like devil's club root. Overhead costs can also exceed $2,000 to open several limited doors. As a result, your cost for the product should reflect some of these so-called R&D costs. You can always drop your price with time, so it is generally suggested that the whole purpose of this venture is to make money, not spend it.

Since the average forager can harvest up to 200 pounds of devil's club root in one day, initial prices for this crop are recommended at somewhere between $4.00 and $2.50 per pound in 1,000-pound orders. This would be in a semi-processed form, like a chip. For further processing, like for retail and manufacturer markets, additional charges should be added.

Eventually, when national markets exceed 20 tons, then the pricing will become more competitive - dropping to $1.50 per pound in 2-ton orders for a chipped form. This might occur sometime in 1988, but not until then and for quantities only "on contract." Remember, this is a crop with similar chemical and physical properties to the imported Siberian ginsengs which sell for more than $60 per pound.

I think that the really good markets will be those which enter this market as a cottage industry. There are a number of immediate products which could be developed with little effort. The first would be to prepare this products as a powder, capsulate it, and sell it under your own label as a Northwest panax Ginseng, with a tradition of use by the Indians of the Pacific Northwest.

Tinctures are always a profitable way to enter a new product into the marketplace as a cottage industry. FDA requirements are simple, as long as you do not make medical claims. Teas are another which might require some further processing, like C/S. Tea bagging would be an instant success, of course, and if you could prepare this crop in that form, there are numerous tea manufacturers who would be more than willing to market this crop under their own label.

Because devil's club root is a regional variant to a commercially important import, the opportunities available for the development of a new market are quite broad and exciting for the starting entrepreneur.

"The Herb Market Report" Resource List

For the past year, OAK offices have received numerous requests for seed sources and other technical information necessary for the commercial cultivation and forage of herbs. As a result, a computerized resource list has been started, and a print-out is now available.

The following print-out is an example of hibiscus, a request from the Virgin Islands.

A second print-out contains all the addresses and other important ordering information on each of the companies referenced. Note that a number of different cultivars are given for this crop.

The cost for this service has not yet been standarized and is negotiable. For the present, we have been asking $10.00 advance payment for each crop, $25.00 for three. A number of crops, like basil, are more than 6 pages of seed sources for various cultivars.

```
HIBISCUS abelmoschus Musk Plant
            2.05/25, 6.15/100, 27.65/500, 49.20/1,000
Hurov's

HIBISCUS Southern Belle Hybrid,mixed colors

NAME OF COMPANY   : PKT : 1/8 oz.: 1/4 oz.: 1 oz. : 1/4" : 1/2" : 1"
Burpee            : 5.75: 10.50  : 17.25  :       :      :      :
Jung's            : .95 : plants 2.25 each:        :      :      :
Stoke's           : .80 : 10.15  :        :       :      :      :

HIBSCUS Dinner Bell Giant
            2.49 each plant or 3/6.75
Henry Field

HIBISCUS Dixie Belle Mix
            : 1.00: 14.85  : 27.45  :        :      :      :
Stoke's

HIBISCUS esculentus Burmese Aphrodisiac
            2.05/25, 6.15/100, 27.65/500, 49.50/1,000
Hurov's

HIBISCIS Hardy Mallow Mixture       : 3.05  :        :      :      :
            : .60 :
Stoke's

HIBISCUS Moscheutos    no prices listed    :        :      :      :
Back Porch

HIBISCUS mutabilis Burma Rose
            1.50/10,  3.30/25,  12.00/100,  54.00/500
Hurov's

HIBISCUS mutabilis Cotton Rose
            2.40/100, 19.20/1,000, 86.40/5,000,  153.60/10,000
Hurov's

HIBISCUS sabdarifera Siam Big Pod Roselle
            4.95/100, 39.60/1,000, 178.20/5,000
Hurov's

HIBISCUS sabdarifera Sierra Leone Roselle
            .95/100, 22.25/500
```

"The Herb Market Report" resources also include access to a number of technical papers useful for crop development. The following example on rosemary is given to show scope, not quantity. There are more than 400 articles on rosemary in OAK files.

The cost for this service varies with the depth of the request. A list of the top ten articles on a given crop is $10.00 advance payment, and $0.50 per additional reference in a specific category (like plant growth or plant physiology and metabolism).

Yakhontova, L.D., et. al. 1971. "A study of Rosmarius officinalis: IV. Isorosmaricin." Chem. Nat. Compd. (Engl. Transl.) 7: 396-398. Translation of Khim. Prir. Soedin. 1971(4): 416-420.

Evstratova, R.T., et. al. 1978. "Level of essential oil and ledol in wild rosemary (Ledum palustra L.) leaves in different vegetation phases [in Russian]." Khim. -Farm. Zh. 12(11): 71-77. CA 90: 51413

Rasmussen, K.E., et. al. 1972. "Terpenes and related compounds. XIX. Quantitative variations of some components of the foliage volatile oil of Rosmarius officinalis in the spring." Pharm. Weekbl. 107: 309-313. CA 77: 58757.

Bos, L. et. al. 1979. "Parsley latent virus, a new and prevalent seed-transmitted, but possibly harmless virus of Petroselinum crispum." Neth. J. Plant Pathol. 85: 125-136.

Wheeler, J.E., et. al. 1971. "Identification of four Phytophthora isolates previously unreported from Arizona." Phytopathology 61: 1293-1296.

Roth, H., et. al. 1973. "Helicella snails infesting rosemary seeds: Methyl bromide and other fumigants for quarantine control." J. Econ. Entomol. 66: 935-936.

BOOK REVIEW:

"Potpourri from Herbal Acres" - A Quarterly Newsletter by Phyllis V. Shaudys. Pine Row Publications, Box 428, Washington Crossing, PA 18977. $15.00/year.

If you have ever felt alone or isolated from others that love herbs as much as you, you won't after you read "Potpourri from Herbal Acres," a quarterly newsletter by Phyllis Shaudys.

It is an information-packed publication for the potential cottage-industry gardener, a place where most of us begin with our interests in herbs and spices. It should be noted that this publication is geared for the home hobbyist and small-scale gardener.

The publication is not without its worth, however, with lots of neat ideas which could be developed into interesting cottage industries. Its primary orientation is toward detailed directions for a large variety of herbal craft items, with numerous receipes that will make your mouth water.

Excerpts of letters and comments from all over the U.S. add to the charm of this publication. There is even a section called herbfest, containing schedules of upcoming events, classes, open houses, workshops and conferences.

They even offer a free herb chart on herb growth, use, harvesting and processing with a SASE.

Workshops

Raleigh, NC - January 11, 1986. A one-day farming workshop. For further information, contact Leo Tew at (919) 782-9338.

New Orleans, LA - January 14, 1986. A one-day farming workshop. For further information, contact Acres, USA at (816) 737-0064.

Kansas City, MO - January 16, 1986. A one-day farming workshop. For further information, contact Acres, USA at (816) 737-0064.

Grand Rapids, MI - January 28-February 1, 1986. Farm conference and 2-day workshop. For further information, contact Nancy Benn of National Ag Products at (800) 851-8588.

Portland, OR - February 15/16, 1986. A 2-day workshop on foraging and marketing. For further information, contact The Western Forestry Center at (503) 228-1367.

Ithica, NY - March 16, 1986. A one-day farming workshop following The National Organic Farm Conference. For further information, contact Walter Pedersen at (607) 243-7502.

Austin, TX - No date yet, workshop forming. For further information, contact Acres, USA at (816) 737-0064

Seattle, WA - No date yet, workshop forming. For further information, contact Joel Radcliffe at (206)-324-9792, or send a SASE to P.O.Box 20695, Seattle, WA 98102.

Organization for the Advancement of Knowledge

OAK

Oak Publishing
1212 SW 5th Street,
Grants Pass, OR 97526
Phone: 541-426-5588

Copyright 1986-2013 © Dr. Richard Alan Miller

The Herb Market Report   Vol. 2 No. 1

Address Correction Requested

Return Postage Guaranteed

BULK RATE
U.S. Postage Paid
Grants Pass, OR
Permit No. 66

Special thanks to James Duke for his insights regarding evening primrose (Vol.1, No.10). Furhter information on James Duke can be found in Vol.1, No.7.

THE HERB MARKET REPORT

for the herb farmer and forager   Vol. 2   No. 2   February, 1986

SWEET BASIL:
The Perfect Annual for the Beginning Farmer

Few plants offer the beginning small herb and spice farmer as much potential as the sweet basil (Ocimum basilicum L). While most spice farms prefer growing perennials, sweet, or common basil is one annual that is so successful that it should be included in any beginning small-farm plan.

As a native to both India and Asia, it is a tender, annual herb of the Labiatae or mint family. Although grown as an ornamental, basil is cultivated commercially in Egypt, France, Turkey, and several of the Soviet bloc countries. India has also become fairly active in recent years, as well as South Africa.

There is a difficulty in classifying the more than sixty varieties of Ociumum basilicum L.. This has been attributed to the plant's polymorphic character and ability to cross-pollinate. This has resulted in creating a large number of subspecies, varieties, and forms.

Ornamental types of basil include types with purple foliage (ie. Dark Opal) or varying growth habits (ie. bush basil). Basils grown for the fresh market should have a sweet flavor and dark green foliage. Those grown for their dried leaves as the end product are usually classified into three main categories.

French basil, reputed to be the sweetest in flavor and darkest in color, is the most valued. Basils grown in the U.S. are noted for their rich color, sweet flavor, cleanliness, and uniformity of particle size. They are often quite competitive on the world markets. Egyptian basils, also known as "Reunion" or African basil, have a somewhat camphoraceous fragrance and different flavor and are usually less expensive.

The reported life zone for most sweet basils range from 44.5°F to 80.5°F, with 23.5" to 165.5" annual precipitation and a soil pH of 4.3 to 8.2.

Production

Basil is usually direct seeded, although some farmers are now transplanting it in the field in late spring after all danger of frost has passed. It will die immediately when exposed to frost. Germination ratios should be at least 80-95% from the seed company. Germ ratios below 70% should not even be used.

With heavier soils, the seed needs to be covered with an anticrustant soil. It should be kept moist to hasten germination and ensure more uniform plant stand. Because the seed is relatively small, they require a well-tilled and uniform seedbed, with better-than-average friability. This will give the best chance for uniform establishment, essential to weed control.

The seed should be planted only 1/8- to 1/4-inches deep. Germination is strictly based on soil temperatures (see graph), with plant emergence occuring within 8-14 days. Lateral branching and growth can be encouraged by trimming the tops of transplants prior to field planting. This procedure can be done in the field when they are about 6 inches tall.

The optimum population density of basil is usually dependent upon the end use. 24 to 36 inch rows recommended, being compatible with existing cultivation machinery. Plants should be spaced 6 inches apart in each row. Large variations in growth and yield may occur due to conditions in climate, plant cultivars, and cultural/management practices.

Seed Sources

For the past year, OAK offices have received so many requests for seed sources, a computerized resource list has been created. Print-outs are available for a fee ($10/crop or $25/3 crops). An example of the print-out for hibiscus was shown in Vol.1, No.12 of the newsletter.

The print-out for basil seed sources is 3 pages long and contains 19 different cultivars. A summary of some of the "best buys" are

Sweet basil - Lake Valley, Agway, Harris and Burpee, by the pound.

Green bush basil - Abundant Life, by the ounce and Lake Valley, by the pound.

Lemon basil - Lake Valley, by the pound.

Lettuce-leaf basil - Companion Plants.

Opal basil - Northrup/King.

A list of more than 100 seed sources (complete addresses) is now available either as a print-out or as tables from OAK for $10. Each of their catalogs has been reviewed and entered into our resource list database. It is continually updated weekly, as new sources are developed. It's a lot of work.

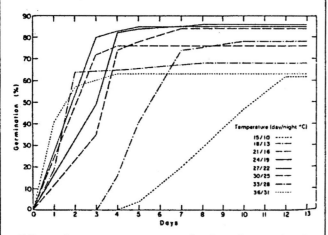

Effect of temperature on germination of sweet basil.

Fertilization

The rate of fertilization application will depend on both soil type and prior history (including previous crops and their fertilizer application). The effects on N- and P-nutrition on the essential oil content of several herbs and spices are shown in the next column, for future reference.

It is suggested that an N-P-K ratio of 1-1-1 be used at first. This can be accomplished by the broadcast and plowdown application of $N-P_2O_5-K_2O$ at a rate of 120-120-120 pounds per acre.[2] A sidedress application with nitrogen, at a rate of 15-30 pounds N per acre, is recommended shortly after the first harvest.

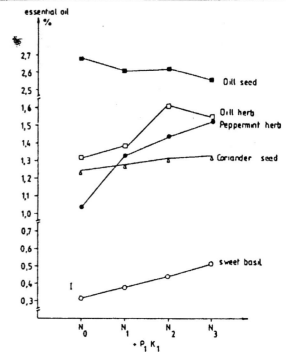

Effect of N-nutrition on the essential oil content.

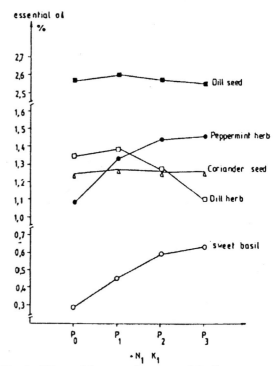

Effect of P-nutrition on the essential oil content.

Irrigation

Most basils are not tolerant to water stress. A regular and uniform supply of moisture is required , usually via either trickle or overhead irrigation systems. When using trickle irrigation, care must be taken not to damage irrigation line during harvests.

During hotter periods, overhead systems of water work best for more uniform growth. This helps hold weeds under better control. With high plant populations, coupled with mechanical cultivation, weeds become much more manageable.

Commercially labelled herbicides for weed control for basil are not available in most states. The presence of weeds markedly decrease the value and quality of dried basils. The only viable techniques for weed control is through the use of irrigation and cultivation techniques/management.

Insects and Disease

There are a number of insects and diseases that may infest basils. Again, there are no pesticides currently labelled for basil. Plants should therefore be constantly monitored for the presence of insects and diseases.

A complete list of the diverse insects and diseases of basil can be found in the important reference "Diseases of Sweet Basil - A Review," Khial Badshah and Zakaullah, The Pakistan Journal of Forestry, July, 1979. pp.188-194.

Harvest

The plant part harvested depends upon the projected use. Basils grown for the dried leaves are usually cut just prior to the appearance of flowers. Plants harvested for oil extraction should be harvested during full bloom. The variations in essential oil content of basil plants as a function of the phenological stage at each period between mowings for Israel is shown as

The cultivation techniques practised with sweet basil in Israel permit harvesting three or four times in a growing season (early spring to late autumn).[4]

The variations in essential oil content of basil plants as a function of the phenological stage at each period between mowings, are shown in Figure 1. The maximum oil content during each period of plant development was found to occur in the full bloom stage.

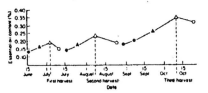

Figure 1. The variation in the essential oil content of *Ocimum basilicum* plants with season and plant phenological stages. ●, vegetative stage; ▲, early blooming; △, full blooming; and ○, seed stage.

The results obtained coincide with the known data that the essential oil content in plants of the Labiatae family increases as the plant approaches the bloom stage. In most cases, plants of this family are harvested at full bloom, if they are intended for oil extraction.[2,4]

During the same phenological stages, the essential oil content of the plant increases toward autumn.

In the Mediterranean area, basil is grown as a short-lived perennial, and 3-5 cuttings are usually taken. In more temperate zones basil may only be cut 2-3 times. First harvests are always low, with second cutting just prior to open bloom, especially when harvested as fresh foliage.

A sickle-bar mower with an adjustable cutting height is most often used to cut the herb. Leaves for fresh-market produce must be cut by hand. The foliage should be cut at least 4-6 inches above the ground to allow for regrowth and a subsequent crop.

When basil is marketed for the fresh produce markets, a continuous supply of leaves is desired. Field harvests and planting dates can be staggered accordingly. A higher yield of herbage and oil results when crops are harvested between early seeding to late seeding stage of growth.

The eugenol content is always highest at late seeding stage. Application of nitrogen has been found to increase growth and yield, in some case as much as 80 kg/ha. This does not affect eugenol content, however.

Processing

Basil is taken for bulk markets as both a dried herb and as an oil. A side-bar cutter will not damage the leaf structure as badly when harvesting the crop for the dried herb markets. Because it is a high volatile oil crop, it can not be sun cured but require special dehydration.

It can be dried fairly easily with good air-flow systems. Initial heats should begin around 85°F and rise gradually to no more than 120°F toward the end of the drying cycle. There will be a tendency for leaf-browning, indicating too much heat and the need for more air flow.

It should be packed in 200-pound bales, wrapped in poylproplyene. Burlap tends to leave an odor. Dried basil must be stored in heat warehouses and inventories should be sold within 1.5 years. It can be further cut with 1/4-inch screens, but has a tendency to powder. Shear mills work best in these situations.

The quality and market price for dried basils is determined by the color of the leaf and volatile-oil retention. The slower the dehydration, the better the quality of herb. This particular herb prefers higher air-flows for faster dehydration and quality of production.

Oil distillation is another form of how this herb is marketed in bulk, primarily through steam distillation. In these cases, basil can be taken with a forage harvester and piggyback system of wagons. The dried fiber, remaining for the distillation process, can be used in the field as trash for a late fall plow-down.

Oil Chemistry

Included among a large number of different types of basil oils are two which have become particularly common in perfumery and flavoring markets. The first is called the true sweet basil oil which is taken from the flowering tops of the Ocimum basilicum L. France and the U.S. being the primary producers, with Italy, Hungary and Spain producing smaller quantities.

The second is the "exotic" or "Reunion" type of basil oil, primarily produced in the Comoro Islands, the Seychelles, and now Madagascar. The two oils can be distinguished by their odor characteristics: the linalool-type and the camphor-type.

The former type also contains estragole, but this material is not typical of the odor of the sweet basil. It does not contain camphor. The latter oil contains more estragole than the linalool-type, and the odor of the "exotic" type is not covered up by the content of camphor. It also contains little or no linalool.

Sweet basil oil has been produced in very limited quantities and now ranks among the more expensive essential oil. Primarily used in fine perfumery and flavor work, it has been a "classic" material in the "Origan" type of perfumes and bases for several decades.

It blends well with the most varied types of perfume materials, e.g. opopanax (bergamot), isoeugenol (clary sage), methylionone (cyclamal), and lime oil (oakmoss) as just a few examples. It also finds some application in flavors, e.g. in the "chartreuse" type of liqueur, and in the high-priced culinary seasonings, meat sauces, and other condiments.

The "exotic" type of basil oil is produced for less money and may be doctored with synthetic linalool (up to 60%!). This less expensive substitute is useful in soap perfumes or other low-cost perfumes as a fair replacement.

A third type of basil oil, known as the "methylcinnamate" type, is produced mostly in Africa, India, Indonesia, the West Indies, and the Balkin States. It is much more fruity and not at all as fresh-green as the "French" basil oil. Its primary constituent is methylcinnamate and could find some use in soap perfumery, especially with availability.

A fourth type of basil oil is the "penolic" type, primarily distilled from Ocimum gratissimum. There are two variations in this product, either high concentrations of thymol or high concentrations of euganol. Euganol is often a replacement to clove oil. The thymol cultivar may substitute thyme productions in some quarters for this important chemistry.

Marketing

More than 2,000 ton of dried basil was imported into the United States in 1985, with similar imports into West Germany. Egyptian basil today lands C/F New York with prices ranging from $0.75-0.85 per pound, while French basils are more than $0.90. Comores

basil oil enters at more than $90 per pound, while Grand Vert ("exotic") basil oil is only $45 per pound.

For perspective, last week, just in the Port of New York alone, McCormick imported more than 28,000 pounds of fancy basil from Egypt, Lyonnais imported 46,000 pounds from Egypt, and Luis Furth imported more than 28,000, also from Egypt. These buyers should be buying domestic productions of this crop. They will, too, when it becomes available.

Basil is used as a fragrance ingredient in perfumes, soaps, hair dressings, dental creams, and mouth washes. Basil oil possesses insecticidal and insect repellent properties. It is effective against houseflies and mosquitoes. It is also a bactericidal and efficient against Salmenella typhosa. Basil extracts have been reported to have antioxidant activity as well.

Other Cultivars

Ocimum sanctum L. (holy basil), an annual native to Australia, India, and some portions of Asia, has a strong, pungent, clove-like odor because of the high euganol content. It is grown extensively in India as a sacred plant to the Hindu religion.

Ocimum citriodorum Vis. or lemon basil has a strong lemon scent, and may have a future as a flavoring substitute. Ocimum kilimandschar Guerke, or chaphor basil, has a strong, pungent camphor odor. Ocimum suava Willd., or tree basil, is a densely woody shrub, reaching heights of 6 to 10 feet and is found everywhere in Africa and India.

Ocimum minimum L., or bush basil, is used as a border plant. It is considered by many to be a dwarf form of sweet basil. The spice basil grown by many American farmers may actually be Ocimum sanctum L. or a hybrid, rather than Ocimum basilicum L.. You must really check you seed source on the precise variation or cultivar when purchasing seed.

Cottage Industries

There are many opportunities available for the small farmer who uses basil as an ingredient for a cottage industry. One of the best examples is given on page 192 in the book THE POTENTIAL OF HERBS AS A CASH-CROP. This describes how to make frozen pesto for the Italian food markets. Net incomes from this form of venture can be more than $4,000 per acre

A pleasant seasoning for your morning tomato juice is basil vinegar. To make this, put one-half cup of slightly crushed fresh leaves (one tablespoon if dried) into a jar with two cups of white vinegar. Let it stand three to five days. Strain the liquid and discard the herbs. Bring the vinegar to a boil. Remove from heat and pour into a preheated sterilized jar. Cap tightly and store in a cool, dark place.

If you are making it for a gift, put a decorative sprig of basil into the bottle before capping. This vinegar is best used within six weeks. Similar vinegars can be made with dark opal basils and apple vinegars. By using tarragon and several other herbs, another cottage industry can emerge, usually with excellent marketing potentials.

Some Technical References

"The Herb Market Report" resources also now offer lists of important technical articles on a given crop for a fee. Not only are these references on a specific crop, they are also organized in specific categories (like plant growth or plant physiology and metabolism). You may write or call for details.

The following are just a few references from more than 400 just on basil now available for your continuing need to grow these crops:

Afifi, A.F., and Dowidar, A.E. 1976. "Effect of volatile materials produced by some members of Labiatae on spore germination and spore respiration of some soil fungi." Egypt. J. Physiol. Sci. 3: 81-92 HA 48: 9285.

Darrah, H.H. 1974. "Investigation of the cultivars of the basils (Ocimum)." Econ. Bot. 28: 63-67.

Darrah, H. 1978. "The clove scented basil: Ocimum gratissimum L." Herbarist 44: 31-37.

Guenther, E. 1969. The essential oils. Vol. III. Individual D. Van Nostrand Co., New York, NY 777pp.

Putievsky, E. "Temperature and daylight influences on the growth and germination of sweet basil and oregano." J. Hort. Sci.(1983) 58 (4) 583-587.

Hornok, L. "Infuence of nutrition on the yield and content of active compounds in some essential oil plants." Acta Hort. 132, 1983 Med. Spice Plants, 239-247.

Pareek, S.K., et al. "Domestication studies on Ocimum sanctum for high oil and euganol content." Indian Perfumer, Vol XXIV, No. 2, 1980, p93-100.

Fleisher, A., "Essential oils from two varieties of Ocimum basilicum L. grown in Israel." J. Sci. Agri. 1981, 32, 1119-1122.

Krishnan, R., "Natural outcrossing in sweet basil, Ocimum basilicum L." Indian Perfumer, Vol. XXV, Part No.3&4, 1981, p74-77.

THE FARM:
A Simple Rotation Program

While visiting the Creative Heath Center in Union City, MI, I had the distinct honor to meet William Mundt. Bill had been invited as a speaker to share his experiences as one of Michigan's first organic farmers. He began as a horse farmer in 1940 and led the way for many organic farming techniques being profitable in Michigan.

Most small farmers know that crop rotation is a good practice, one way to foil disease and insect pests. When closely related plants are grown in the same spot season after season, pests increase, feeding and breeding without interruption. Moreover, some crops deplete soil nutrients, while others, like nitrogen-fixing peas and beans, may contribute to soil fertility.

The following rotation is a summary of procedures carried on Bill Mundt's 200 acre farm, west of Marcellus, MI:

Sod - Clover - Alfalfa - - - - Plow in spring.
1st Year - Corn - for harvest - Plant May 15 - June 1.
2nd Year - Corn - (manure added) - for harvest
3rd Year - Corn for plow down - Broadcast 1.5 to 2 bu./acre.
  Plant May 15.
Buckwheat - (plow corn) plant buckwheat on July 1.
Incorporate 1st Buckwheat into soil, and plant 2nd Buckwheat
  on Aug.1.
Incorporate 2nd Buckwheat into soil on Sept. 1.
  (Note: incorporate Buckwheat into soil when in flower state.)
3rd Crop - plant Wheat for harvest.
Or plant Rye for winter cover and plow in spring and plant to
  Corn for harvest.
Or - plant to Oats for winter cover.
Oats will winter-kill. Incorporate into soil in spring to plant
  Soybeans for harvest (note no weeds).
If Hay is wanted seed in Cereal crop and leave for Hay after
  Cereal has been harvested.

The suggested techniques of Bill Mundt's can be modified for many perennials which will need to be moved every third or fourth year. This outlined program is one used by a very successful organic farmer, and may serve as a model for your own crops and soil requirments.

Once the tree is down, the bark is easily stripped by making longitudinal incisions and peeling off sections which tend to roll into large "quills." The bark is then laid out on tarps in the sun to dry, being turned every day. The inner bark is protected from the sun by the curving of the bark inward. This "red" color is what determines the market-quality. The bark is then chipped into one inch pieces and packed into 20 to 80 pound burlap sacks for shipping.

Since the tree is part of the Buckthorn family, it grows from rootstock. This means that if the tree is semi-harvested, it will "bleed" to death. By chopping the entire tree down, the rootstock will send up further shoots which eventually make the tree larger (several trees now exist where there was once only one).

Commercial cultivation of cascara segrada is under way in Oregon, Washington and British Columbia. However, there remains abundant supplies of naturally growing trees which exceed even future export demands. It is easily grown from seedlings within its natural range.

Current suppliers such as Pacific Coast Cascara Bark Co., I.P. Callisons, and Penik Corp (aka Western Crud) sell a chipped bark, packaged in burlap sacks at $0.54 per pound (current year-new) and $0.75 per pound (year-old), F.O.B. Portland/Seattle in large tonnages. Cascara exports from Washington and Oregon last year were 400 ton and 500 ton, respectively. Both states have exported this crop to Europe for more than 40 years.

The average forager of cascara bark can usually peel more than 300 pounds in one day, presuming availability of trees which are close to each other. The key is to locate a good stand along the coastline. Most Forest Services and Railroad lands are available and well-documented, with free brush permits for this crop. Sometimes a timber company might cut the tree when clearing land for a logging venture.

Green bark (wet) is usually sold to collection sites at $0.12 to $0.20 per pound. The bark is then dried and chipped further and sold to collection trucks from the various "buying stations" from $0.35 to $0.48 in burlap sacks. The weight-loss when drying green bark is less than 45%. Watch for mosses and other foreign material.

Most retailers which would like to sell powders, or the larger pharmaceutical houses which want to extract the oils for those markets both prefer to buy year-old bark. Price variations depend on the season, but range from $0.85 per pound in tonnage to more than $1.75 per pound in 100-pound quantities. During the early spring, before the cascara has begun to be harvested, prices for year-old bark (in tonnage) can rise considerably. This year it was up to $1.40 per pound.

While the total global use in 1984 was about 1,000 ton, the world markets could be expanded to more than 2,000 ton. There are shortages now, and a number of states (like Idaho) could consider this a minor cash-crop. Structurally, a cooperative could collect bark from several parts of a state, marketing the product as a wholesale middleman. For those too small for inventory/credit situations, the cooperative could offer a cash-on-the-spot basis, similar to a buying station for some large agri-business.

Larger quantities could be handled even without good weather, where tarp/sun-cure methods have been used. Green bark can be chipped first and then dried via a corn dryer or similar continuous-feed dryer system. Propane heat sources are the cleanest and cheapest. The barks can be dried at slightly higher temperatures, ranging up to $140^{\circ}F$.. A loading hopper and bagging scale works the best for filling sacks, especially if a commercial sewing machine is available to stitch the bag (with a lable). Polypropylene is a prefered sack when working in large quantities.

A Note from the Editor

The response to our work in the forage of non-timber forest-floor crops and other noxious weeds in Southern Oregon has been overwhelming. As a result, a number of 2-day intensive workshops are now being offered. The emphasis is toward marketing. Dates now scheduled are

April 13th (one-day), Gold Beach, OR. Contact Marge Johnson (503) 347-9389.

April 20/21st (2-day), Portland, OR. Contact Monti McHone (503) 760-2996.

June 22/23rd (2-day), Portland, OR. Contact Scott Browder at The Western Forestry Center (503) 228-1367. Field-hikes/Camp.

THE POTENTIAL OF HERBS AS A CASH-CROP, by Richard Alan Miller will be available next month. Write Acres, U.S.A., P.O.Box 9547, Kansas City, MO 64133 for pre-publication price and tapes of previous workshops.

Getting Back to, and Using Your Roots

The table below classifies root crops by **HARVEST TIME** (spring, summer, fall), **CYCLE** (annual, bi-annual, perennial), **PREPARATION** (raw, baked, boiled/simmer, " water change, roasted, flour, candied), **MEDICAL PROPERTIES** (stomachic, carminative, digestive, laxative, tightens bowels, cholagogue (liver), emmenagogue, diuretic, diaphoretic, astringent, skin wash, " poultice, hemostatic, demulcent, bronchials, sedative, stimulant), and **CONSTITUENTS** (starch, inulin, sugar, oils, tannin, albumin, resin, gum, fat).

Rows (top group):
Angelica, Arrowhead, Arrowroot, Arum, Beet, Burdock, Carrot, Cattail, Chicory, Comfrey, Dandelion, Ginseng, Horseradish, Jew. Artichoke, Licorice, Lovage, Marshmallow, Osha, Parsley, Parsnip, Potatoe, Radish, Salsify, Sassafras, Soap root, Sweet flag, Turnip, Wild ginger, Yellow dock, Yellow pond lily

Rows (bottom group):
Black cohosh, Blue cohosh, Couch grass, Echinacea, Goldenseal, Madder, Mugwort, Oregon grape, Orris, Pleurisy root, Rhubarb, Sarsaparilla, Soapwort, Valerian, Wild yam

Workshops

Portland, OR - February 15/16, 1986. A 2-day workshop on foraging and marketing. For further information on this and future Portland events, contact The Western Forestry Center at (503) 228-1367.

Ithica, NY - March 17, 1986. A one-day farming workshop following The National Organic Farm Conference. For further information, contact Walter Pederson at (607) 243-7502.

Fairbanks, AK - March (tentative). A one-day farming workshop. For further information, contact Charles Walsh of ARCTIC (botanicals Division) at (907) 452-8251 x208.

Austin, TX - No date yet, workshop forming. For further information, contact Acres, USA at (816) 737-0064.

Seattle, WA - No date yet, workshop forming. For further information, contact Joel Radcliffe at (206)-324-9792, or send a SASE to P.O.Box 20695, Seattle, WA 98102.

POTPOURRI FOR HERBAL ACRES

A quarterly newsletter for $15/year. Information-packed for cottage industries and the home gardeners. Pine Row Publications, Box 428-OAK, Washington Crossing, PA 18977.

BOOK REVIEW:

<u>Wild and Exotic Mushroom Cultivation in North America</u>. Geraldine C. Kaye. Farlow Reference Library and Herbarium of Cryptogamic Botany, Harvard University, Cambridge, MA 02138. 1984. 32pp. $4.50.

Written by a specialist, this hard-to-find information will be of lasting interest to a wide spectrum of both scientific and popular readers. The explosion of interest in growing and eating different varieties of edible mushrooms over the past ten years has been phenomenal.

The booklet is divided into seven sections: 1) Introduction and Acknowledgments; 2) Bibliography; 3) Organizations (includes mycological organizations, cultivation research centers, amateur cultivation groups, cultivation classes, etc.); 4) Sources of Spawn, Equipment and Supplies; 5) Commercial Growers/Suppliers of Mushrooms; 6) Booksellers; 7) Indexes and Equivalent Names (scientific names with literature and sources, common names and botanical equivalents, index of organizations). I think you get the idea....

Of particular interest to me was section No.2 on Bibliography. This consists of books and papers, usually with an analytic summary of contents. It was divided into several parts: General to Introductory Works; Scientific Works; Practical Treatment (General and Desirable Crop Species; New Species in Commerce; and Periodicals.

For those interested, this is mushroom season....or will be, shortly. The more you become aware of these natural resources as forageable cash crops, the more you will become aware of the diversity of opportunities available through foraging. Overall, we recommend reading this and related books on this subject.

Organization for the Advancement of Knowledge

OAK

Oak Publishing
1212 SW 5th Street,
Grants Pass, OR 97526
Phone: 541-426-5588

Address Correction Requested

Return Postage Guaranteed

The Herb Market Report   Vol. 2   No. 2

THE HERB MARKET REPORT

for the herb farmer and forager   Vol. 2   No. 3   March, 1986

THE FARM
Some Important Considerations for the Beginning Herb Farmer

Spring is just around the corner, buds are beginning to show on trees in most regions of the country already. For those of you who plan a project with an alternative crop like herbs for the first time, an overview and farm plan on what you need to do is critical at this time.

Questions like "what should I plant?" and "how much money do I need?" must have answers before April. Before you can even begin to approach answers to these types of questions, however, a bigger need exists for an overview toward your approach. This is especially true when attempting to develop specific herbs as cash crops.

The following suggestions are commended for consideration when developing your overview and farm plan:

Overviews

All new crops should be cultivated in 2-acre feasibility studies for at least two years before expansion. Smaller acreages will not give a close cost-of-goods production figure, data critically important for any successful expansion program. Each crop has its own idiosyncrasies. You must become familiar with the plant before you put further money into it for development.

Most successful small herb farm ventures use what is known as a polyculture situation. This is where more than six crops are grown, rather than a monoculture program. What this gives to the small farmer is protection against saturated markets, giving him better stability in both marketing and cash-flow. If a crop market saturates, that crop and be easily rotated out of the farm plan without affecting his other crops. The beginning herb farm should start with about 12 acres; 6 crops, each on a 2-acre parcel.

Often, the land you own is not appropriate for the desired crop. An example would be the lack of irrigation. When working small ventures, appropriate land is

rentable for simple the taxes, water ditch costs, and often 10% of any gross sale. This is known as sharecropping, and is an excellent way to invest your nestegg into crop development (rather than land payments and earnest moneys). With a lease-option, you might even be able to buy the land from profits off the crops. That is the "old fashioned" way most farmers aquired land.

The need for farm equipment is similar. There are plenty of small farms in a given community who are already well-equipped. Often they will be willing to "custom farm" your fields at rates about $20/acre for each pass. With established marketing for a given crop, a "custom" farmer will take his payment in crops, the standard is 40%. Crop selection is often made on the availability of specific tools. There is no sense in growing chamomile if a combine or bean-harvester is not available.

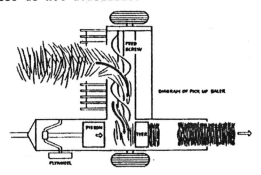

All new crops <u>must</u> be grown with so-called "organic" techniques. Very few herbs and spices have been "labeled for use" with most pesticides and herbicides via EPA. While some small farms have used sinbar to control grasses in mints without inspection, that will not be true in the near future. It is especially true when attempting to import to such countries as Germany and Japan, who have much tougher laws than FDA.

Your crop selections should be designed for export. Direct marketing only moves money from one part of a community to another. Exporting, however, whether it is out of the county, state, or country, brings new dollars into that community. It also restores the identity of that community. When you produce a product that was previously imported, now you are also balancing trade deficits. This is where small farm agriculture will find its stability.

If you are exporting, transportation becomes the single largest expense other than labor. This is why most herbs and spices are sold in a dehydrated form, the "cube" in a truck is worth more money. While most produce trucks are worth $2K, most filled with a dehydrated herb or spice is worth more than $10K. This variation in transportation-costs/pound often makes the difference between closing a sale with a distant port, or not. The bottom line is landed costs, even though most herbs are sold FOB/freight-collect.

The value of a crop is often predicated on the processing done to it prior to shipping. This is why many traditional spice crops are harvested for distillation as an oil. Often the best way to enter the marketing of a new crop is as a cottage industry, where smaller acreages can have greater net incomes. Marketing options are also broadened.

Many current farms have too many acres in cultivation. This was how a number of them got into trouble in the first place. The first question a farmer with traditional crops should ask is "what is my annual income needs?" Since most crop alternatives can net as much as $2K/acre, this will indicate how many acres will be needed after expansion to full production. This will leave some large parcels available, and free the small farmer for more important things to do, like marketing.

What should be done with these larger parcels, not needed to produce net incomes? The farmer might consider putting it into timber, creating topsoil for his great grandchildren. Topsoil is not a "renewable" resource, and is only created, by and large, from forests. There is a need for us to assume a form of "soil Stewardship" toward our childrens' future with agriculture.

Getting Started

Since most of you would like to begin a project this spring, certain options are no longer available. First, one rarely begins a perennial from seed in the field. The problems with it growing faster than the weeds becomes a serious problem. Therefore, most perennials are developed in nurseries in the winter for a spring planting. This is often quite expensive, averaging more than $0.085/plant. The average need for

perennials is 10K/acre, or more than $900 per acre for nurserywork.

There are numerous sources for greenhouse and garden supplies. The best seen for the home gardener with limited greenhouse facilities is the Gardener's Supply Co. (128 Intervale Road, Burlington, VT 05401). While their prices are high, their quality and diverse offerings make them a viable resource.

E.G. Geiger offers similar tools for the beginning farmer, only their prices are oriented toward larger needs. They can be reached at 1-800-4GEIGER. "Greenhouse Manager," a monthly periodical, offers a semi-annual All-Industry Buyers' Guide. You can find any supply needed with this directory. Write Branch-Smith Publishing (120 St. Louis Ave., Fort Worth, TX 76104).

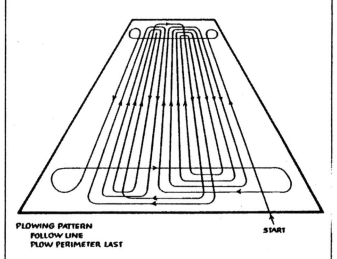

PLOWING PATTERN
FOLLOW LINE
PLOW PERIMETER LAST
START

Most new farmers begin their perennials in beds outdoors in the spring, set for easy hand cultivation during the summer. The plants are then moved in the fall into rows for a following-spring cultivation (1987). The new rows are often mulched heavily to protect the new rootlets from hard frosts. In cases of fast-growing perennials, like oregano, a late-summer move into rows allows some layering before the dormant season.

Seed for annuals should be ordered now. The main problem with most seed companies is their lack of attention to specific cultivars and contaminated seeds. It is often worth paying a little more from a smaller source, knowing that the seedman's reputation is on the line. We will have an article on seeds in a following newsletter. Perennial seed can be ordered next month. Both should have detailed plans on how you plan to get them started, and where.

Deciding where to put specific crops is an artform. Like reading the racing forms, soil survey maps can give you a lot of tips on your land. We have found that plugs taken for chemical surveys are useless. The noxious weeds growing on your field will often tell you more about soil deficiencies and what additives are needed than any other form of soil survey. Their history and regions of control become important factors on techniques used to "organically" cultivate.

Most beginning farms start with 2 or 3 annuals, and 4 perennials. Annuals give experience in cultivation problems, while the perennials are still set in beds for hand-cultivation. One should not expect to show a profit off of first-year productions, even from the annuals. You will find more success if the annuals are put up as a cottage industry the first year, helping add to net profits. 2-acre productions are usually too small for bulk marketing interests. 2 acres of dill, however, put up in 1-pound sacks is quite profitable during canning season.

Sometime before spring, you should go visit the county extension office and obtain a copy of their noxious weeds and native plants lists. As you become more familiar with local weeds, it may be that some of them can be developed as supplemental forms of rural income. In the deserts, for example, there is chapparal and mormon tea. Both are currently of some commercial importance, and both are currently being imported. Recognizing a natural resource from a noxious weed can often underwrite a small farm venture.

There are other examples of how noxious weeds can become more important than the crop in cultivation. In Iowa, for example, burdock often infestates with corn. The farmer is constantly struggling to eliminate the burdock, usually at a loss on production. Burdock, however, is a major produce in Asia, the various countries eating it like we might a carrot. In other words, burdock is worth 4-times the money as a root crop than the corn off the same acreage.

The most important thing to remember is that 1986 is suppose to be a "learning year," not one to show big profits and solve your financial problems. It takes time to learn a new crop. Often the soil will actually show you which crop should be grown, like the burdock example. There will be a lot of handwork at first. The key is to learn how to cut time, using tools and techniques.

Some Points on Marketing

The most common problem with beginning farmers is their security in the sale of a crop. As a result, many go out to prospective markets and ask what they are willing to buy. Most do not like to be bothered, less than 10% might even attempt growing something that year. It is recommended that you don't bother a buyer until you have something to show him from your first year's production. There is no substitute for proof of production.

If the buyer likes what he sees, he will usually want to buy it on the spot. Most wholesale buyers buy on a spot basis, like most other commodities. The buyer does not need to know that you have only limited productions (2-acre), just show him what is available. The key is to secure a contract each year to meet your cash-flow requirements for the projected expansion program. Whatever else you do, please remember not to attempt rapid growth. That is how agriculture got into this current problem in the first place.

There is always lead-time in closing a sale. Most of the larger buyers must secure more than 200 products, each from at least five to ten sources. My approach is to send a one-page description of my crop, including terms-of-sale, with a small sample attached. If they like the price, terms, and small sample, they will then ask for a larger sample, usually 2 pounds or more. Some crops may take as long as six months before a sale. This is normal, for a number of reasons.

There are situations where even though you product is better and cheaper, the buyer will not commit to a purchase. Why? One reason might be trade. There are some companies that sell products to a foreign country. Since they do not want to be paid in the currency of that country, they take a trade in one of their commodities, usually a spice or drug plant. Isn't that interesting? There is more, but that is another story.

Chapter 9 on Bulk Marketing should be thoroughly reviewed, especially the graph on page 159. What this indicates is that often crops are harvested at the very time most buyers are at their lowest cash-flow period. This means that they are not in a position to buy crops when they first become available. The small farmer should attempt contracts for future productions. This gives both the farmer and buyer security.

All first attempts on herb and spice farming should be seen as speculation. With this perspective and approach, there should be no expectations, either on production or marketing. Your primary purpose is as a feasibility study toward more lucrative crops. The key is to enter marketing slowly. Most expansion programs show a 2-acre production on a given crop for 3 years, expanding into 10 acres within 6 years. With 6 to 8 crops in a similar production, market securities are established.

WORKSHOPS:

Ithica, NY - March 17, 1986. A one-day farming workshop following The National Organic Farm Conference. For further information, contact Walter Pederson at (607) 243-7502.

Fairbanks, AK - April 30, 1986. A one-day farming workshop. For further information, contact Charles Walsh of ARCTIC (Botanicals Division) at (907) 452-8251 x208.

Kailua-Kona, HI - No date yet, workshop forming. For further information, contact Brian Tibbetts at (808) 322-2321.

Austin, TX - No date yet, workshop forming. For further information, contact Acres, USA at (816) 737-0064.

Seattle, WA - No date yet, workshop forming. For further information, contact Joel Radcliffe at (206)-324-9792, or send a SASE to P.O.Box 20695, Seattle, WA 98102.

Grants Pass, OR - No date yet, workshop forming. For further information, contact OAK at (503) 476-5588.

Potpourri for Herbal Acres

A quarterly newsletter for $15/year. Information-packed for cottage industries and the home gardener. Pine Row Publications, Box 428-OAK, Washington Crossing, PA 18977

Royal Doulton Water Purification Systems

American Embassies, in over 40 countries, use Royal Doulton water purification systems. The most basic element, earth, in the form of a ceramic outer shell with bacteriocidal silver components traps bacteria to below one micron in size.

Activated carbon forms the inner core of the Royal Doulton filter cartridge. It is removable, easily cleaned and replaced, for extended use. Home, farm, hospital, school and industrial applications. Prices from $100.

Write Royal Daulton of Oregon, 543 Hussey Ln., Grants Pass, OR 97527. (503) 479-2951. Manufacturing ceramic water filters since 1827.

Companion Plants

400 varieties of herb plants and seeds, both common and exotic. Catalogue $1.00 deductible COMPANION PLANTS, Rt.6, Box 88HR, Athens OH 45701

NEWS RELEASE

The following article was printed in the weekly "Research Institute Recommendations" newsletter, an important publication from The Research Institute of America, Inc. (589 Fifth Ave., New York, NY 10017). This was from March 7, 1986/Vo.37, No.10:

"Despite the crisis in farming, there are some high hopes in agriculture. They involve little known plants & forest crops with industrial possibilities.

"...Kenaf is one example: Presently raised in Georgia, Texas and Florida, it's a replacement for cotton & imported newsprint, and in last-mentioned form has been used by more than 10 publishers. Big market foreseen within 5 years.

"...Crambe: In mustard family, source of seed oil for nylon, other items.

"...Guayule: Shrub that's found in the Southwest & Mexico, this is one of only two known species that can produce natural rubber on commercial scale.

"...Meadowfoam: A wildflower of the Pacific Northwest, the USDA says that it may be a key source of oil for lubricants, waxes, etc.; Japan uses it now.

"Agriculture Dept. is currently cultivating a few items of these and other crops on an experimental basis, says it has already identified prospective buyers."

The following article was printed in USA Today on 3-5-86, titled "N.Y.: Urban herbs earn way:"

"BRONX - Nestled among the abandoned buildings, vacant lots and urban decay, an herb farm grows in the South Bronx.

"Glie Farms started four years ago by former IBM Corp. workers Gary Waldron and Jean Lobasso, is the largest year-round producer of fresh culinary herbs in the Northeast.

"This year Glie Farms doubled its capacity by building a 14,000-square-foot hydroponic greenhouse to grow basil, tarragon, oregano and parsley as well as exotic salad greens such as nasturtium leaves.

"Glie began with five employees as an economic development project for the poverty-stricken South Bronx and sold herbs in the New York City area.

"Now it's a for-profit business with 50 employees, and it sells to restaurants, supermarkets and specialty stores in 15 states. Lobasso says growing herbs 'lends itself to inner-city neighborhoods' because of the large amount of hand labor needed."

THE POTENTIAL OF HERBS AS A CASH-CROP is now in print and available.

Organization for the Advancement of Knowledge

LECTURES, WRITING, RESEARCH   1212 SW 5th Street, Grants Pass, OR 97526

HERB FARMING AND FORAGING TAPES — by Richard Alan Miller

If you haven't been able to attend a workshop yet, enjoy Rick's informative lecture style in your home or car! Most tapes contain pertinent questions and answers from participants, bringing up points not necessarily covered in Rick's books.

AL

#1 RECOMMENDED READING & RESOURCES (90 min.)
Introductory material on getting started in an herb-related business. How to find pertinent info., the best texts, and source directories on marketing, trucking, plant identification, etc. These evaluations will help you determine how to invest your limited $ in reference books best suited to your needs.

#2 WEED CONTROL, CROP FUTURES, SEED SOURCES (90 min.)
Learn how to acquire and read soil maps; farm plans, crop rotation, controlling weeds; FDA approval; red clover, lemon balm, apple mint, sage, etc.

#3 MILLING: GRADES, STANDARDS, & PROCEEDURES (90 min.)
How to prepare your product for manufacturers so you get a higher return.

#4 BULK DEHYDRATION & STORAGE (60 min.)
Includes specific techniques, examples of farmed and foraged products, dryer design for efficiency and economics.

#5 MARKETING (60 min.)
Wholesale buyer's needs and requirements, how to do a bulk mailer. etc.

#6 FORAGING (60 min.)
Locating products; brush permits; potential problems; notifying local authorities; cleanup; staying on task; minimum harvest requirements. Some foragable products: locale and use.

#7 FORAGED CROP EXAMPLES (60 min.)
Cascara, Bay, Baby's Breath, Horsetail

#8 FORAGED HERBS & THEIR USES (60 min.)
From RCC class "Herb Use in Home and Industry," with Q. & A.

#9 COTTAGE INDUSTRY EXAMPLES (60 min.)
From RCC class: examples include marketing of an herbal salve and manufacture of gourmet pesto from basil.

#10 HERBAL TEA & TOBACCO FORMULAS--TINCTURES (60 min.)
Mu tea; yogi tea; cinnamon spice; orange spice; lemon spice; red racer; licorice spice; light lavender; night cap tea; golden dawn, etc. Blending, brewing, and other stove-top alchemy, for yourself, for gifts or market. Also "spring tonic," nerve-calming tea, "brain" tea, and appetite-curbing tea ("OB tea").

#11 BUSINESS PLAN EXAMPLE (Retail Herbstore/Deli/Bookstore) (60 min.)
How to evaluate your potential for success in a small business. Making a business plan includes Purpose; Orientation; Inventory Needs; Capital Equipment; Cash Flow; summary Statement of Funds, Bio. or qualifications; advertising needs; legal services; mail order services, etc.

#12 FDA & DANGEROUS HERBS (30 min.)
Food and Drug Administration's "Hit list."

Make checks payable to: O.A.K.

SHIITAKE:
The Oak Mushroom

The two primary edible mushrooms which are presently cultivated in the world are the common button mushroom, <u>Agarius bisporus</u> L., and the oak mushroom, <u>Lentinus edodes</u> (Berk.) Sing.. Both are excellent ways to supplement rural incomes.

The cultivation of the button mushroom was begun in France and developed in Europe, England and USA for use mainly in Western dishes. In recent years, it came to be cultivated in the Orient such as South Korea and Taiwan, primarily for export.

The oak mushroom, on the other hand, is the product indigenous to the Orient and widely used in Oriental dishes. It is mainly cultivated in Japan, South Korea, Taiwan and the People's Republic of China.

Known as "Shiitake" in Japanese, the oak mushroom has been served as an elixir of life to the Orient for its unique taste and flavor for hundreds of years. The texture can be compared to moist lobster and crab meat.

In Japan, production is now more than 160K MT (metric tons) of this mushroom per year. This means than more than 440 metric tons is consumed each day! 60 per cent is sold dried and about 40 per cent is sold fresh. In 1978, the United States imported 274 MT of Shiitake in dried form. That has now increased to more than 536 MT in 1983.

With prices ranging from $15 to $28 per pound (dry-weight), this represents an annual import of over $25M in 1983. Whereas, the US consumes the button mushroom which is grown on manure compost with numerous herbicides and pesticides, the oriental consumes a chemical-free oak mushroom.

Shiitake contains minerals such as calcium, phosphorus and iron, vitamins B_1, B_2, D_2 etc., as well as proteins, carbohydrates and lipids. Proteins in oak mushrooms consist of valuable amino acids such as glutamic acid, alanine, adenine and leucine, etc. which make up the peculiar flavor and taste.

Nitrogen-free extract includes trehalose, mannitol, pentosan, methyl pentosan, etc. which gives it good taste. Phosphorus, iron and calcium in crude ash are essential for the growth of bones and teeth. Vitamins included are B_1, B_2, C, ergosterol and probably A and F. Vitamin B_2 promotes the growth and vitamin C is effective for the prevention of scurvy.

As ergosterol (provitamin D_2) is converted to vitamin D_2 by ultraviolet light, dried oak mushroom contains a relatively high content of vitamin D_2 which promotes the translocation and deposit of phosphorus and calcium in the body. This prevents rickets and lymphatic constitution and helps the growth of bones and muscle.

Cultivation

There are two ways to grow Shiitake mushrooms: 1) Under controled conditions indoors, the mushrooms can be harvested in as little as three to four months. 2) Outdoors, it normally takes up to two years for a harvest, but requires much less work and capital to set up. These two distinct forms of cultivation are known as log farming and sawdust culture.

The growing process for log farming actually begins four weeks before planting, when two- to six-inch-diameter trees are harvested and cut into logs three to four feet long. This is best done during the winter, to capture the sugars stored in the dormant wood. Ash, hickory, maple, horebeam, chestnut, beech, and aspen have all been used successfully.

After four weeks of "aging," the small logs are drilled every eight inches in a log. Dowels made from wood chips innoculated with Shiitake mycellium are pushed into the holes. The usual size is 3/4 inches long by 5/16 inches wide.

The dowels are sold by a small network of dealers who offer quart jars containing 350 to 400 sterilized pieces of wood that have been impregnated with shiitake spore. A quart sells for between $10 and $15 and provides enough dowels to inoculate 17 to 25 logs.

After the impregnated dowels are pounded in flush with the bark, the wounds are then sealed with wax. This step prevents moisture from escaping and keeps rival spores from invading. The ends of the logs are also sealed with a latex paint, for the same reason.

After inoculation and sealing, the logs are piled in a moist, shady area. Forests are perfect. They are then covered with burlap for further shading. It now takes about two years for the mycelium to impregnate the log and begin fruiting. But, when production begins, the logs will yield mushrooms for as many as six years.

The growth of oak mushroom fungus depends largely on the environmental conditions such as temperature, humidity, oxygen, and light. In particular, the environmental conditions suitable for the mycellium of vegetative ohase and for the fruiting body of reproductive phase are quite different.

The mycellium grows at 50-90% air humidity, 65-75% being the most suitable. Fast growth of mycellium is observed at 40-50% moisture in log culture period. Optimum temperature for the formation of fruiting body in oak mushroom is in the range of 50-60°F with a slight difference depending on the strains.

The fruiting body is formed well under conditions of a slight temperature fluctuation between day and night rather than a constant temperature. Though direct sunlight is not necessary, some scattered light is needed.

High moisture content is also needed for the development of fruiting body. Thus 45% of moisture content in mushroom logs and 80-90% of air humidity are preferable. The mushroom can be harvested after 7 days at 50°F temperature and within 4-7 days at 62°F.

During the mycellium growth cycle, the logs are cross stacked and stored in a damp area. Sunlight should not be permitted to heat the logs. In order to allow uniform growth, the logs are reversed once or twice during the growth cycle. This also permits inspection of the logs for good mycellium growth.

Logs in which the mycellium is well developed can be placed for natural absorption of rain or immersed in water to produce fruiting bodies. Movement of the logs must be handled with care to prevent damage to the bark and any mushroom buds.

The logs are placed in an upright position for ease in harvesting the mushrooms. As a brace, long boards or barbed wires are placed in a proper growing environment. Logs are stood against the brace alternately from each side. The number of logs per square meter of growing area is 10 to 12.

Following harvest, the logs are then cross stacked in a damp environment again for at least 12 weeks. The fruiting cycle can be repeated for 4 to 5 years thereafter.

Marketing

Fresh Shiitake mushrooms bring between $2.50 and $6 per pound, while the dried version can fetch upward of $12 a pound. Each log that is inoculated will produce about two pounds of mushrooms over its life. That means that a grower could expect an income of $1,500 per cord of logs, minimum.

The market for fresh Shiitake in the US is very strong and growing. The import volume alone is growing more than 15% per year. While it is unlikely to replace the common button mushroom, it is growing in popularity as sources of supply increase and as more consumers become familiar with oriental cooking.

There are a number of advantages to the Shiitake mushroom: The fresh forest mushroom resists bruising and spoiling, are easily dried, rehydrate well, and impart a full-bodied flavor and aroma. They are larger than the white button variety, with brown or speckled caps that are three more inches wide. They may be eaten fresh, dried and kept up to 13 months, canned, or pickled. Fresh, they almost taste like meat itself.

In addition to their culinary benefits, forest mushrooms offer amenities on the production side, also. For example, they do not use up valuable farm land, need only scrap timber to grow on, don't require fertilizer or pesticides, are not particular about the weather, and have a low start-up cost requirement.

Most important, Shiitake can be easily dried in sunlight.

Sources for Further Information

Dr. Yoo sells a booklet and kit to inoculate about one cord of wood. The kit includes a drill bit and 500 wood chips. The complete kit costs $21.50, while the booklet ordered alone is is $2.50. (Dr. Yoo Farm, P.O.Box 290, College Park, MD 20740).

Several companies in the United States are working on kits for indoor production of Shiitake. One soon available is from Thompson & Morgan, Inc., the British seed firm. (P.O.Box 100, Farmingdale, NJ 07727). Their indoor Shiitake kit ("Black Forest Mushroom") produces for up to eight months.

There are several books on the subject as well. Shiitake Gardening by Bob Harris is $3.00. Cultivation of Shiitake, the Japanese Forest Mushroom, on Logs by Gary F. Leatham is $1.50. Both are available from Mushroompeople, P.O.Box 158, Inverness, CA 94937.

BOOK REVIEW:

Herbs, An Indexed Bibliography, 1971-1980.
James Simon, Alena Chadwick, and Lyle Craker.
Archon Books, CN. 1984. 770pp. $69.50.

While there are numerous books in print on the folklore and ethnobotanical uses of herbs, what the small farmer now needs is access to contemporary research. Simon, Chadwick, and Craker have done this with their new book Herbs, An Indexed Bibliography, 1971-1980.

The purpose of this book becomes obvious when it is first opened up. There are more than 7,000 entries from scientific journals, books, research reports, magazines and industrial journals. All are referenced in a massive, ten-part subject classification. They are chemistry, botany, bionomics, horticulture, production ecology, culinary studies, pharmacology, perfumery, natural dyes, and ornamental application.

Many of the articles and references, unfortunately, are in other languages than English. Remember, while herb and spice farming is fairly new to the United States, many other countries have been studying these crops for centuries. Some of the more important studies have been translated, and the reference will note that via brackets.

The book is divided into three parts, the first being a narrative description of sixty-four important herbs. This gives general information and up-to-date facts about each herb. Following each narrative are bibliographical references that are organized according to the subject classification.

Part two is the subject classification, and is most of the body of the book. Part three is a list of other books on herbs, bibliographies, reports, conferences and numerous other important references. This text is almost a must for any serious herb farmer who needs specific technical information to complete his cultivation aspects these new crop options.

James Simon is an assistant professor of horticulture with Purdue University. Alena Chadwick is a reference librarian at the University of Massachusetts (Amherst). Craker is a professor in Plant and Soil Sciences, also at Amherst. All are still quite active and should be seen as important resources for the small herb and spice farmer.

Organization for the Advancement of Knowledge

OAK

Oak Publishing
1212 SW 5th Street,
Grants Pass, OR 97526
Phone: 541-426-5588

Address Correction Requested

Return Postage Guaranteed

NOTE FROM THE EDITOR

You will note an attempt to make this newsletter even better than previous issues. This is a direct result of your inputs as readers. We would like to take that one step further by asking you to share your insights, problems and possible solutions, and ideals. We encourage you toward writing about your work. If enough of you respond, we can add another page to the newsletter, giving you access to each other via editorials.

We really appreciate receiving the many diverse catalogs and resource lists. As you can see, this exchange is beginning to pay off and a network is developing.

rd

The Herb Market Report　Vol. 2　No. 3

THE ENCYCLOPEDIA OF ALTERNATIVE AGRICULTURE: *for Urban and Semi-Rural Communities*   NEW CENTURY EDITION

THE HERB MARKET REPORT

for the herb farmer and forager   Vol. 2 No. 4   April, 1986

COTTAGE INDUSTRY:
Southern Oregon as a Prime Example

Southern Oregon has some very interesting geography, creating natural habitats for a large and diverse range of wild flowers, botanicals, and other non-timber forest-floor products. Its weather and other seasonal factors has made it a prime area suitable for the cultivation of numerous herbs and spices.

Originally one of the world's largest hop producers in the 1940's, southern Oregon has had a history of successful herb farming ventures. One of the most successful peppermint farms in the world was, for years, situated just outside Grants Pass.

Over the last ten years, however, the national trend toward slumps in agriculture has had its impact. Today, the major cash-flow for southern Oregon is now recreation and tourism, not agriculture.

While agriculture has taken a back seat to more lucrative forms of employment, southern Oregon has recently begun to show signs of recapturing its identity as a farming community. While the farms are much smaller today, there is, nevertheless, a general trend of the farm toward herbs and spices more than any other form of agriculture.

Because the trend has been for smaller acreages in cultivation, cottage industries have formed the foundation for the marketing options available to these new pioneers in small farm agriculture. The original concept of a cottage industry was one of a manufacturer in a rural setting, probably working from their home.

Their advantage to the community was seen on several levels. Not only did they broaden the marketing of local products, they also brought new money into the community because of their export orientation. As the community grew, so did these private, home industries. Today these local entrepeneurs are considered critical to the health and growth of southern Oregon's rural communities.

The diversity of marketing options to farmers interested in herbs and spices as cottage industries is unbelievable. The small farmer who chooses not to market, either by direct or bulk marketing channels, can find a number of profitable alternatives by forming a series of cottage industries around their crops.

Profit margins can be increased by more than 400 percent in most situations. While these profit margins are necessary for most structures involving distributions, a number of other important benefits emerge for the rural community.

Aside from the economical benefits, there are the human development and community benefit aspects. It makes residents more aware of the natural resources available, thus creating further cottage industry opportunities. A number of technical information sources are created, usually including marketing and farm-management training programs - primarily through local County Extension offices and Community Colleges.

Ed Smith of Herb Pharm

It also provides employment, needed now by these communities more than ever before. Cottage industries help build the community-owned economic structure, using local resources. This helps the community to recapture its identity, as in the case of southern Oregon.

The best way to approach an understanding of these diverse opportunities is by example. Herb Pharm of Williams, Oregon is typical. Currently manufacturing tinctures, salves, syrups, liniments, and some tablets, Ed Smith and his wife Sara grow most of their needed botanicals on less than 10 acres. Known as "Herbal Ed," his interests in herbs began in the 1960's with the alternative counter culture movements.

His first exposure to herbal pharmacy began with extensive travels through Africa, Asia, and South America. In the Third World, 90 percent of the ailments are treated with folk medicines.

Now recognized in the field as an expert in botanical medicines, Ed Smith lectures nationally on herbal pharmacy and theraputics. These range from garden clubs to rooms full of medical doctors, including the Harvard Medical School. As a result, there is a limited effort in the marketing of Herb Pharm, as the products essentially sell themselves. Herbal Ed has become such a well-known figure in his field, his business has doubled every year, with less than 1 percent budget toward advertising.

Herb Pharm advertises via seminars and a mail-order catalog (available by writing Box 116, Williams, OR 97544). Seven years ago they grossed only $10K, today they are well over $100K and growing. As a cottage industry, Herb Pharm has given growth to others in his neighborhood.

One neighbor, for example, now makes four times the cash income growing echinacea root for Ed as he did with carrots on the same piece of ground. As Ed grows, so does the community, as he has more and more farmers growing herbs locally to support his marketing. This creates new economic opportunities.

A great example is Herb Pharm's latest experiment: pickled bull whip kelp. As an annual brown algae from local shores along the coast, bull whip kelp is considered a problem with most fishing industries. Yet it is unbelievably nutritious and potentially holds promise as another cottage industry.

Herb Pharm's catalog now also features books and some herbal laboratory equipment for other communities just getting started with their own cottage industries based on herbal preparations. What are Herbal Ed's goals for the future? His newest project is setting up a thin-layer chromatography laboratory to study his plants in more detail, and writing.

Debby and Jim McLennan live near Brookings, Oregon. The coast of southern Oregon has been known for years to be one of the few places in the world where lilies can be successfully grown. Having grown up in this tradition, Debby began to cultivate numerous other flowers, including baby's breath, statice, and other flowers suitable for dried flower manufacturing.

The result is some of the finest dried flower wreaths and herbal baskets available anywhere. As a cottage industry, she now can provide limited employment to the community to meet manufacturing deadlines for numerous projects, including kits for the home hobbyist.

While her marketing has been confined to local and regional florists, she now has a number of her products in Safeway Stores. Less than one-half acre of flower production can produce more than 300 wreaths and other dried products for market. Since most of her products begin marketing at $20 each, she now can average more than $20K per acre by manufacturing her crops into cottage industry items.

Marketing seems to be her major problem, although colorful mail-order brochures, sales representatives and wholesale distributors may offer more growth than she desires.

Debby McLennan is considered an exceptional artist in her various designs, and her products are quite unique as dried flowers. As a cottage industry, dried floral arrangements are quite common. So she decided to develop kits for the home hobbyist. Last year's flowers and those which fragment are used in creating pot pourris, a vast and growing industry, nationally. Her future in growth, however, will lie with the larger mail-order houses. With volume sales, jobs are created and more land is put into cultivation.

Pinnacle Orchards of Medford, Oregon is a typical mail-order fruit and gift industry. They began in 1937, marketing pears in wooden lug boxes, eventually growing to iced-down railroad cars. Medford pears found their way to all the major markets in the U.S., and they became famous. That same year marked the beginning of Pinnacle's mail-order catalog business. That first holiday catalog featured the "Queen of Pears," the Doyenne du Comice.

Steadily, the business grew, and the catalogs were expanded to add other gourmet items. Until recently, Pinnacle Orchards was like a treasured family secret. Not many knew about their catalog. Those that did made their pears and apples a gift-giving tradition.

In 1980 a merger was made and the mail-order gift lines were expanded. Their catalogs are works of art and offer a number of different cottage industries from local growers and producers. They serve as a cottage industry based on other cottage industries, primarily acting as a marketing channel. Here is an example of one cottage industry offering support marketing for more than 50 others, mostly local producers.

Alan Kapular and Alan Venet used seed to sprout their business. Peace Seeds started 6 years ago as a business that grows seed plants, ranging from the common vegetables to the more exotic flowers and fruits. The company carries about 3,000 different varieties of seed, and includes such plants as tobacco, carob, luffa, and even herra flax (grown for its fiber).

Peace Seeds is also interested in heirloom varieties, used primarily for the home grower. These are superior varieties which do not have good shelf life, necessary for large agriculture.

Kapular's academic background in biology is astounding. He holds a doctorate in biology and life sciences, and has written some interesting and important papers on plant biology. His interests in herbs began at 18 when he collected rare and exotic seed from the Amazon basin.

As a gifted child with the traditional chemistry set in the basement, Dr. "Al" now uses his fields as a research facility to develop new hybrid variations via gene mixing. He has also climatized several important spices for southern Oregon herb farmers.

Seen from this perspective, a company like Peace Seeds is the "root" of all other cottage industries in herbs and spices. It is a gene pool. Every night he pollinates each squash by hand. With 50 different

beans, there is a tag on each ovary to keep the genes straight. The seeds are harvested at their prime, husks and chaff winnowed away, cleaned and packaged into small manila envelopes inscribed with their now-famous logo: "Seeds are atoms. Peace is grown." More information and a complete catalog is available by writing directly to Peace Seeds (1130 Tethrow Road, Williams, OR 97455).

Cottage industries are an excellent way for the small farmer to market his crops. The purpose of these examples is to overview the scope of possibilities available when growing herbs and spices on small acreages. The only limiting factor seems to be the imagination.

The profit-margins available are excellent when one adds further processing to their crops. The advantages of these markets is that they allow the individual marketing without large land commitments. These, and other factors, stabilize the small farm and guarantee its survival for the future.

HERB FARMING & FORAGING TAPES by Richard Alan Miller

If you haven't been able to attend a workshop yet, enjoy Rick's informative lecture style in your home or car! Most tapes contain pertinent questions and answers from participants, bring up points not necessarily covered in Rick's books.

Note from the Editor

It seems that there are some major marketing trends and directions beginning to develop around the use of essential oils. The news release regarding McCormick's use of scent for their annual report is only the tip of the iceberg.

The April issue of OMNI magazine, for example, also features a major section on testing your "scentsability" by including a special paper impregnated with several different scents. It is included with a test prepared by the Clinical Smell and Taste Research Center at the University of Pennsylvania.

It now appears that some new markets are developing for the essential oil producers. Odors are processed in the primitive part of the brain, the section concerned with animal and nonverbal action. They are also related to memory, and it is our opinion that this will become a major new form of communication.

You will note that we have included several publications from Allured Publishing in the book review section. This is to give you a better access and perspective on these changing marketing trends. A review of current essential oil markets can be found in Vol.1, No.11 of "The Herb Market Report."

WORKSHOPS

Fairbanks, AK - April 30, 1986. A one-day farming workshop, part of a larger conference on agricultural alternatives. For further information, contact Charles Walsh of ARCTIC at (907)-452-8251 x208.

East Coast - No date yet, workshop forming. For further information, contact Walter Pederson of NOFA-NY at (607)-243-7502.

Kailua-Kona, HI - No date yet, workshop forming. For further information, contact Brian Tibbetts at (808)-322-2321.

Austin, TX - No date yet, workshop forming. For further information, contact Charles Walters of Acres, USA at (816)-737-0064.

Seattle, WA - No date yet, workshop forming. For further information, contact Joel Radcliffe at (206)-324-9792 or send a SASE to P.O.Box 20695, Seattle, WA 98102.

Grants Pass, OR - No date yet, workshop forming. For further information, contact O.A.K. at (503)-476-5588.

Pot pourris from Herbal Acres

A quarterly newsletter for $15/year. Information-packed for cottage industries and the home gardener. Pine Row Publications, Box 428-OAK, Washington Crossing, PA   18977

MAJOR MARKETS

The following are import statistics for aroma chemicals, as reported by the Bureau of Census. This was taken from the 3-10-86 issue of "Chemical Marketing Reporter." This figures only reflect these specific items entering the Port of New York.

Many of the aroma chemicals listed are from herbs which can be feasibily grown in North America. There are many, many more which are not even listed or monitored. We recommend that you begin to research some of these as potential cash crops for domestic production and export.

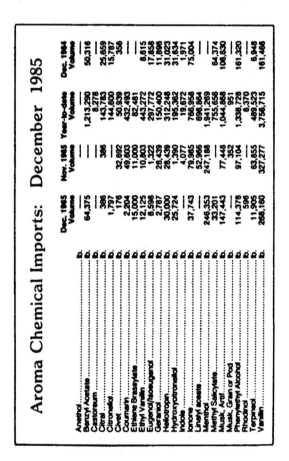

Aroma Chemical Imports: December 1985

OAK library files are beginning to grow because of your questions and inputs. If you should want further information regarding aromatic chemistry and potential sources, please write. That is how many of our articles are chosen for publication.

JOJOBA: A Brief Introduction

Jojoba [<u>Simmondsia chinensis</u> (Link) Schneider] is a dioecious desert shrub that is native to the Sonoran Desert of Arizona, California, and the Mexican states of Sonora and Baja. It may be found growing from sea level to altitudes nearly 5,000 feet and in areas that receive as little as 5 inches of rainfall.

The jojoba plant in the wild has a life expectancy of 100 years and may be even as long as 200 years. In the lower rainfall areas the plants may only be 2 to 3 feet tall but 6 to 8 feet tall (and even taller) in the higher rainfall areas. It may take 25 to 30 years for a seedling to produce seed, especially in the lower rainfall areas.

Jojoba is a rather nondescript, unexciting looking shrub with grayish-green dense foliage. Johoba is either a female or a male plant and you can not tell the difference from a distance. It is only determined when the plant blooms.

The flower buds begin to develop in later summer. In late winter or early spring as the male bud grows, it will change to a yellow color and release its pollen. The female flower is small and inconspicuously pale green, much like newly formed leaves. But when pollinated, it will begin to grow. In late summer, it produces the much sought after acorn-sixed jojoba seed.

Jojoba is wind pollinated. In nature, the jojoba plant is usually restricted to well-drained, coarse, desert soils and coarse mixtures of gravels and clays.

Jojoba seeds vary in size from that of a coffee bean to a large peanut. A single mature shrub may produce as much as 5 to 10 pounds or more of seeds per year.

It was at the University of Arizona in 1933 that it was discovered that the jojoba seed did not contain just another vegetable oil, but instead it contained liquid wax. The only other source of this liquid wax is the now endangered sperm whale. It is the liquid wax that makes jojoba commercially valuable.

Jojoba made its debute as a commercial entity in 1971 with the ban on the importation of sperm whale oil. This amounted to more than 55 million gallons of oil per year! With commercial ventures beginning in earnest, presently in the U.S. there are about 50,000 acres under cultivation.

The oil from jojoba is a long-chain fatty acid which is esterfied with a long-chain alcohol molecule. This is distinctly different from the triglyceride oils of other seed crops. This oil has a multitude of uses due to its high resistance to oxidation; these uses range from lubricants to cosmetics, from food to pharmaceuticals. Another striking feature is that 50% by weight of the jojoba bean is oil.

The oil, which commands most of today's attention because of its high cash value, is in high demand. From a "Newsweek" article dated 3-19-84 states:

"in 1977 the National Academy of Sciences estimated that there was a market for 254 million pounds of jojoba for a multitude of uses, if the price was right. But even 1984's bumper crop is expected to be a mere 2 million pounds. It is estimated that 7.5 million pounds of the oil could be used every year simply as an antifoaming agent in the fermentation of penicillin. Its low coefficient of friction and its compatibility with modern plastics made it seem a promising lubricant for artifical hearts, and its tolerance for high temperatures indicate that it might serve as both a valuable additive to automobile transmission fluids and a low-fat cooking oil which would never go rancid."

In addition to the oil, a much overlooked byproduct is the jojoba meal (after the oil has been squeezed out of the bean). While 50% of the bean is oil, the other 50% is meal. The meal is high in protein (30%), containing all but one of the known essential amino acids. When detoxified, it can be used as a feed suppliment for cattle, and eventually hogs.

Detoxifying the meal is a relatively simple process using a <u>Lactobacillis</u> type bacterium. Selected strains of <u>Lactobacillus acidophilus</u> and <u>L. bulgaricus</u> were found to grow well on jojoba seed meal and reduce the levels of simmondsin and other cyano toxicants. After standing for 21 days at 26°C on a 30% moist jojoba meal, <u>L. acidophilus</u> 629 lowered total toxicant levels 95-98%. Ammonia can be used to facilitate the detoxification.

<u>The treatment of jojoba meal with a Lactobacillus resembles an ensilage process.</u>

The growing of jojoba on a commercial basis is a rather expensive operation when considering the price of land, the extensive hand labor required during the first 3 years, and the high cost of water. Never the less, the return on ivestment at today's prices seems to make it a very attractive venture.

In 1984, for example, beans sold for about $2.00 a pound. A mature plantation yields up to 4,000 pounds of beans per acre. This means a return of some $8,000 per acre each year. It should be pointed out that this crop is also very labor-intensive.

Should the price even drop to $1.00 per pound (a price successfully competing with other lubricants and even sperm whale oil), the return would still be about $4,000 per acre, not including the value of the ton of meal produced.

While this makes jojoba a very attractive venture, it should be pointed out that the cosmetic markets are now saturated with the oil. With the current political games involved with OPEC and current oil sources, the chances of the lubricant/oil-additive markets developing now are very slim. This market will be important, however, within the next ten years.

An interesting legal aspect regarding initial jojoba growers and the law was described in the Fall, 1985 issue of "Herbalgram" (Vol.2, No.3). Six to eight years ago, many initial investors were approached with the lure of investing in tax-deductible jojoba plantations in Arizona.

The plan was to write off the investment of initial production and planting costs in the first year. They would then get a return in six to eight years (like ginseng) when the crop was ready for its first harvest. They would also realize a gain through appreciation in land values.

The IRS, however, disallowed the straight deductions, citing a 1976 tax law (Section 278) in which fruit or nut crops grown on trees, orchards or vineyards grown by syndicates (including limited partnerships) must capitalize pre-production costs. This means that the up-front costs must be amortized over a period of years, not written off entirely.

The jojoba growers had wanted to write off 80% of these cost in the first year. This would give the investor a 40% after-tax benefit (assuming a 50% tax bracket). There is a pending study to redetermine this law. Further information can be gotten directly from Carroll Whittaker, Ph.D., Jojoba Growers Association, 3320 E. Shea Blvd., Suite 290, Phoenix, AZ.

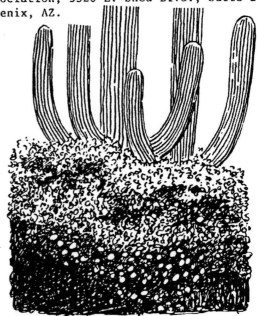

NEWS RELEASE

"Crambe: a new crop for Iowa?" is an interesting article submitted by John Tarnish of Carrol, IA. It is from the January issue of "Iowa REC News:"

"Crambe may sound like a cross between a cranberry and a mulberry, but it's actually a new crop that could someday be a money-making export for Iowa.

"A bushy, scraggly looking plant, crambe is an annual herb and a member of the mustard family. Its tiny seeds contain a non-edible oil that is valuable to industry because of its high erucic acid content. Erucic acid gives oil stability under high temperatures and is used in lubricants for jet engines, for continual casting of steel, and as a rubber additive and plastics component.

"Unlike many chemical compounds, erucic acid cannot be economically duplicated in the laboratory; it must come from plant sources. In the past, supplies of erucic acid have come mainly from Canadian rapeseed.

"But Canadians needed an edible oil for their own use more than they needed an industrial oil to export. So, plant geneticists bred most of the inedible erucic acid out of the seed, and a new type of rapeseed plant, called "canola" was born.

"Factories now need a new supply of oil that contains erucic acid. A major chemical company would like to see more Iowa farmers growing crambe which is 20 to 30 percent higher in erucic acid than rapeseed.

"ISU Agronomist Don Woolley thinks Iowa's climate and growing conditions are nearly ideal for growing crambe. Crambe is a cool-season, drought-tolerant crop. Recommended planting date is early April, and harvest is in early July. No specialized planting or harvesting equipment is required and the plant has few diseases and insect pests.

"Weed control is probably one of the biggest challenges to growing crambe, and researchers continue to experiment with combinations of herbicides. Treflan, Ramrod and Basagran will control weeds, but the Environmental Protection Agency will have to approve their use on crambe, Woolley said.

"After oil is removed from crambe seeds, the remaining by-product can become a high-protein (40 percent) livestock meal. The meal has been approved for cattle, but before it is approved for hogs, sulfur compounds must either be removed or bred out of the plant."

NEWS RELEASE

The following article titled "McCormick Scents Profit" was printed in the 3-10-86 issue of "Chemical Marketing Reporter:"

"McCormick & Co., Hunt Valley, MD-based seasoning and flavor producer, is again gaining the attention of readers of its annual report by producing a document that "smells.

"This year the scent selected to represent the 3,000 different products marketed by the company is something McCormick calls "Chinese Five Scent." The actual spice product is a blend of six spices - anise, fennel, ginger, licorice root, cinnamon and clove.

"The scent of :Chinese Five Spice" was applied to the 32,500 copies of the company's 64-page 1985 report by a Baltimore, MD printing firm, Wolk Press, Inc. The scent is contained in a varnish-like substance the color and consistency of honey which is rolled over the pages after the ink dries.

"Figures in the report show the firm's net sales of $873M in 1985 were up from $788M the previous year, but net income of $27.8M was down from $54.6M.

"The company has attracted attention in recent years by using allspice, curry powder, pumpkin pie spice, vanilla, cinnamon, cloves, and nutmeg to scent annual reports to smell like some of the products it sells. The "cinnamon edition" in 1977 is believed to have been the first time the process was used for an annual report.

"An added bonus this year, McCormick says, is a 20-page guide to a gourmet spice line the company launched last Fall, the first significant change to the line since its introduction in 1959."

BOOK REVIEW

"Cosmetics & Toiletries" - A monthly international magazine of product development from Allured Publishing Corp., P.O. Box 318, Wheaton, IL 60189. $45/year.

This is the only specialized magazine edited for those involved in research and development of new cosmetic products. It covers the formulation of cosmetics more thoroughly than any other publication and is widely read throughout the world, since 1906.

The August issue is the Cosmetic Bench Reference, an encyclopedia of cosmetic materials. This encyclopedia is the first annual directory of cosmetic materials. It contains the information that the cosmetic chemist requires for production development work.

This convenient, complete and up-to-date listing of all cosmetic materials immediately becomes the standard reference for formula development and formula registration purposes. This information is critical for any beginning cottage industry in cosmetics.

BOOK REVIEW:

"Perfumer & Flavorist" - A bi-monthly international business magazine for the flavor and fragrance industry from Allured Publishing Corp. (address given). $55/year.

This magazine covers the creative, scientific and commercial aspects of this spec-ialized business. The editorial program deals with information on the essential oils and aroma chemicals used in flavors and fra-grances.

Reports are published on the scientific and commercial news from such groups as American Society of Perfumers, The Society of Flavor Chemists, The Fragrance Materials Association, Flavor & Extract Manufacturers' Association, The British Society of Perfumers and similar groups worldwide.

"Perfumer & Flavorist" is the only regular magazine reporting on new developments in growing, processing and supplying essential oils, as well as the chemistry and manufacture of aroma chemicals that are used in the compounding of fragrances and flavors. All issues feature "Progress in essential oils" by Dr. Brian Lawrence.

Allured Publishing Corp. also offer a series of books on the subject of cosmetics and flavoring materials which we recommend. They include The Chemistry and Manufacture of Cosmetics (deNavarre), Perfumery & Flavor Materials (Bedoukian), and the two-volume Essential Oils: 1979-1980 and 1976-1978 (Lawrence). All considered, this is a very useful publisher for these topics.

Organization for the Advancement of Knowledge

Oak Publishing
1212 SW 5th Street,
Grants Pass, OR 97526
Phone: 541-426-5588

The Herb Market Report   Vol. 2   No. 4

THE HERB MARKET REPORT

for the herb farmer and forager   **Vol. 2   No. 5   May, 1986**

HALOPHYTES: Salt-Tolerant Plants of the Future

There is a new set of plants now being studied for the future. These crops, known as halophytes, will sprout and grow on sandy beaches irrigated with seawater. It is an old dream: to figure a way to put the expansive coastal lands and their billions and billions of gallons of seawater into yielding nourishing crops for the future.

Conventional studies in this area have focused primarily upon ways to desalinate the salty water. The other is to find a cultivar that turns out to tolerate brine. These studies have examined closely such unlikely garden spots as estuarine swamps, tidal flats, and numerous other regions where vegetation thrives on brackish water.

An astonishing variety of salt-tolerant flora, or halophytes, have been discovered. Some found are comparable, or even superior, in nutritional value and crop yields to rice, wheat, alfalfa, and other such staples. The implications of such discoveries are quite exciting from a commercial standpoint, and several private agencies are now going forward with specific studies.

The Problem

There are some 20,000 miles of desert coastline in the world, nearly twice the total U.S. coastline. Another billion acres of desert, about 10 times the area of California, overlie saline aquifers. Every year another half-million acres becomes too salty for conventional farming because of saline accretions resulting from irrigation.

In all, since the earliest farmers learned to irrigate, some 25% of the Earth's irrigated cropland has become too salty to farm. Specifically, 12.7% of the agricultural real estate in California and up to one-fourth of the land within the lower Rio Grande valley have serious salinity problems.

Desalination efforts so far have managed to produce only about 750,000 acre-feet of fresh water per acre. An acre-foot refers to the volume of water necessary to cover one acre to the depth of one foot. The volume of desalinated water amounts to only one-sixth the discharge from the Colorado River.

While these statistics are discouraging, this does indicate clear and compelling evidence of the value of developing a halophyte agriculture. For example, a quarter-million square miles of the U.S. - a full twelfth of the continental land area - overlie reachable aquifers with a salinity of 3,000 parts per million.

While that is only one-tenth the saltiness of the ocean, it is three times the salinity that many conventional farm crops will tolerate. It is also far less salty than the water halophytes can drink. Two-thirds of the United States has what is considered slightly saline water, containing from 1,000 to 3,000 parts per million (ppm) of salt.

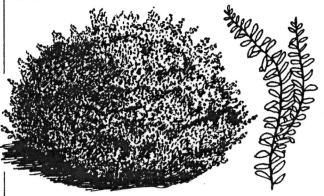

Atriplex

In all, however, the U.S. has access to more than 18.5 billion acre-feet of readily pumpable saline groundwater. About three billion acre-feet, a volume of water comparable to Lake Michigan, could be available in the critically water-short mountains of the West.

Why are these halophytes so important? One answer is that man depends upon just 30 species of plants to provide the preponderance of his sustenance: 85% of our food, 95% of our calories and protein. Eight species of cereal alone supply three-quarters of all our food energy and that only three - wheat, rice, and maze - provide three-quarters of that energy. If only one new plant could be added to this list as a primary food, and it could be grown from a saltwater irrigation, there would never again be world hunger.

Specific Cultivars

More than 75 different halophytes have been studied from expeditions around the northern Gulf of California and Baja California. Of these, only one type, Salicornia europaea (pickleweed), will germinate in the salt water. It was found that all would grow better on less salty water. This means that if they were grown in areas like the Colorado basin, they would benefit from the "sweeter" water.

Distichlis palmeri (Palmer's grass) is only found in the northern Gulf of California in less than a dozen small estuaries. It produces a grain used by the Cocopa Indians. The tides act on Palmer's grass like a giant threshing machine, rocking the plants back and forth, separating the seeds into long windrows on the beach. They can be easily swept or vacuumed quickly because of this phenomenon.

The seeds of Palmer's grass can be eaten like peanuts, the seeds do not accumulate salts like the rest of the plant. The seeds contain 80% soluble carbohydrate, and can be used for making breads. As a primary source for starch, they compare with rice and corn.

Another traditional Indian halophyte is Batis maritima, or saltwort. It is reported that the Seri Indian eat the roots and stems. It's a bit salty for me. Pickleweed, used as a salad ingredient in England, is less salty and is a more likely candidate for continued research.

The most interesting halophyte studied thus far, however, is the genus Atriplex, or saltbush. This family of plants are a lush, velvet, silver-green carpet of shoots. Even before the salt is removed, barclayana, another species of Atriplex, looks to be an excellent additive for livestock and poultry feeds. The yields/acre using saltwater irrigation is similar to most hay-crop yields using normal water.

Plant Processes

The botanical process that enables Atriplex and other halophytes to survive in heavily saline areas is not completely understood. Halophytes not only exclude salt but also can absorb it and deal with it internally by one of several strategies.

All plants open their leaves to absorb carbon dioxide. When they do, water evap-

orates, and they then have to take up more water through the roots. This process is called transpiration. For every gram of dry matter produced, there is anywhere from 200 grams of water for a desert plant to a typical 500 grams of water passing through a crop plant.

If there is salt in the water, then it is actually distilled fresh water that leaves the plant. The salt is left behind, either at the roots or in the plant. Energy is required to exclude, sequester, or excrete this salt. This costs the plant in growth and total production.

This map shows many areas with shallow saline groundwater. Though too salty for conventional crops, this water could easily support halophytes.

Normal transpiration can be compared to a paper towel with one end placed in water. The submerged end draws in water to replace the water evaporating from the exposed end. But put one end of the papper towel in a salt solution, while it still acts as a wick, it will become salt-encrusted.

Cytoplasm is intolerant of salt concentrations, and all the living cells in this "paper towel" would be furiously pumping salt out just to stay alive. An older theory holds that halophytes are just like regular plants, except that they have the ability to pump salts out as fast as the salts enter.

A nonhalophyte filters out the salt leaving it at the roots, but that mechanism cannot tolerate a high level of salt. The salt creates a bottleneck and cuts down on the plant's water supply. The halophyte apparently relieves the bottleneck by admitting a certain amount of salt in with the water.

Some green succulent plants, like pickleweed and saltwort, deposit the salt in a vacuole, a small cavity surrounded by a membrane in which the salt is trapped, and kept in the leaf.

Others, like Distichlis, or Palmer's grass, excrete the salt through the leaf via special excreting cells. These are not the cells through which water ordinarily is lost. Another mechanism, one most of the Atriplex plants use, secretes the salt outside the leaf through salt cells on the surface of the leaf. These cells become so bloated they burst, and the next tide or rain carries the salt away.

All of these mechanisms require energy. Every time a plant has to pump a salt molecule, it uses energy made from photosynthesis to pump salt instead of it being used for growth. This is primarily why most plants grown in salt water grow more slowly, no matter how salt-tolerant it is.

As well as giving them a distinctive silvery glister, the presence of salt on their surface also gives Atriplex plants a briny flavor. There is from 14 to 20% protein in the leaf (similar to alfalfa), but growing it in saline water makes the plant very salty. This is because about one-third of the weight of the plant is salt. There are some studies to remove the salt from chopped halophytes by floatation, but those are not yet affective for current markets.

The highest halophyte yields are similar to most hay crops, averaging about 3 ton per acre in dehydrated biomass. With all the available landmass with access to saline groundwater, halophytes are now seen as important cash-crops for the future.

Royal Doulton
Water Purification Systems

Potpourri from Herbal Acres

THE FARM: Fertilizers and Water Quality

"National Greenhouse Industry" - A quarterly newspaper. Dr. Francis X. Jozwik (editor), P.O.Box 217, Mills, WY 82644. $10/year. (Special $5/year introductory offer).

Formerly "National Greenhouse Gardener," this fine newspaper offers basic theoretical understandings with specific answers to daily situations, especially for the beginning nursery. It is well done for the lay, making difficult subjects easier to understand.

The January, 1986 issue dealt with fertilizers and water quality. This article is very articulate and has numerous tables and math to illustrate important principles. The modern use of artificial soil media demands attention to nutritional needs of crops due to increasing expenses.

The following is a hypothetical model of increased profits brought about by more efficient management of fertilizer application:

1000 plants sold at $5.00 each minus $4.50 production cost each = $500.00 profit. ($5000 - $4500 = $500)

If prices can be increased 5% through improved plant quality due to better nutrition, the following profit results.

1000 plants sold at $5.25 each minus $4.50 production cost each = $750.00 profit. ($5250 - $4500 = $750)

Profits have increased 50% by realizing a 5% increase in quality. Costs of production are not likely to increase since the improvements are made through a more balanced nutrition program - not by using more dollars worth of fertilizer.

There are a number of factors which need to be considered when devising a fertilizer program. From Table 3, the following checklist of those factors are given as

Checklist of Factors to be Considered When Devising a Fertilizer Program.

A. pH characteristics of fertilizers should be compatible with desired pH range of soils.
B. Essential fertilizer elements must be present in balanced portions.
C. Low salt index fertilizers should be chosen whenever possible.
D. Fertilizers which supply more than one essential element are generally more desirable.
E. Nitrate forms of nitrogen are usually safer, especially in artificial soil mixes.
F. Be sure precipitation is not occuring in fertilizer solutions.
G. Double check all calculations.
H. It is safer to underfertilize slightly than to overfertilize.
I. Relatively small amounts of trace elements can be toxic to plants.
J. Ammonium toxicity and the carbon-to-nitrogen ratio of soils must be considered when deciding upon types and amounts of nitrogen to fertilize with.
K. Soil pH and other factors can alter the availability of nutrients.
L. Availability of essential elements is more important than physical concentrations.
M. The types and portions of soil mix ingredients may affect the type and amount of fertilizers used.
N. Different species of plants may require different forms and concentrations of fertilizers.
O. One fertilizer formula will not work under all circumstances.
P. Water characteristics must be considered when choosing fertilizers.

The article continues with techniques for mixing fertilizer solutions, measuring soluble salts, how to avoid plant damage due to high soluble salts, and numerous other sections on water quality and how to recognize fertilizer and water quality problems. Table 7 offers some visual diagnostic characteristics of some major disorders caused by fertilizer or water quality imbalances:

I. First Symptoms Characterized Mainly by Various Patterns of Leaf Chlorosis (Yellowing).

A. Tissue between the veins of leaves becomes yellowish, the veins remain darker green. Restricted in earlier stages to leaves at the tips of stems. Diagnosis: Iron deficiency. Manganese deficiency is less common but may show the same early symptoms except that dead spots often develop in the yellow areas. Both deficiencies are common in high pH or cold, water logged soils.

B. Gradual yellowing and scorching of leaf edges and tips. Not restricted to younger leaves at the tips of stems, lower older leaves are just as likely to suffer. Much of the leaf may remain green but yellowish color becomes more evident towards the edges. Pronounced darker green color not distinctly restricted around leaf veins. Growth stunted. Diagnosis: Two common possibilities, 1) Ammonium toxicity, especially common in artificial soils and on poinsettia crops, 2) gradual accumulation of soluble salts in the soil to high levels.

C. Entire leaves, especially on the lower parts of plants, lack a good green color or become more or less evenly yellowish. Growth stunted. Diagnosis: Nitrogen deficiency.

II. Leaf Chlorosis is Not the Main Characteristic.

A. Plants decidedly stunted with a deeper green color early on, later often becoming purplish. Diagnosis: Phosphorus deficiency.

B. Lower, older leaves develop dead spots or more generalized dead areas usually near the tips and margins first. Diagnosis: Potassium deficiency.

HERB FARMING & FORAGING TAPES by Richard Alan Miller

If you haven't been able to attend a workshop yet, enjoy Rick's informative lecture style in your home or car! Most tapes contain pertinent questions and answers from participants, bring up points not necessarily covered in Rick's books.

All tapes are $2.50, flat rate/advance payment (includes postage). For further information on specific tapes, write OAK, 1305 Vista Drive, Grants Pass, OR 97527.

Note from the Editor

The First International Herb Marketers Conference has been set for July 21-23. The conference will be held at the Sheraton Hotel in W. Lafayette, IN (near Purdue University). This conference will provide a forum for nationally recognized growers, marketers and researchers to discuss a wide range of topics for the commercial grower and marketer of herbs.

This three-day intensive conference will feature lectures, small workshops and tours of Purdue University's three-acre research with aromatic, spice and medicinal plants. A trade show exhibiting specialized equipment, books and herbal products will be located at the conference.

West Lafayette, Indiana is located two hours south of Chicago and one hour north of Indianapolis, IN. For further information concerning preregistration and the conference, contact Dr. Jim Simon, Department of Horticulture, Purdue University, West Lafayette, IN 49709. It would be a nice way to meet each other and begin forming networks for information and marketing options.

A sad note to say that Dr. James Duke of Herbal Vineyard will be moving to Thailand. Jim has become a very important contributor to the growth of herb and spice farming over recent years (ref. Vol.1, No.7 of HMR), and we will miss his insights and humor.

For those interested, Jim recorded an LP with a studio group in Nashville of songs from his new book HERBALABUM. It's not bad, and is probably an "herbal" first. Since he will be leaving for northwestern Thailand soon, he has turned distribution over to Tom Wolfe of the Smile Herb Shop, 4908 Berwyn Road, College Park, MD 20740. The cost is $10.00 plus $2.00 postage/handling.

The Forage of Stinging Nettle

Stinging nettle (Urtica dioica L.), also known as common nettle, can be found in most parts of North America, including Alaska. While prefering moist areas and deep woods, it can be found in ditches, riverbanks, and even sagebrush deserts.

Nettle is a perennial with creeping rootstock. The stalk is erect and soft in the early months, becoming woody (barkish) with flowering stages of growth. The leaf is heart-shaped, finely-toothed, and tappering to a point. The green flowers (June-September) are in long branched clusters, springing from the axils of the leaf. The stem is square-stalked. The whole plant is downy, and covered with stinging hairs.

History

Dried nettles can be fed to livestock and poulty, and are even cultivated in Sweden and Russia for that purpose. It has been used as a folk remedy for cancerous ulcers, inflamed tumors, and as a hemostatic (a substance that will prevent bleeding or promote clotting of blood).

The genus Urtica is derived from the latin word uro, to burn. The common name of nettle is said to be derived from Noedl (a needle), probably from the sharp sting (Dutch). This makes sense in that the plant was used as the thread in Germanic and Scandinavian nations before the introduction of flax. Its fiber is very similar to that of hemp or flax, and it has been used for the same purpose, making cloth of the finest texture down to the coarsest, such as sailcloth, sacking, and cordage.

Chemistry

Fresh plant material contains 80 um vitamin B_1/100 gm and 15.7 mg chlorophyll.

The sting is due to acetylcholine, histamine, and 5-hydroxytryptamine. Betaine choline and lecithin also occur in the leaf. Carbonic, formic and silicic acids are also reported in the leaf, with phytosterins and tannin.

Mode of Action

Gastric irritation, burning sensation of the skin, edema, and urine suppresion. It is used as a diuretic and some commercial hair growing stimulants. A decoction of nettle yields a beautiful and permanent green dye, used for woolen stuffs in Russia.

Preparation and Dosage

An efficient hair tonic can be prepared from nettle by simmering the young plants in a quart of water for 2 hours. The liquid is then strained and bottled. Well saturate the scalp every other night. This prevents the hair falling out and renders it soft and glossy.

The sting of the nettle may be dissipated by heat, enabling young shoots to be eaten as a pot-herb or salad green. Homeopathic remedy uses the plant to treat skin diseases and complaints (externally).

Toxicity

There is little or no toxicity when the plant has been boiled. The juice of the plant contains lecithin, and is its own antidote when rubbed on the affected spot (due to the histamine-like substances found in the bladders within the leaf). Juice from dock (Rumex) or touch-me-not (Impatiens) which grow in the same area have the same beneficial action.

The sting may also be cured by rubbing the part with rosemary, mint, or sage leaves. The North Coast Indians say that wherever a toxic substance grows in the forest, the antidote will be growing right next to it. In this case, they most often use bracken fern juices, which also contain lecithin.

Harvest

Nettle should be harvested before the plant goes into the flowering stage. When young, the stems are still green saplings and can be cut as an herb. If the plant stems begin to bark, they are worthless. The green saplings can be cut twice during a season (similar to catnip), and can be sun-cured. The crop needs to be turned often to prevent browning of the leaf.

Some companies will even accept the herb in baled form, if dried properly. A large sickle or scythe can be used, especially automated versions (like brush hogs). First cuttings can begin as early as May, and then again in August.

European imports are only leaf, rather than herb. If the company you wish to service requires leaf only, the sun-cured herb can be processed with a edible bean harvester-combine, similar to peppermint leaf production. Bean harvesters are used because they have a conveyor to the hopper, rather than an auger (which tends to fragment the leaf into powder).

If leaf is sought from the harvest, then it is best to let the stem form a bark. This allows easier drying and separation of the leaf with a combine-type action. If herb is sought, then a medium condition is required on the stem to have it dry uniformly with the leaf.

Reforestation

Since nettle grows from a rhizome, cutting it only stimulates further growth. As a point to remember with most rhizomes, if it is left to go to flower, there is usually a 60% loss of rootstock while seed is produced. This is one reason why it wants to be cut before flower formation. The stem is also more marketable at this stage.

It should be remembered that in most states, nettle is considered a noxious weed. As such, many communities might object to its cultivation for machine-harvesting. Special permits may be required and you are recommended to consult your local County Extension office for details. Regions like New York and Michigan could probably cultivate this as a cash crop with very little problems. Yields are estimated now at more than 3 ton per acre (dry weight) on two cuttings.

Marketing

The price variation on nettle herb can range from $0.45 per pound in tonnage to more than $1.30 per pound in C/S forms of 100-pound quantities. Leaf enters the Port of New York at $0.65 per pound and begins marketing at $0.85 per pound.

Most regional herb companies buy more than 4,000 pounds annually, with larger wholesalers wanting to buy 5-ton quantities. Nettle is used in both food, drug, and cosmetic industries. Most all of it is now imported from either Germany or Soviet bloc countries (Bulgaria and Yugoslavia).

An average forager can harvest well in excess of 1,000 pounds wet material in one day, presuming the location of good stands. It has about a 50% weight-loss, so it is considered an excellent crop for foraging. When stands can be found with more than 4 acres of flat terrain, it can be machine-harvested for really excellent profits.

Some of the larger recreational parks will actually harvest the nettle before the park is open for the public. These crops are usually burned. They can be taken for no cost, just for removing them from the park. By paying the Parks Department the standard $0.01 per pound, both you and the Parks Department can benefit from the relationship. Once the crop has been dried, it can be hand-fed into a baler (or combine) and sold.

GINSENG

Major Markets

The following are import statistics for some selected essential oils and spices, as reported by the Bureau of Census (reprinted from "Chemical Marketing Reporter." These figures only reflect these specific items entering the Port of New York.

Many of the crops listed can be grown in North America. As you will note, these lists are far from complete, and there are many, many more crops not even monitored at this time. We recommend that you begin to research some of these as potential cash crops for domestic production and export.

Seed and Spice Imports: December 1985

		Dec. 1985 Volume	Nov. 1985 Volume	Yr-to-Date Volume	Dec. 1984 Volume
Anise seed	lb.	215,946	177,297	2,135,178	103,035
Basil	lb.	384,672	542,300	4,028,882	366,030
Caraway seed	lb.	828,823	900,495	7,930,637	608,527
Cardamom	lb.	57,930	57,102	447,298	9,483
Cassia	lb.	2,101,038	1,447,030	24,092,258	2,965,891
Celery seed	lb.	719,310	620,732	5,617,728	931,247
Cinnamon, unground	lb.	168,592	186,091	3,2708,874	548,206
Cloves	lb.	103,460	157,296	2,474,971	145,661
Coriander	lb.	312,992	633,795	5,437,991	716,572
Cumin seed	lb.	460,725	420,241	8,688,236	738,408
Dill seed	lb.	64,247	23,784	988,593	75,032
Fennel seed	lb.	581,527	372,360	3,545,299	350,578
Ginger root	lb.	509,901	1,536,118	12,347,766	1,348,523
Laurel leaves, crude	lb.	42,109	101,273	891,157	216,696
Mace	lb.	30,863	—	636,916	15,755
Marjoram, crude	lb.	141,202	179,078	870,058	39,703
Mint leaves, crude	lb.	12,720	22,951	406,135	4,584
Mustard seed, whole	lb.	6,854,555	10,352,241	87,830,658	5,590,860
Nutmegs, unground	lb.	375,771	323,552	4,665,917	313,474
Origanum, whole	lb.	829,200	1,011,542	7,905,598	1,109,511
Paprika	lb.	2,154,679	1,300,925	19,061,759	1,882,740
Pepper, black, unground	lb.	6,232,818	4,089,680	60,452,740	9,238,898
Pepper, red, capsicum	lb.	926,051	615,782	13,645,796	845,897
Pepper, white, unground	lb.	956,474	489,399	10,498,644	—
Pimento, unground	lb.	212,134	206,090	1,533,224	105,836
Rosemary, crude	lb.	30,690	44,382	979,078	42,255
Sage unground	lb.	225,032	544,275	4,301,669	451,778
Tarragon, crude	lb.	9,849	19,851	103,050	20,999
Thyme, crude	lb.	165,227	131,960	2,051,291	80,331
Turmeric	lb.	180,997	408,398	4,630,200	92,674
Vanilla beans	lb.	188,718	113,977	1,638,274	126,042

Essential Oil Imports: December 1985

		Dec. '85	Nov. '85	Yr. to date	Dec. '84
Anise	lb.	5,637	4,997	41,836	---
Bergamot	lb.	7,925	7,227	69,275	2,601
Bitter Almond	lb.	1,430	—	112,548	13,746
Camphor	lb.	17,637	—	153,214	---
Caraway	lb.	430	3,139	13,244	661
Cassia	lb.	62,849	16,169	554,191	26,076
Cedarleaf	lb.	400	850	23,717	404
Cinnamon	lb.	2,271	4,494	140,894	4,480
Citronella	lb.	26,741	38,007	1,369,755	39,638
Clove	lb.	9,958	70,215	1,298,313	217,235
Cornmint	lb.	3,571	12,460	291,773	29,212
Eucalyptus	lb.	13,156	39,392	498,597	17,814
Geranium	lb.	22,601	2,885	107,866	8,809
Grapefruit	lb.	15,475	14,112	189,415	220
Lavenders	lb.	14,813	9,937	135,790	9,515
Lemon	lb.	351,551	232,273	2,200,425	149,973
Lemongrass	lb.	---	22,000	135,518	20,000
Lime	lb.	23,189	122,111	1,373,394	27,120
Linaloe (Bois De Rose)	lb.	3,968	12,674	146,062	30,357
Neroli	lb.	29	132	750	47
Nutmeg	lb.	26,626	54,892	239,292	33,318
Orange	lb.	751,978	2,051,028	9,845,097	709,952
Origanum	lb.	641	---	5,558	1,212
Orris	lb.	84	80	2,559	46
Palmarosa	lb.	---	1,190	17,026	1,578
Patchouli	lb.	9,259	42,198	544,857	40,123
Peppermint	lb.	---	662	9,925	240
Petitgrain	lb.	5,455	8,881	174,342	5,136
Pine Needle	lb.	2,400	---	201,074	8,856
Rose	lb.	2,769	12,074	93,412	5,831
Rosemary	lb.	10,919	1,102	74,076	2,154
Sandalwood	lb.	13,279	2,208	55,715	8,825
Thyme	lb.	926	882	26,165	110
Vetivert	lb.	5,070	4,409	155,782	14,071
Ylang Ylang or Cananga	lb.	14,635	24,352	93,065	2,225

Book Review:

PEACEFUL VALLEY FARM SUPPLY, 1986 Catalog. 11173 Peaceful Valley Road, Nevada City, CA 95959. (916)-265-FARM. Catalog is free upon request.

As much as I love color photos, I feel good when I find a business that is ecologically focused. The 1986 Peaceful Valley Farm Supply catalog is literally packed with information, interesting services, and most important: their prices are fair.

Their primary marketing includes organic fertilizers, soil amendments, beneficial insects, bare root and container-grown plants, bulbs, and appropriate tools. Consultation services use natural growing methods. Of special interest: the most complete list of biological pest controls available to date.

We recommend their catalog, and it should be mentioned that they have an international reputation for reliability on their products and information. From their catalog: "Growing with nature is far more rewarding than offending it with poisons. We show you how to make poison unnecessary."

Book Review:

"LADYBUG" - A regional economy journal and newsletter. Mary Lehmann (editor), 218 7th. St., Boonville, MO 65233. $6.00/year

This is a charming newsletter with an interesting mix of information. There are some editorial philosophy intermixed with book reviews and previews on upcoming conferences from different angles - and levels of effect on farming and local economic structures - that touch all of us - in different ways.

I first met Mary at an ACRES, USA conference back in November, 1984, and was impresed with her wit and insights toward the political aspects of farm agriculture. Her newsletter is used as a network for various farmers to contribute ideas and thoughts to one another - something HMR would like to encourage.

Many talk about the pain of living in a small town and watching it die as businesses die and the town's moneys go elsewhere. She states the need for change in philosophy and attitudes/dedication needed to keep small towns alive. Her thoughts apply to so many places in the U.S. today: "We

continued

want small town charm as long as we don't have to work for it."

I like her newsletter and would like others like it to begin to form networks for a community-access of new information. The $6.00/year subscription includes membership, the newsletter, a 1987 calendar and the LLLibrary. She is a very outspoken woman, and I'm sure she would like to hear more from individual farmers attempting alternative farm ventures.

Book Review:

"PERMACULTURE with NATIVE PLANTS" - A network newsletter. Curtin Mitchell (editor), Box 38, Lorane, OR 97451.   Donation.

This is a regional network newsletter, designed to exchange information among individuals who are interested in growing and using native plants. Their purpose is to develop appropriate use of the multiple resources in the Pacific Northwest forests. While it is a free publication, contributions are always welcomed.

As a networking newsletter, it is an excellent example of how to organize a local region toward identifying their natural resources and then developing programs to maintain them for the future. Issue #4 discussed a variety of local Pacific Northwest weeds and their varied uses and how they interrelate with other plants and flora.

One section has an ongoing discussion on edible wild plants for the region. This issue included detailed write-ups on 9 different plants. These included latin/common names, uses, soil nutrient requirements, propagation, plant associations with insects and weeds, various problems and hazards with harvest, and a request for reader inputs.

For what it is, Curtin Mitchell is to be complimented. What he has created is a model for other communities, and how they might begin their own networking newsletter. This is the first important step toward rural economic development. As a form of communications, it is essential to a local community and should be encouraged for each region.

Organization for the Advancement of Knowledge

Oak Publishing
1212 SW 5th Street,
Grants Pass, OR 97526
Phone: 541-426-5588

Address Correction Requested

Return Postage Guaranteed

BULK RATE
U.S. Postage Paid
Grants Pass, OR
Permit No. 66

The Herb Market Report | Vol. 2   No. 5

THE HERB MARKET REPORT

for the herb farmer and forager   **Vol. 2 No. 6   June, 1986**

COLTSFOOT HERB:

An Alternative Ingredient for Tobaccos

Coltsfoot (<u>Petasites frididus</u> [L.] Fries var. <u>palmatus</u> [Ait.] Cronq.) is a spectacular plant which grows throughout the Pacific Northwest. It has a number of "cousins" with similar chemistries and properties which have been harvested from both the East Coast and the Mid-West since the 1930s. This includes <u>Tussilago farfara</u> L.

Also known as butterbur, coughwort, British tobacco and gowan, the purplish-white flowers occur before the leaves are formed, and usually wither back in the early spring. This makes the plant difficult to identify. It was historically used by Indians in the Northwest and Canada as a salt substitute, much in the same manner as the leaves from cow parsnip.

All the various types of coltsfoot require rich, damp ground to support its heavy bulk and is generally found in areas of substantial rainfall. The <u>Tussilago farfara</u> L. can be found along roadsides from eastern Quebec to Pennsylvania, Ohio, and Minnesota. The West Coast varieties are found along northern beaches of British Columbia, Washington, Oregon, and California, wherever the earth has been removed to make roads or logging trails.

The flowering stalks of these plants appear first in the spring with white-purplish blossoms. There are usually several stalks 3 to 18 inches high, arising directly from the rootstock. Each bears a single flower-head. Each flower-head has numerous tubular disk flowers in the center, surrounded by ray flowers. They open only in sunny weather. The ripe seed head looks somewhat like that of a dandelion, only much larger.

Some time after the flowers appear, the leaves begin to emerge on long erect stalks directly from the rootstock, also. They range in size from 3 to 15 inches wide and in the shape resembling a horse's hoof. The lower surface of each leaf is white with densely matted wooly hairs. Occasionally leaves appear at higher bracts in older plants, and are deeply lobed into seven to nine divisions.

History

The silky seed (or <u>pappus</u>) was once used for stuffing pillows and mattresses. The root, with wine, is still used as a folk remedy for hardening of the liver. It is also still used as one of the most popular of cough remedies.

The dried leaves were used in cough medicines for colds and bronchial catarrh, or smoked with other herbs for asthma and coughs. The smoke from the herb is said to be anticholinergic (like atropine) and a demulcent against persistent cough (like that from a smoker).

Homeopaths prescribe the tincture of the whole plant for obesity and excessive eating habits. For lung congestion or consumption, coltsfoot is combined with elderflowers, ground ivy, horehound and marshmallow and smoked. The fresh leaves, or juice, is also used for a bad, dry cough or wheezing and shortness of breath.

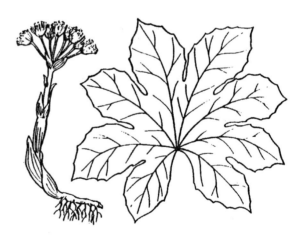

The leaves can be made into a pleasant salty seasoning by burning the dried leaves, then powdering the resultant ashes. The native method was to roll the green leaves and dry them thoroughly. They were then set afire on a flat stone and the ashes collected.

Chemistry and Mode of Action

Coltsfoot contains a number of agents, including acrid essential oils, a bitter glycoside, tannin, caoutchouc, a saponin, a resin, several acids, and pectin.

The only therapeutic value the leaves possess (according to FDA) is as a demulcent, due to the high mucilage. The ingredients appear to have little activity in the concentrations used. There may also be some astringency due to the tannins. There are no reported cases of coltsfoot poisoning. Since the therapeutic activity is rather low, poisoning is unlikely.

Harvest

A gas-powered weedeater can cut out large stands fairly quickly, flailing the stem and leaf for faster drying. The high mucilage does make this crop a little more difficult to dry, with weight-losses up to 85%. The higher moisture means that the crop needs to be taken to a dehydrator within one day of harvest.

The plant can be dehydrated without leaf-browning, but needs good ventilation and stem-conditioning. For this reason, shade-drying is usually not workable, as the product must be turned every hour. A good dehydrator with large air flow systems will usually take care of the crop without heat.

The leaf and shoots are harvested after the flower-heads begin to disappear, sometime in June and early parts of July. This not only leaves the rootstock, but the seed has already dropped to the ground. The underground stems preserve their vitality for long periods when buried deeply, so that in places where the plant has not been observed previously, it will often spring up in profusion after the ground has been disturbed. It is very difficult to extirpate.

On the West Coast, coltsfoot can be picked freely along the coastal shelf but should not be harvested east of the Cascades or Rockies, where it is rare.

Marketing

The price for coltsfoot herb ranges from $0.40 per pound in short tonnages as a "whole" product to more than $1.80 per pound when sold as a C/S in 100 pound quantities. The herb is currently imported and not produced at all domestically any more. This is probably because most import houses only import 5 tons annually.

The entire domestic market-need for coltsfoot is probably less than 40 ton annually at this time. That appears to be changing, however (see cottage industry section). It is a perfect early spring crop because European and Indian imports do not begin until June or July.

An average forager can harvest as much as 3,000 pounds of wet product in one day, resulting in over 300 pounds of marketable product after dehydration. The key is to find large enough stands to stay on task, rather than having to move from one small stand to another. Typical plots of coltsfoot which are feasible usually run approximately 1/4-mile and are about a ditch wide. You will need at least a dozen such stands for several days work, averaging more than 2 ton, dry-weight.

Cottage Industry Example: Coltsfoot, Inc.

About two years ago, Kevin Rowley, now on the Board of Directors of The Southern Oregon Herb Gatherers' Association, Inc., made up several samples of an herbal chewing substitute for tobacco. It was an excellent idea, and his friends encouraged him to develop the product for mass-market distribution.

The following descriptions are meant to describe what is necessary to begin marketing such types of products. Such businesses as Root Diggin' Nation Herb Co. (advertized in this issue) might follow this example as a means of also developing their own marketing of cottage industry products.

First, you must form a corporation. Most begin with a C-type, and change with expanded sales (for tax purposes). Kevin not only registered his company (Coltsfoot, Inc.), he also trade-marked (TM) his first product, namely "Golden Eagle" Herbal Chew. This protects his names, advertizing, and formulas.

Next, he developed pricing which could be competitive with exisiting tobacco products. The single most important rule is that the suggested retail price must be 400% more than the total cost-of-goods produced. If it is less, there is a more than 75% chance that you will not be in business next year. He had to cut costs by seeking better sources of supply. This includes packaging and labels.

An attractive logo, letterhead, press release, display flier, and distributor's net price list were then developed. These are your sales tools, necessary in communicating information to customers, media and buyers. Kevin's forms have been included in this newsletter as representative of approximately how they should look and what kinds of information is necessary.

From the price sheet, you will note that he has UPC codes. This is now absolutely necessary in order to enter any warehouse today. He also had to get FDA approval on his ingredients and label. This is required for the next important requirement: product liability. Good luck with this one.

The best way to obtain product liability is as a rider on an existing insurance company, usually on a fire-and-theft policy for your inventory and manufacturing warehouse. With current questions in the insurance

world, it is best to seek companies in larger cities already familiar with these forms of policies. This may take some time.

From there, most of the sales problems lie with cash-flow requirements. Kevin sought out a CPA firm who could do some proforma cash-flow projections of cash requirements for several typical mass-market purchases. This would give him an idea of how much he could realistically sell without overcommitment.

With these tools, Kevin was now ready to contact the world with his product. It took him one year to get to this point. From there, a sales person was brought in to begin negotiations with numerous distributors. A first list was prepared, including more than 200 distributors, and a bulk mailing (with permit) was made.

First year sales for this product is now estimated at more than $250,000. At some point, with luck, he may have to consider a line-of-credit from his bank. This is a much better way to proceed than taking on money-partners. Why? Kevin now has the option of selling his business to a major company who might want to expand this product and become an open corporation.

Coltsfoot, Inc.

P.O. BOX 5206 • GRANTS PASS, OR 97527 • PHONE (503) 476-5588

GOLDEN EAGLE Herbal Chew

NEWS for immediate release:

Golden Eagle Herbal Chew is a new non-tobacco product developed by a Grants Pass, Oregon company, as a safe alternative for users of so-called "smokeless tobacco" products, such as chewing tobacco and snuff. The Surgeon General's report states that "....use of smokeless tobacco represents a significant health risk... can cause cancer... and can lead to nicotine addiction..."

Golden Eagle Herbal Chew is a solution to this health dilemma faced by thousands who use these "smokeless tobacco" products. The herbal chew contains absolutely no tobacco or tobacco by-products, but is made entirely from a special blend of natural herbs, and is a pleasant-tasting alternative to tobacco.

Golden Eagle Herbal Chew is manufacturered by Coltsfoot, Inc., P.O.Box 5205, Grants Pass, Oregon 97527. For further information, write the manufacturer or call (503) 476-5588.

GOLDEN EAGLE
Herbal Chew

All-Natural Herbal Chew
Contains Absolutely NO Tobacco
Pleasant-Tasting Alternative to Tobacco
Timely, Unique and Exciting Product
Refreshing Scent, Too

Ingredients: Pure Vegetable Glycerin,
Coltsfoot (herb), Cinnamon, Bee Pollen,
Orange Peel, Angelica (herb), Hawthorne (herb),
and Tang Kuei (herb).

Manufactured by: **Coltsfoot, Inc.**   (503) 476-5588
P.O. BOX 5205 • GRANTS PASS, OR 97527 • U.S.A.

Distributed by:

Coltsfoot, Inc.

RE: DISTRIBUTOR'S NET PRICE LIST

All prices are subject to change without notice.

EFFECTIVE DATE: June, 1986.

TERMS: Net 30 days.

SHIPPING: F.O.B. Grants Pass, Oregon.

PACKAGING: Unit = 1.2 oz. plastic cannister.
Roll = Ten (10) cannisters.
Case = Nine (9) rolls.

Cube = 10" x 8" x 8" or 640 in³
Tare = 8 oz.

UPC No. = 0-86085-98440

MINIMUM ORDER: Ten (10) Cases.

Quantity	Unit Cost	Cost/Case
10 Cases	$ 0.90	$ 81.00
20-50 Cases	$ 0.88	$ 79.20
75-100 Cases	$ 0.85	$ 76.50

Call for pricing on larger orders (over 100 Cases).

CONTACT: Richard Alan Miller,
Sales Manager.

Notes from the Editor

Domestic basil (see Vol.2, No.2 of HMR) is reported in to be in very short supply this year. This has driven the prices for "fine grades" up by more than $0.40 per lb. Current prices for this quality is now more than $2.85 per pound, while other import grades remain unchanged.

Look for an article in "The Furrow" magazine next month on herb and spice farming. This is a publication by John Deere Mfg. Co. and is the first major indication of national interest these forms of alternative agriculture. They also plan further stories in this area, including an article on how foraging can supplement rural incomes and economic development.

There are numerous important conferences, workshops and meetings on-going each month around herb and spice production (and related areas of alternative agriculture). The lists are so large that they are not publishable in this newsletter. However, since we do keep a monthly update, this list is available to subscribers as a service with a SASE. Be sure to specify the month of interest.

Two of the best lists can be found in the newsletters "Potpourri for Herbal Acres," (see Vol.2, No.1 of HMR) and "The Business of Herbs," (see Vol.1, No.8 of HMR). Other excellent newsletters include "Herbalgram," a publication from the Herb Research Foundation (P.O.Box 12602, Austin, TX 78711) and "Quarterly Newsletter," published by The American Herb Association (P.O.Box 353, Rescue, CA 95672).

The Massachusetts Cooperative Extension Service publishes an interesting and quite useful newsletter "The Herb, Spice and Medicinal Plant Digest," (University of Massachusetts, Amherst, MA 01003). The spring issue had some very interesting reviews of parsley production, including an article on specific cultivars by Dr. Jim Simon (see Vol.2, No.3 of HMR). He is also part of the First International Herb Marketing Conference set for July 21-23 in W. Lafayette, IN (see Vol.2, No.5 of HMR).

Potpourri from Herbal Acres

A quarterly newsletter for $15/year. Information-packed for cottage industries and the home gardener. Pine Row Publications, Box 428-OAK, Washington Crossing, PA 18977

HERB FARMING & FORAGING TAPES by Richard Alan Miller

If you haven't been able to attend a workshop yet, enjoy Rick's informative lecture style in your home or car! Most tapes contain pertinent questions and answers from participants, bring up points not necessarily covered in Rick's books.

HERB/SPICE PRODUCTION IN EGYPT AND ISRAEL
A Comparison of Methods and Development

Since ancient times herbs and spices have been cultivated and traded in both Egypt and Israel. The Bible mentions the tithing of herbs and spices, while the earliest records of herbs as medicinal plants dates from the age of the Egyptian pyramids, some four thousand six hundred years ago. The 'Ebers' papyrus, discovered in 1874, documents over eight hundred medicinal plants used in ancient Egypt, many of which are still growing there today.

Later in history the region became a through route for spices on their way from the Orient to the new markets of Europe. A rich class of Arab merchants and princes grew up on this trade, which was to last from the first century B.C. until the 15th century when the Portuguese found a sea route around Africa to India and the Far East, and thus broke their hold on this valuable trade. Today the Middle Eastern herb/spice trade is no longer a source where vast fortunes are made. In fact, herb production was not even mentioned in the 1980 World Bank report on the Arab Republic of Egypt. It is there in fact, however, accounting for $1.7 million in exports to the U.S. alone for the year 1981.

In Israel, the commercial production of herbs and spices has recently taken a new shift; previously production was largely for home consumption, being grown mostly by small Arab farmers. About ten years ago, however, the Israeli Ministry of Agriculture became interested in the possibilities of a modern herb/spice industry in the country, and by now at least three Israeli companies are currently involved in export production.

Because the highly technical nature of modern Iraeli herb/spice production contrasts with the labor intensive methods used in Egypt, perhaps this brief study will provide some insight into the development of this relatively minor 'crop' and its attendant advantages for each method.

The present trend in Egyptian agriculture is toward cash crops such as oranges, potatoes, and, to a small but growing extent; herbs and spices, a trend largely the result of falling returns on grain and traditional Egyptian cash crop - cotton. Cotton production, still Egypt's main export cash crop and raw material for industry, has been hampered to a certain degree by the nature of of the State 'cooperative' monopoly marketing system which leaves the cotton farmer with only 60% of the true value of his crop, but herbs and spices, like potatoes and citrus, are free of government controls on marketing and production.

Methods of Production: Egypt

Bedding for herb plants in Egypt is largely a hand dug activity, herbs being grown in either seeding beds or planted directly to a field bed. The principle in both is a square with a level base, the seedling bed measuring 4 sq. m., the field bed 2 sq. m. Within these squares at intervals of 30-50 cm are ridges on which the herbs are planted and around which water may flow from an open irrigation canal at each irrigation cycle, from one bed to another until the farthest bed from the source is filled, at which point the mud wall to this bed is closed. This is repeated until each bed is 10 cm deep, or 6 cm in the seeding bed.

Much of the growing information presented here came from Dessimi, a village on the west bank of the Nile approximately 70 km south of Cairo. Here, as in most of Egypt, there is little rainfall during the year, all forms of agriculture thus being dependent on irrigation. Herbs and spices are no exception; if anything, they are more dependent on regular supplies of water than other crops. In many respects, problems exist here in the cost and ability to irrigate that are typical. Dessimi, like much of the Nile Valley, is over seven meters above the water table. The Government supplies water at a rate of one Egyptian pound/50 piasters for 200 cubic meters, or enough to supply one feddan (0.42 ha) for one watering. This water, however, can be supplied only 20 days/mo., effectively five days of every 10, and pumping system breakdowns often interrupt the schedule.

The Dessimi farm studied here had its own artesian well and electric pump, a facility few farmers have to rely on when the Government system is not working. But the cost of this water is four times the Government system's water. High returns, therefore, have to be achieved and maintained to make the use of this well economically viable. Offsetting the higher costs, however, is one major advantage this farm's artesian well has over the Government-supplied water: it is clean and free from bilharzia, a debilitating disease found in slow-running or stagnant water.

Herbs grown at Dessimi include anise, caraway, coriander, fennel, basil, marjoram, spearmint, cornflower, marigold, chamomile, and great mullein. Exported yields of seed per faddan of the first four of these, for example, show:

anise	250/350 kg/feddan
caraway	470/900 kg/feddan
coriander	470/700 kg/feddan
fennel	330/470 kg/feddan

In September-October, five to six seeds are planted by hand every 30-40 cm in an irrigated field bed. The next irrigation is carried out after germination, about one week later. After one month, when the plants should be about five cm high, the crop can now be thinned, leaving only the best plants in each group.

Pests and diseases include aphids and other insect pests which are sprayed once they become a nuisance; 'Lancer,' a total plant killer, is used before planting to kill all the weeds; however, when the herbs are growing, only hand weeding is carried out because of the expense of selective herbicides. Helmenthosporium fusarium, a fungal root disease occuring in saturated soils, can devastate a crop of seed or leafy herbs, and is a major risk factor. Fumigation of the soil is a remedy but impractical.

Fertilizer is applied to these seed herbs as follows: Organic: 30 m³/feddan animal manure prior to planting. Inorganic: 60 kg/feddan during first two months.

The harvest is in April, the crop being cut down by hand with a sickle, then put under canvas on shelves for a week to dry, after which it is beaten by hand on a stone to remove the seeds. Seeds are then collected and sieved on a 1.5 mm² holed sieve, plant debris remaining while the seed falls through. The seed should then be sieved again - though not all producers do this - to extract grit and sand which fell through with the seed. This is done on a 0.5 mm² sieve which holds the seed while letting the small waste fall away. All this sieving is done by hand.

Methods of Production: Israel

A realistic comparison of herb production in Egypt and Israel will, of necessity, focus on the difference between labor-intensive and machine production. In Israel, where herb production on a commercial scale was introduced a decade or so ago, the emphasis is on the use of tractors to construct row bedding, multiples of herbicides to cut weeding to minimum, specially designed and constructed herb/spice harvesters, sprinkler and drip feed irrigation systems. The Hevel Ma'on group of kibbutzim in the Negev, for instance, have built a processing plant involving a chain of machines linked by conveyor belts and including a solar-heated dryer, various rubbing machines, mechanical sieves, and air separators. Such methods would, of course, fail to make full use of the vast human potential as a valuable resource in Egypt. Nevertheless, the use of appropriate technology through adaptation of some of these methods is gradually being developed in the latter country. An export company in Alexandria has constructed two herb machines, one an electric sieve, the other a flower crusher, both designed and built by a young engineer in Alexandria. The more modern factory atmosphere there provides and appropriate compromise since the machines still require workers to fill and operate them.

The most promising fundamental change in Egyptian herb production is one that would revolutionize agriculture in general there, namely the introduction of a national pipe-fed irrigation system to replace the present canal network. The advantages would include erradication of water-carried diseases, minimizing loss through seepage and evaporation and the employment of a substantial number of workers in a constructive and productive new industry. Costs would be considerable, but considering the benefits, long-term and immediate, the idea may be one whose time has come. Certainly the technical and scientific know-how in Egyptian universities and research institutions is recognized worldwide as outstanding.

Exports: The World Market

Egypt exports a fair proportion of her total produce to the U.S.: in 1980, according to U.S. Department of Commerce trade figures for imports for 1976-1981 inclusive, 61% of all basil exported from Egypt went to the U.S., and a general figure of 30% could be put to five other herbs exported to the U.S. that year. The American market seems to be very relevant to Egyptian herb production:

Table 1: Increase in metric tonnage of herbs/spices exported by Egypt to the U.S., 1976-1981

	1976 Egypt	1976 Total*	1981 Egypt	1981 Total*
anise seed	93.8	478.1	200.2	524.2
basil leaf	150.3	412.3	573.1	744.9
caraway seed	162.2	2795.0	312.0	3031.2
fennel seed	82.8	872.3	254.4	1416.0
marjoram leaves	161.4	310.2	299.2	343.0
mint leaves	71.1	138.1	163.9	214.7

*Total imports to the U.S. to illustrate the market potential via increase in imports as a whole, 1976-1981.

Table 2: Herb Prices F.O.B. 1981 in U.S. $/metric ton

	Egypt	Europe
anise seed	$1,779.7	$3,091.3
basil leaves	839.6	1,162.0
caraway seed	792.0	1,077.0
marjoram leaves	1,036.8	1,605.1
oregano leaves	1,046.0	2,088.6

The difference in price between European and Egyptian herb exports is so great that some unscrupulous European countries have been known to import Egyptian produce, clean it, and re-export it as their own countries'.

Israel, the newcomer to herb production in this region, exports its herbs at or near European prices, $2,062.2 per metric ton of oregano in 1981, for instance, compared to Egypt's $1,046.0. A concerted effort by Egyptian producers to prepare a cleaner product, free of impurities, will initiate a reputation internationally for reliability and consistency of quality, which in turn will induce the higher prices that Egypt needs to compete equally with other producers.

Government Role

Much of Irael's success in its herb/spice industry can be attributed to positive government involvement. The agricultural extension service, acting as a conveyor of research and information between the Ministry's research centers and the producers, brings together in the "Council of Vegetables' opportunity for democratic discussion of the allocation of State grants for research and new projects. This team - farmer, government research extension service - thus makes maximum use of all parameters of the industry's development.

In Egypt, the Ministry of Agriculture and the University of Cairo's herbarium are directing medicinal herb research through many of their facilities. There is evidence, too, that recognition of the value of interaction on the field level between all components of successful production is to be a prime factor in the development of herb/spice 'crops,' as well as in other agricultural fields.

Book Review

PLANTS FOR PROFIT: A Complete Guide to Growing and Selling Greenhouse Crops. Francis
X. Jozwik. Andmar Press, Mills, WY 82644.
c1984. 334pp. (Hardback). $39.95.

Last month's issue of HMR included some
tables from the quarterly newspaper "National Greenhouse Industry" by F.X. Jozwik. I
was very impressed and wanted to review his
new book PLANTS FOR PROFIT. I'm very glad
to have had the opportunity to review this
new book.

PLANTS FOR PROFIT is organized extremely well and contains a goldmine of factual
information. Even the most experienced
grower will find this text well worth the
money. It covers the commercial greenhouse
business from A to Z in a logical, easy to
understand manner.

Difficult technical subjects are ex-
plained step by step so anyone can master
this material easily. This includes specific directions for schedules, fertilizers,
soils, pest control, and most important:
marketing. It is this part of the book which
we found most valuable.

Francis Joswik has been intimately associated with floriculture for the past 15
years as the owner-manager of a successful
greenhouse operation in Wyoming. He received
a Ph.D. in Plant Sciences from U. of Wyoming
and began teaching plant physiology at Wisconsin State University. It was this background which prepared such a well-organized
text for other greenhouse managers.

We strongly recommend PLANTS FOR PROFIT
for any who manage a greenhouse or who have
interest in marketing such crops as bedding
plants, flowering pot plants, and foliage
plants. His chapters on business management
and how to grow plants that sell make this
text almost invaluable for any who wish to
enter alternative crop markets.

Organization for the Advancement of Knowledge

Oak Publishing
1212 SW 5th Street,
Grants Pass, OR 97526
Phone: 541-426-5588

Copyright 1986-2013 © Dr. Richard Alan Miller

The Herb Market Report   Vol. 2 No. 6

THE HERB MARKET REPORT

for the herb farmer and forager   Vol. 2   No. 7   July, 1986

A GROWER'S GUIDE TO RHUBARB PRODUCTION

by Bernard H. Zandstra and Dale E. Marshall
    (from "American Vegetable Grower," 12-82)

Rhubarb is a member of the buckwheat (Polygonaceae) family. A number of species are cultivated for medicinal purposes, but rhubarb is the only one used for food. Other vegetables in the family include garden sorrel and patience dock. The Polygonaceae family contains a number of common weeds – wild buckwheat, knotweed, Pennsylvania smartweed, ladysthumb, red sorrel, and curly dock. Rhubarb (Rheum rhabarbarum, formerly R. rhaponticum) is sometimes also called pie plant.

Rhubarb is one of a small group of vegetable crops in which the edible portion of the plant is the leaf stalk (petiole). The leaves, which contain calcium oxalate that makes them poisonous to humans, should never be eaten. Although it is rather low in vitamins and minerals, it does contain significant amounts of calcium, potassium, and vitamins A and C.

Most rhubarb grown in the U.S. is frozen by processing companies for later use in pies. Most of it goes into bulk pack for institutional or commercial use, but about 10% is sold in consumer-sized packages. A smaller amount is sold fresh, mostly in roadside markets and local stores. Some rhubarb is grown in the field, and then dormant crowns are moved into hothouses in the fall for forcing during the winter. All forced rhubarb is sold fresh. Forcing is declining steadily, however, because of the large amount of labor involved and increasing energy costs.

Varieties currently used for commercial production can be classified as green-, pink-, or re-petiole types. Green varieties have petiole that are almost completely green when grown in the field. The petioles of red types are almost completely red, while pink types vary in shade from pink to red.

The yield for pink and green varieties in Michigan is 10 to 18 ton per acre in a single harvest. Red types average 50% to 75% the yield of pink and green types. Although red color is desired by processors, they produce less so pink types are most commonly grown for processing.

Besides color and yield, absence of seedstalk production is the main characteristic for which varieties have been selected. Little or no seedstalk production is desired, since seedstalks interfere with harvest and inhibit production of leaves and petioles.

A number of varieties are grown for commercial production. Those that produce well in Michigan are Canada Red or Chipman (very red), Valentine (red), Strawberry (pink), Sutton, Sutton Seedless, or Red Right Through (pink), and MacDonald (pink). Victoria, an old green type, is usually not grown for field production because of its all-green color. It is commonly grown for forcing, however. In the hothouse, it produces bright red petiole.

Of these varieties, Victoria is the heaviest producer of seedstalks, followed closely by MacDonald, Strawberry, Red Right Through, and Sutton. The others produce fewer seedstalks.

Field rhubarb production (1980 figures) in the U.S. is concentrated in three states: Washington (275 acres), Oregon (250 acres), and Michigan (200 acres). In addition, Washington grows 125 acres and Michigan grows 80 acres for hothouse forcing.

Rhubarb requires temperatures below 40° F to break dormancy and stimulate production of leaves and petioles. Foliar growth declines when daytime temperature exceeds 80°F. It does best where average diurnal temperatures during the summer are below 75°F and where average winter temperatures are below 40°F. This includes most of the northern half of the U.S. and all of Canada. Rhubarb can be grown successfully at high elevations in some southern areas.

Rhubarb buds begin to open as soon as temperatures exceed 45° to 50°F in the spring. In Michigan this is mid to late March. The young shoots and leaves are susceptible to frost, but usually outgrow the damage. A hard frost (25°F or lower) will severely injure the petioles. If they are damaged by a frost, it is usually wise to chop them off to let new ones come up.

After the petioles are harvested in May or early June, new shoots emerge. Foliar growth declines during the heat of July and August, but resumes again in September. During this period, the roots build up reserves for the next year's growth. In cooler, northern regions, growth is not curtailed during the summer, and a second harvest can be taken in August. If a second harvest is anticipated, make sure the crop receives 1 inch of water per week between harvests, either from rain or irrigation.

Rhubarb is a perennial plant (it comes up from the same crown each year). A good field will stay in production for 10 to 15 years if properly maintained. Extra care in selecting a site, clearing it of perennial weeds, and cover-cropping or fallowing the year previous to planting will pay off in bigger yields and longer productivity. Rhubarb grows best on fertile, well-drained soils that are high in organic matter. It can tolerate pH as low as 5.0, but does best at 6.0 to 6.8.

Planting

The planting site should be prepared the season prior to planting. It is essential that rhubarb be planted in a field free of perennial weeds, and relatively free of annual weeds. Quackgrass is especially a problem. Since no herbicides are presently registered for perennial weed control in rhubarb, the field should be cleaned up in the cropping season previous to planting rhubarb. For instance, Roundup could be applied the previous spring and the field then planted to a crop for which Roundup is registered. After the crop is harvested, the field would be prepared for planting rhubarb the next spring.

Manure adds active organic matter to the soil, increasing aeration and water-holding capacity. Apply 15 ton per acre and work it into the soil the season before planting. Plant a fall cover crop and plow it down in the spring.

Before planting, broadcast and disc into the soil 200 pounds N, 200 pounds P_2O_5, and 200 pounds K_2O per acre. This amounts to 1000 pounds 20-20-20 or the equivalent. These amounts of P and K can be reduced if soil tests high in P_2O_5 or K_2O.

Propagation

Rhubarb is propagated by planting root divisions, which are often called eyes, buds, or sets. These can be obtained from a nursery, or by cutting large crowns into pieces. A planting set should contain a bud and a large piece of root. Roots for replanting can be dug in the fall and stored in a cool place where they won't freeze or in the spring. The roots should be dug late in the fall after leaves have frozen off, or very early in the spring before the buds begin to grow. Seeds should not be used for propagation because they are often not true to type.

If you plan to use your own old crowns for dividing and replanting, select and mark vigorous, healthy crowns the previous season. Avoid weak, diseased, or off-variety plants. A large crown three or more years old should produce 8 to 10 divisions for replanting.

Plant the roots as early in the spring as possible. Roots should be in the ground by the middle of May in all locations. Keep roots below 40°F before planting, if possible, to prevent sprouting. If planting in dry soil, or if dry weather follows planting, irrigate once each week until the roots are established.

The roots should be planted 4 feet apart in 4-foot rows. Plant on a grid so that the rhubarb can be cultivated in two directions. Cut trenches about 6 inches deep with opening shovels, then mark the field across at 4-foot intervals. Plant the roots at the intersection of the trenches and marks. Be careful to keep the rows as straight as possible in both directions. If mechanical harvesting is anticipated, plant

18 inches apart in 4-foot rows, with no concern for cross cultivation.

Plant the roots so that the buds are about 1 to 2 inches below the soil surface. Cover the root with soil and press it firmly. The soil will settle so that the buds are just below the soil surface.

Cultural Practices after Planting

Additional fertilizer is not necessary the year of planting. In subsequent years the rhubarb should be topdressed or side-dressed with 100 pounds N (200 pounds urea or 300 pounds ammonium nitrate) when shoots are between 2 and 10 inches high in the spring. Every three years apply a complete fertilizer (500 pounds of 20-20 per acre, or the equivalent) as a broadcast or side-dressing in the spring in place of the N alone. Apply a second sidedressing of 50 pounds N per acre after harvest to stimulate regrowth.

Cultivate the field as necessary to control weeds. Avoid damaging the crowns during cultivation. When pre-emergence herbicides are registered for use on rhubarb, cultivations after harvest may become unnecessary.

Seedstalks should be cut down as they are produced, especially before harvest in the spring. Once a plant has produced seedstalk, production of petioles decline. The seedstalks are usually removed by walking through the field and cutting them with a knife.

Harvest

Stalks should not be picked the year of planting, since food from the leaves is needed to nourish the roots for the next year's growth. One light picking may be taken during the year following planting if the plants are vigorous. Beginning the second year following planting (when the plants have been in the ground for two years), you may harvest the entire plant. Cut stalks at the soil line and pull them out individually. All the stalks of a plant can be cut at one time, or pulled selectively over a four- to six-week period. Cut leaves off after cutting the stalks.

Time of harvest depends on the variety as well as location and temperature. Generally, harvesting begins in May or early June. When rhubarb growth during the summer is vigorous, a second harvest may be made in August. Stalks should be firm at harvest; when harvested too late, the stalks become pithy and tough.

A commercially available mechanical rhubarb harvester developed by the USDA group at Michigan State University's Agricultural Engineering Department can recover 60% to 70% of the crop in a once-over harvest. Research is improving recovery in conjunction with spacing and variety studies.

Postharvest

Harvested rhubarb stalks must be protected from rain since unprotected ends will "broom" (split). Fresh rhubarb stalks in good condition can be stored for two to four weeks at 32°F and 95% relative humidity. The stalks should be packed in crates that are stacked to allow ample air circulation

Weed Control

Paraquat is the only herbicide that has a tolerance established for use on rhubarb. It is in the process of being registered for use by Chevron Chemical Co., and should be labeled for use in 1983. It will be applied as a dormant spray to kill emerged annuals and to suppress emerged perennials. Paraquat does not have pre-emergence activity and will not affect weeds that subsequently germinate.

Weed control is especially important the year of planting because rhubarb is a poor competitor. In subsequent years, heavy weed pressure will reduce plant vigor and yields. Weeds are also hosts for insects that attack rhubarb. For instance, curly dock is an alternate host for rhubarb curculio, the most important insect pest of rhubarb. Quackgrass is a host for the potato stem borer, which is becoming a major pest in some areas. Cultivation and hand hoeing remain the most effective methods of weed control until pre-emergence herbicides are labeled for use with rhubarb.

Pests

Rhubarb curculio and potato stem borer are the most important insect pests, but are usually not economic pests if the crop is kept free of weeds.

Phytophthora crown rot is the most important disease of rhubarb. The idsease attacks the base of the petioles, causing them to rot off. If infection continues, many petioles may be affected and the crown eventually killed. It is usually only a problem in poorly drained soils. Infected plants should be dug and removed from the field.

Viruses can also infest rhubarb and small, stunted plants that otherwise appear healthy may be infected. Avoid using these plants for replanting.

Note from the Editor

Last month was a major advancement for the growth of herb and spice production in the U.S.. USDA issued two SBIR grants, both for $50,000 each, and BIA (Bureau of Indian Affairs) issued one to the East Plateau Indian Cooperative (EPIC). I received one of the USDA grants, and the other two went to students from previous workshops.

My grant (#8600849) was titled "A Processing Facility for Botanical Alternatives as Cash-Crops." The technical abstract read as

"The collection of wild botanicals and non-timber forest floor products has long provided gainful employment for many living in the rural sections of the United States. As a result of a course taught on this subject, a group of students formed a profit-sharing cooperative to harvest and market these crops. Acting as a model for rural economic development, 12 further cooperatives were formed in 8 states. They interface with each other through marketing and trucking.

"A centralized processing facility is proposed which will strengthen marketing options, profit-margins, and allow a number of cottage industries to emerge. It will serve as a model for other communities and how they might access their own natural resources. A national newsletter already exists for education and information needs.

"It acts as a centralized point of collection for crude botanicals, many of which are currently imported. It will provide business opportunities and jobs in rural situations which have very limited options toward economic development. Not only can it serve as a model toward balanced trade deficits in these and related crops, it will serve as an important example toward rural economic development."

The second USDA-SBIR grant went to Tom Johnson, of Buffalo, SD. The title of his grant was "Herb Production as an Alternative Cash Crop." His technical abstract read as

"Because the crops that are presently available to the small farmer are no longer profitable, there is a need to develop alternative crops. Herb and spice production shows great promise in providing an alternative. The herb and spice market demand far exceeds domestic production. Therefore the U.S. is importing herbs and spices from other countries to meet the demands that exist. If the small farmer is to be successful in providing these crops for the present markets, he must have information in the areas of: Crop Selection, Crop Production, and Market Preparation. This information must be relevant to the climate, soil types, and markets that the small farmer will have available.
"The result of having the data available for successful U.S. production of herbs and spices, would be rural economic growth and development from dollars that are presently being spent in foreign countries."

Tom Johnson's grant represents a farm plan study to determine crop selections and production, and market preparation. He may be contacted directly by writing T.J. Enterprises, Box 21, Buffalo, SD 57720. Whenever you request information from private individuals, it is only correct to include a SASE. He is a farmer and does not have the time to answer your questions. His grant, however, may be available similar to mine. He did a nice job on his grant-writing.

The third grant was submitted by the American Indian Community Center of Spokane, WA. Their award came from the Administration for Native Americans, part of the BIA. Their purpose was a "Proposal for the Formation of the East Plateau Indian Cooperative." It read as

"The East Plateau Indian Cooperative (EPIC) represents the first attempt by Indian people in Spokane to create a business and marketing vehicle which will help lead to community self-sufficiecy. The Cooperative will provide market access for products created or har-

vested by Native Americans throughout the region. Established in accordance with state and federal laws, EPIC will represent community interests because each participant will have one vote and will exert control as both owner and member. EPIC is a democratic means of organizing human and financial resources in order to enhance the economic well-being of the entire Indian community."

"....In the second case, a market demand exists for botanical and herb products which grow naturally throughout the region and which are used in the production of cosmetics, drugs, florals, and food. The objective will be to work with Indian groups, individuals, other cooperatives, and a marketing agent, in order to procure purchase orders for items such as mullein, yarrow, and baby's breath. Harvesters will process and sell these products with the expectation of a reasonable return....."

For more information on this grant and a broader scope on their objectives and goals, contact either Raymond Reyes or John Engel, American Indian Community Center, E. 801 Second Ave., Spokane, WA 99202. Again, I recommend a SASE for any follow-up correspondence.

The 2nd International Permaculture Conference is scheduled for August 8-10 at The Evergreen State College in Olympia, WA. Speakers include Bill Mollison, Masanobu Fukuoka, and Wes Jackson. The theme is titled "Regenerative Systems for an Abundant Future." I will be interviewing the first two speakers for ACRES, USA and HMR on Friday, with a 1.5-hour presentation scheduled from 3:30-5:00pm that evening.
For further information, please contact Permaculture Institute of North America, 6488 Maxwelton Road, Clinton, WA 98236, or by calling (206) 426-2375. It promises to be a most interesting conference. It is then followed by The International Federation of Organic Agriculture Movement's Biannual Conference, Aug. 18-21, University of CA, Santa Cruz, CA.

Potpourri from Herbal Acres

A quarterly newsletter for $15/year. Information-packed for cottage industries and the home gardener. Pine Row Publications, Box 428-OAK, Washington Crossing, PA 18977

PRICE VARIATIONS FOR CRUDE AND PROCESSED BOTANICALS

The following tables, (F)-(3) and (F)-(5), are from grant #8600849 on a processing facility and its advantage in price variations from crude and processed botanicals.

Not only does processing increase total gross sales by more than 150%, more than 108 man-hours are needed. This means new jobs and rural economic development.

(F)-(3) Harvest Schedule - Forage/Farm Plan:

The following list of botanicals represent crops which already have a history of production in the region selected for the centralized processing facility. They do not reflect a number of other dried floral and forest products also produced and marketed from this region of Oregon.

A number of private farm ventures have also begun for 1986 markets which are not represented on this harvest schedule. As the processing center becomes more established, these and other new ventures will benefit through broader marketing options provided by the proposed facility.

CROP	1984 (lbs)	1985 (lbs)	1986 proforma (lbs)	Price ($/lb)	Gross ($)	Form	Firm	Season
Aspen Leaf	3,500	7,000	10,000	1.50	15,000	forage	coop	July-Sept
Bay Laurel Leaf		4,000	4,000	1.00	4,000	forage	private	Feb-April
Cascara Bark		7,100	20,000	0.75	15,000	forage	coop	May-Sept
Catnip Herb	2,000	4,000	10,000	0.55	5,500	forage	coop	June/Aug
Chaparral Leaf			10,000	1.00	10,000	forage	coop	Aug-Oct
Chicory Root		4,000	4,000	0.60	2,400	forage	coop	Nov
Coltsfoot Herb			4,000	0.80	3,200	forage	coop	June
Comfrey Leaf		4,500	50,000	0.45	22,500	farm	private	June/Oct
Devil's Club Root		460	4,000	2.50	9,000	forage	coop	Open
Eucalyptus Leaf		815	4,000	0.65	2,600	forage	private	Dec-Jan
Lovage Herb			2,000	0.80	1,600	forage	coop	Aug
Mistletoe Herb	400	650	2,000	0.35	700	forage	coop	Oct
Mugwort Herb			2,000	0.55	1,100	forage	coop	July
Mullein Herb	1,340	4,800	10,000	0.65	6,500	forage	coop	July
Nettle Leaf		4,200	10,000	0.65	6,500	forage	coop	June
Oregon Grape Root	5,100	9,400	10,000	0.70	7,000	forage	coop	Open
Peppermint Leaf	20,000	50,000	200,000	0.65	130,000	farm	private	July/Sept
Pipsissawa Herb	4,000	4,000	10,000	0.75	7,500	forage	coop	Open
Shave Grass Herb	740		4,000	0.60	2,400	forage	coop	Sept
Spearmint Leaf		40,000	60,000	0.55	33,000	farm	private	July/Sept
Strawberry Leaf		5,000	20,000	0.35	7,000	farm	private	July
St. John's Wort		500	2,000	0.65	2,600	forage	coop	Aug
Yellow Dock Root		480	4,000	0.65	2,600	forage	coop	Nov
Yerba Santa Leaf	1,500	880	2,000	1.00	2,000	forage	coop	July

$ 299,700

HERB FARMING & FORAGING TAPES by Richard Alan Miller

If you haven't been able to attend a workshop yet, enjoy Rick's informative lecture style in your home or car! Most tapes contain pertinent questions and answers from participants, bring up points not necessarily covered in Rick's books.

(F)-(5)   Price Variations for Crude and Processed Botanicals from the Forage/Farm Plan:

The following list of botanicals, scheduled for a 1986 harvest, show the advantages and profit-margins available when processing these crops from crude productions. While 1984-5 crops were sold to only five major processors, processed products can be sold to more than 200 regional buyers.

Not only will profit-margins and marketing options broaden, a number of local cottage industries will emerge with the availability of processed botanicals. While the percentage of processing is somewhat arbitrary, they are based on previous experiences with demand-needs.

CROP	1986 proforma (lbs)	Forager Price - COD	Crude-Bulk Price	% to be Processed	C/S-cut 100# quant.	C/S-cut 1# quant.	Special (tbc, ect.)	Powder-cut 100# quant.	Powder-cut 1# quant.	Gross sales Processing	Man-months Foraging/Processing
Aspen Leaf	10,000	1.25	1.60	20	3.50	4.50	6.50	8.00	10.00	10,000	6
Bay Laurel Leaf	4,000	0.60	1.00	20	2.00	2.50	3.00	4.00	6.00	1,200	2
Cascara Bark	20,000	0.45	0.75	50	1.30	1.75	2.20	2.20	2.80	20,000	10
Catnip Herb	10,000	0.35	0.55	50	1.00	1.50	2.00	2.50	3.50	7,500	4
Chaparral Leaf	10,000	0.65	1.00	50	1.25	1.60	2.20	1.80	2.20	8,000	3
Chicory Root	4,000	0.40	0.60	80	0.85	1.00	1.25	1.70	2.20	4,000	2
Coltsfoot Herb	4,000	0.55	0.80	100	1.00	1.25	1.40	1.80	2.20	4,000	2
Comfrey Leaf	50,000		0.45	50	0.80	1.25	1.70	2.20	2.80	30,000	10
Devil's Club Root	4,000	1.80	2.50	100	4.50	5.50	8.00	10.00	12.00	16,000	4
Eucalyptus Leaf	4,000	0.45	0.65	50	0.80	1.10	1.40	1.60	1.80	2,500	2
Lovage Herb	2,000	0.55	0.80	100	3.00	4.00	4.35	4.50	5.00	4,000	1
Mistletoe Herb	2,000	0.15	0.35	50	0.75	0.95	1.50	1.60	2.00	1,000	1
Mugwort Herb	2,000	0.35	0.55	100	0.95	1.25	1.40	1.80	2.20	3,000	1
Mullein Herb	10,000	0.45	0.65	50	1.45	1.80	2.20	2.60	3.00	7,500	4
Nettle Leaf	10,000	0.45	0.65	50	1.45	1.80	2.00	2.45	2.90	8,500	4
Oregon Grape Root	10,000	0.55	0.75	80	1.35	1.85	2.20	2.40	2.90	12,000	6
Peppermint Leaf	200,000		0.65	20	1.35	1.60	1.80	2.20	2.60	72,000	20
Pipsissawa Herb	10,000	0.55	0.75	20	3.10	3.50	3.70	4.00	4.40	8,000	4
Shave Grass Herb	4,000	0.25	0.45	100	1.25	1.60	1.80	2.20	2.65	5,000	2
Spearmint Leaf	60,000		0.55	20	1.10	1.40	1.60	2.00	2.20	24,000	10
Strawberry Leaf	20,000		0.35	80	0.80	1.20	1.40	1.80	2.20	24,000	6
St. John's Wort	2,000	0.45	0.65	100	1.25	1.70	1.90	2.00	2.40	4,000	1
Yellow Dock Root	4,000	0.35	0.65	50	1.30	2.80	2.50	3.00	3.40	6,000	2
Yerba Santa Leaf	2,000	0.65	1.00	50	2.30	2.65	2.80	3.20	3.80	4,000	1
										$ 286,200	108

BOOK REVIEW:

Cleaning & Reconditioning of Spices, Seeds & Herbs. American Spice Trade Association (ASTA), 580 Sylvan Ave., Englewood Cliffs, NJ 07632. 41pp. $ 20.00.

This small text is a critical "must" for any considering processing of their bulk herb and spice productions. It covers many aspects and details not covered in my book THE POTENTIAL OF HERBS AS A CASH CROP (Chapter on "The Art of Processing"). Not only does it cover the basic principles of cleaning, it also considers the physical considerations necessary for diverse products.

There is a recommended cleaning equipment chart, and descriptions of various equipments used in both cutting and sifting of products. This section is probably the best written on the subject. Not only is it clear and readable, specific principles of operation and features for each is shown through both text and artwork.

The appendix includes a glossary of terms and how to contact manufacturers for further information on how they need to buy your final products. All in all, it is a very important addition to the grant we just received for setting up a processing facility for herbs and spices. I strongly recommend this text for all potential processors.

ASTA has an additional educational materials price list available. You might want to review these titles for additional information on many of the spices and herbs sold in the U.S.. The list includes some technical articles and reprints which I have found quite useful in my own work.

Organization for the Advancement of Knowledge

Oak Publishing
1212 SW 5th Street,
Grants Pass, OR 97526
Phone: 541-426-5588

THE HERB MARKET REPORT

for the herb farmer and forager   Vol. 2 No. 8   August, 1986

HMR INTERVIEW:
Bill Mollison on Permaculture and Ecosystems for the Future

About two months ago, Charles Walters, editor for <u>Acres, USA</u>, asked if I might not get interviews with Bill Mollison and Masanobu Fukuoka for future use in his paper. Both were to be speakers at The 2nd International Permaculture Conference, August 8-10 at the Evergreen State College, in Olympia.

This turned out to be a working conference, with more than 60 other presenters from all corners of the world. Masanobu Fukuoka is the author of THE ONE-STRAW REVOLUTION (Rodale Press) and several other texts on <u>natural farming</u>. Many in the world now consider him the Master Farmer of Japan. I will share this interview with you in a later issue of HMR. Both these interviews, and the conference as a whole were "events," and well worth the time.

Bill Mollison is an Australian ecologist who writes, lectures and demonstrates his concept of "permaculture" as a self-sustaining, consciously-designed ecosystem for the farm. Permaculture has been described as an integrated system of design, encompassing not only agriculture, horticulture, architecture, and ecology, but also money management, land access stategies, and legal systems for communities and businesses.

Through his consultant work, Mollison is instrumental in the actualization of his vision of regions containing integrated self-perpetuating plant and animal species. These ecosystems operated themselves as low maintenance-high yield areas because of such principles as stable diversity and energy efficiency. If it sounds complex, the theory is carefully described in his two books PERMACULTURE ONE and PERMACULTURE TWO, and its practice is outlined in his forthcoming title, PERMACULTURE: A DESIGNER'S HANDBOOK (1987).

Mollison has worked for both governmental agencies and private individuals. He is often the keynote speaker at worldwide conferences on the environment. His background includes teaching environmental psychology as well and environmental design. In 1981, he received the Right Livelihood Award, which is considered by some as the "Alternative Nobel Prize," for his visionary designs. His current thrust includes the training of amateur permaculture designers, the preservation of historical farms in "land trusts," and promoting ethical investments and community economics. Mr. Mollison is President of the Permaculture Institute of North America.

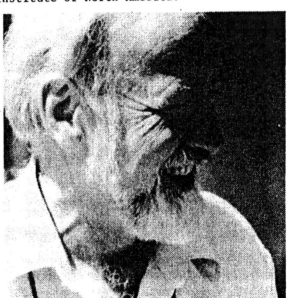

HMR: I'd like to begin by asking how you arrived at your theory of permaculture or perennial agriculture?

MOLLISON: In the early 50's, '53-'59, I was working in forest ecology for the CSIRO, (Commonwealth Scientific Industrial Research Organization), in Australia, and I was dealing with a complex of about 26 plants and 5 animal species. I jotted in my diary, I think about '59, that I thought we could construct durable ecologies, and there it rested. By the '70s, I think we were all aware of the need for sustainable agricultures. In '72 I retired from the world for two years. By '74 I had developed the permaculture idea, which was consciously-designed agricultural ecologies.

HMR: I understand that at one time you had gone into the wilds and had some personal experiences that lead you toward your theories?

MOLLISON: Well, I think that's true. I spent about 25 years working in the field, mostly in very thick forests, or in remote areas. And I kind of withdrew from society in '72 into the wilds. I did the usual thing: I cleared a couple of acres of garden and mulched it down, built a barn and a house, and sat there. I hadn't been sitting there longer than three weeks and I realized I wasn't going to change society. So when I came out of that hole in the bush, I came out with the intention of making a difference.

It wasn't long before I published PER-MACULTURE ONE. Then I gave up my work at the University [of Tasmania]. I was lecturing there in post-graduate work in environmental science. I set up the Permaculture Institute, because by '75-'76 I'd started to design systems for people from urban to rural situations. My first design was a conglomeration of backyards in the city of Melbourne. And right after that was a design for a guy that ran horses for the Olympics. So, I did about 500-600 of those designs, got a lot of feedback from people on them, and decided I had enough skill to teach design. I started in '81. It's now '86 and we've taught a thousand designers worldwide.

HMR: I'm really impressed, by the way, with your work....it's most interesting. Just what is your theory about, what is the basis for your theory of permaculture?

MOLLISON: OK. It's conscious design. It's strange, in fact it's eerie that since a few centuries B.C. when the Chinese developed a landscape planning service called fung-shui*, we have never in modern times developed a similar design service based on aspects of shelter, sun absorption on slopes, etc.*[According to John Michell, fung-shui was "a kind of town and country planning measure attempting to preserve the harmony of the countryside....It was based on a sublime metaphysical system in which scientific and poetic truth harmoniously united." -ed]. All of that is in there. So, I'd say PERMA-CULTURE ONE is the first book on conscious design of agriculture. And that is very eerie, considering we've been agriculturalists for centuries, and we haven't written a book on design.

So, by design, we mean how do you manage the winds, and the light and the sun on a property to get a high productivity. Now, in 1942, your Forestry Department put out a little booklet called TREES, and to a large extent it dealt partly with trees on the farm, and it showed net gains of 16-30%, particularly in lambing and cattle losses, a tremendous gain. It showed crop gains of an average 20%, if the area was well wind-breaked. Now well wind-breaked means windbreaks designed not to reduce the crop's yield, but actually to increase it, because there are several possible interactions between a windbreak and a crop. What we look for is a "plus-plus" reaction; there the windbreak benefits the crop, and the crop the windbreak. So, these all have to be highly specified trees and materials.

Back to the domestic situation - your need to have to earn - that is what makes a lot of farmers have to walk off the farm. They just can't sustain the domestic costs and pay loans, and so on. A lot of farmers I know have managed to hang on to farms simply because they've paid a lot of attention to the fact that they can eat off the farm and the domestic energy supplied off the farm. Now you can hang on through some hard times if that's the case. If it's not, you have to have an income.

We started doing whole-farm designs in Australia because we're a dry country, and so is the Great Basin and Midwest, and California in the summertime. [see Mollison's forthcoming booklet ARID LAND PERMACULTURE, 1988]. Water was our central design factor, and I don't mean pumping water up from 2,000 feet down at $2,000 a month. I mean we very carefully designed methods of rainwater harvesting on property, tried to regard the property and what was on it as to what we had to deal with, and to get the least inputs into production that we could.

HMR: So, bringing this more into a focus, if you could summarize in one paragraph, could you explain the basis of permaculture?

MOLLISON: I'll try and do it for you. Permaculture is a consciously designed landscape system, which deals with the management of crops, water and animals on the land and which also puts that in context with the correct legal, financial, and land-access strategies, and marketing, and trade.

HMR: That leads to my next question. You have indicated that your theory is not technically oriented, but depends on intuition...

MOLLISON: That's true. We're not looking

for expertise in agriculture and forestry. We're looking for the expertise to know where forestry and agriculture fit together, the connection between disciplines is where we look.

HMR: It has been indicated by a group in Southern Oregon [part of Tilth], that your plan was too detailed and technically oriented for commercial farm use. Perhaps you would like to make some comments on that?

MOLLISON: I'd love to. It's certainly not so. A lot of our stuff is commercial. It's carefully designed to be commercial. I must say, in the first place, our greatest demand is still plotting for self-reliance, in and around, the households, and always will be. That's society's single greatest cost. 46% of our income goes toward food. 29% is energy. That's 75% of the income on those two items. So you can see the huge benefit to society if we can cope with those to the amount of capital we're freeing in effect. We always did have inquiries from farmers. However, as they are a minority of the population, it's a minority of inquiries. Still, we've designed all kinds of farms from rangeland, wildlife farms to very detailed one-acre farms supporting people with specialty crops.

HMR: You speak of interacting relationships between species. Perhaps you could explain that a bit....

MOLLISON: I'll go a little further and call it "guilds." You can't put a successful orchard in without having some nitrogen fixation. Some of the best of those things are trees. If you have a frost problem, you need a frost defense. We can get a frost defense with a small legume called tagasaste and grow avocado in areas which frost is quite hard. So you have physical protection of the other crop as part of the guild and you have an underground root association, releasing nitrogen, as part of the guild. Then if we set through that keyaha, which is an insect-attracting plant for predatory wasps, some of the unbelliferra crops, like a few fennel scattered through, we then bring in the predators of small insects feeding on the fruit system.

   Next we put under that a foraging system to pick up all the wind-drops and all the cast-off fruit. There's a special pig bred for that [it's called a Glauster old spot], and it's bred not to root, but to effectively forage orchards. It's always been bred for that purpose. Another alter-

native is in your old agricultural journals. They say if you run successful apple orchards with 70-90 chickens per acre, you get all your fertilizer and effective pest control. So, put in a good program of foragers, insect free plants, physical defense of the trees, and a very good windbreak specifically designed to be of benefit to apples.

   Tamarack, as a windbreak, will reduce an apple crop and eliminate a citrus crop! But, if we put as a windbreak hadioliacus with an understory of Siberian pea tree, we'll get more apples, and more health in the crop. So we pick the windbreak for the crop. Then we do the physical layout. If we need more heat, we'll put in high-radiation trees, the darkest side on the off-sun side of the crop, and we'll radiate heat into the crop. If we have a desert situation, we'll put a deep windbreak, and allow the temperature of the incoming -winds, 30-40°F, and so on.

   Now, this is a guild we've set up, and the guild all centers around the apple. Now under the apple, apples will not stand in grass. They stop infiltration of light and they put out specific chemicals to inhibit root growth of apples. So under the apple we put a small apple garden, and specifically the spring bulbs which lie all around the cultivation and yielding system.

HMR: Washington State now uses mints.

MOLLISON: Yeah, mint, spring bulbs, nasturtium; anything that is not grass. We allow a very small proportion of grass; clover covers, and we've got a very fine situation. If we have any pests in, we might actually have to add a few frog ponds.

HMR: Would you define your use of the word "stewardship?"

MOLLISON: Yes, I think every good farmer, in fact, everybody I've considered to be a patriotic farmer, in that they have a love of country in the deepest sense, (and a lot of farmers have that), everyone of them would rather leave the land and soil improved after their tenure of the land. And so what the good farmer regards himself as, is a temporary "steward" of the land to hand it on in trust to the future. Not specifically to their children, but to the future people of their area. And they can achieve that in a lifetime by putting the land into a farm trust, and by laying out a very long-term development plan for it. And the trust can insure that the plan continues beyond their lifetime.

We've lost some fantastic farms in the United States. Smith's Tree Farm, Luther Burbank's Nursery Farm, I could mention another six, all should have been land-trusted. Professor Meador's little farm in Vermont should be land-trusted. This is where your crops came from, your new species came from, where your new ideas were thought up and demonstrated. And they don't belong even to the United States; they belong to the world! I'd like some American who feels really patriotic about land to set a trust to purchase those key farms that demonstrate principles, forever. They should be run as farms and run for their purposes, but they should be set up as land-trusts, which I believe to be more valuable than many of the trusts that we've set up for our buildings.

HMR: Moving forward, I have picked up a quote where you ask yourself, "What does this land have to give me?" Can you explain.....

MOLLISON: Yes, well sometimes you walk on the land and you have the crop. People say, "I've just bought some land I want to develop a crop." I'll give you and example. I had a young bulldozer operator in Australia. He'd just bought some really run-down cattle land. He had a bulldozer and he put some dams in. Then he said, "Will you come onto my farm and tell me what I ought to do here?" He had nice dams there which he had stocked with trout. "How are they going?," I asked him. "Fine," he said. "I got some eight pounders out of them." "When did you put them in?," I inquired. "Last year," he replied. And the place was swarming with grasshoppers; it was overgrazed.

I said, "You've got your crop; your crop is grasshoppers!" On a 1.8 to 1 conversion ratio you can get a pound of trout for every pound and a bit of grasshoppers. You can trawl those grasshoppers just like you trawl fish. So, the other thing is, grasshoppers go for yellow, so if you float yellow balloons on the dams, you get a rain of grasshoppers into the water. So that's what he did, and he had his crop. The land might already have its crop on it, and yet you might want to change that crop, and you will come out worse off.

For instance, we have a pasture grub that runs at 20 ton to the acre living in the first four inches of the soil. If you covert it into turkey, you're talking 5 ton of turkey to the acre, just for a small soil-skimming operation daily. But they're still trying to get rid of the pasture grub!

And yet that land can barely sustain a sheep on four or five acres. So where's the trade off between a 120 tons of protein and 40 pounds of protein as sheep? So, wherever we see that the crop is already there we've come out on top. And we have nothing to do..

HMR: Next question, in your second book PERMACULTURE TWO, you have referred to Fukuoka's principles of "non-violent cultivation and natural farming" [see THE ONE STRAW REVOLUTION and THE NATURAL WAY OF FARMING]. What are your views on this?

MOLLISON: I think Fukuoka is a genius! What he did (and nobody's quite realized it, as such) is that he stacked, or folded time. Instead of waiting until you've harvested your crop, then appear for cultivation and sowing, he sowed the next crop into the standing crop. At the right time, so that when you hit it off, your second succession is well under way. And that was genius! So what's more, it meant you didn't cultivate, and you went from soybeans into barley, or in his case, rice, rye, rice, rye. So he gathered extra time, and that is also extra capital.

HMR: Considering your theory of cooperation, or the "no-force" theory, are there then no plants that are out of place and therefore considered weeds?

MOLLISON: Plants are innocent. They are all doing a job, and expressing that job to the best of their abilities. To see a patch of thistle is to see a disturbance, and it's being mended fast. If you put a thistle under an apple tree, you can call it a glove artichoke, right? You see, the soil under that artichoke will be twice as good and thick with worms compared to soil without the artichoke. So, it's a soil mender. We don't see it as that; we don't see a weed or invasion species warning us that there is some collapse starting. For instance, we work with gorst in the Pacific Northwest. With gorst we can get to rain forest in four years. Without gorst it takes 20 years. In wet climates it grows great. Burn it and you get more of it. So we roll a tractor roller through it, then put in a first succession tree crop (like acacia or alder), and a second or third succession tree down the alley that was rolled down. The gorst nurtures and nurses the crop.

HMR: What about a place like the Midwest where there's been considerable erosion of topsoil, and the soil blows from one field to another?

MOLLISON: Yes, I've been forced down twice by severe dust storms in wheat areas. The land is in collapse. You need to pick up the dust origins which are always downwind and in between the crop you start "pitting." You use a large wheel and you pit the ground. The minute you pit the ground the dust storms stop, because you've roughened the surface. Don't pit in the crop, but all around it.

We've pitted 600 square miles around Ellis Springs, Austrailia and we get no more duststorms, whatever. They used to close the airport every fortnight. After we've pitted we work our windbreak sequence: talk to the farmers, talk to the government, get our support for the windbreaks, and make the windbreaks a highly productive pile of fun. We start from the downwind area with stategy. We have to work with government and finance to make sure that windbreak is going to be highly productive for the farms downwind. We advance from the downstream and, upstream. And we create a highly stable situation. The other thing you have to do is leave a record for the future - to say why you did all this.

HMR: How do you go about planning a permaculture farm? What are your first steps?

MOLLISON: Well, the first step is to look at the farm, and the skills and wishes of its occupant. If they're in steel we can do something about that. If they're lawyers we can run a bit of legal system on the farm. We use the skills of the occupant and let them define what they want to do. On top of what they have defined, we also suggest what is very wise to do. Then we set about the ground detail planning. But that always with us involves the social factor.

For instance, recently we've been linking urban people in need of some energy source, like firewood or diesel, to individual farmers who grow the plantation. They prepurchase the product. Basically, we don't any longer look at a primary product as being the main potential income of farmland. There are three products. Social products is very high. 80% of the product of our farmers is from social product (offering facilities to people in towns, etc.). The second income is in the production of an energy crop. We have a travelable diesel system we take around. You put

sunflower seeds in one end, it presses it, puts the oil through a catalyst, gives you diesel ine, then regenerates the catalyst. Its a small unit about as big as a dinner table, on a trailer. So, it takes 1/100th of your crop to provide the fuel. You can provide off-farm fuel.

Solid wood is the best income per acre, for abroad. Unless you process it fairly high on the roadside, it runs $80 a ton, or $800 a ton in smaller 5 lb. packages. That means an average acre produces $5-6,000 in firewood year in and year out. Any person in the city would like to have a piece of that. That means two rented acres give him a small income and all their fuel. So fuel is an eternal crop and there is never enough fuel.

Clean water is another crop. Some farms you'll purchase every quarter of an hour, if you have a spring that tests out as potable. That's your problem in the United States - to get any water that tests out as drinkable. In some farms the whole value of the farm is coming out of the hill every ten minutes. You've got an endless trade in clean water.

HMR: Can you explain your use of such terms as "Zones," "Sectors," and "Interfaces?"

MOLLISON: Real easy. When you zone a property from where you start in the morning with the tractor, you zone it in terms of the number of times you can afford to visit that area. For instance, move your household garden a hundred feet from the house and you've lost it! You'll never harvest it efficiently and you can't guard it. Move it within 20 feet of the house boundary and you'll feed yourself forever with hardly any effort.

Out time is 20-40 minutes a week. That's less time for us to grow our food than to actually walk to the shop and back, providing we have it right outside the kitchen door which is Zone 1. Zone 2 is domestic species. The chicken house is on the edge of Zone 2, and they range in Zone 2, then bring all the manure to the edge of Zone 1, where we use it on the garden. So the chickens do the work; try to be smarter than your chickens.

Sectors define against incoming energy, designed to survive the onslaught energy - too hot or too cold winds, sunsector. Put up the defenses in sectors to guard the energy or deflect it to benefit you. With those two things, zoning and sectoring the soil, you also pay attention to any benefits of slope and carefully orientate all your units to the sun or wind. You've got a rational, ideally efficient lair.

An interface is like edge harmonics. All crop scientists tell you that you can't sample a crop at the edges, you've got to walk into the crop. At the edges the yield is abnormally high (sometimes anomolously low). The goal is to try to plant a field that is nothing but this high-yielding edge. For example, if the edge is four feet deep, then we plant solid eight foot deep sections. What is next to that edge? If it is bare ground we get a pretty good yield, but if it is alfalfa that yield is higher. So put strips of 8 feet of grain, 8 feet alfalfa. A double edged section gives superior yield.

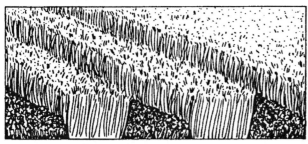

- continued next month -

HERB FARMING & FORAGING TAPES by Richard Alan Miller

If you haven't been able to attend a workshop yet, enjoy Rick's informative lecture style in your home or car! Most tapes contain pertinent questions and answers from participants, bring up points not necessarily covered in Rick's books.

NEWS RELEASE
Upjohn Tests Herb Compounds

The following news release was observed in "Chemical Marketing Reporter," August 4, 1986. It is a quiet reminder that many of the major pharmaceutical firms are looking for new sources of chemistry.

"Upjohn Company says it has entered into a research agreement to sceen and develop compounds derived from Chinese herbal medicines that have never before been studied in the west.

Under the agreement, Shanghai Institute of Materia Medica has provided Upjohn with reseach quantities of compounds isolated from 10 Chinese herbal medicines used for centuries in China for treatment of a wide range of human disorders, including cancer, cardiovascular disease and central nervous system malfunctions.

"'This agreement is a significant step in our worldwide research endeavor and provides an interesting complement to our expanding use of rational, targeted drug discovery and development techniques,' says Jacob C. Stucki, Upjohn's corporate vice-president for pharmaceutical research.

"Upjohn says it intends to apply advanced techniques to test the compounds for their maximum biological activity. 'We can't be sure that any of them will offer more therapeutic benefit than what might already exist in the pharmaceutical marketplace,' Upjohn concedes. 'However, they have not appeared in the scientific literature before, and we're excited to have this unique opportunity to test these compounds and enhance our discovery efforts.'"

Among those recommended for study include several classed as anti-tumor drugs, including Cephalotaxus harringtonia (Plum Yew). These 'specialty' markets for specific chemistry now looks to be very lucrative - with a contract in-hand, of course.

Potpourri from Herbal Acres

A quarterly newsletter for $15/year. Information-packed for cottage industries and the home gardener. Pine Row Publications, Box 428-OAK, Washington Crossing, PA 18977

THE CULTIVATION AND MARKETING OF FRENCH SORREL

French sorrel (<u>Rumex scutatus</u> L.), native to Europe, is a hardy perennial and belongs to the Polygonaceae family. It is the most commonly cultivated of the sorrels because of its broader, more tasteful leaves. In many respects it is identical to the narrow-leaved garden sorrel (<u>R. acetosa</u> L.), and should not be confused with wood sorrel (<u>Oxalis acetosella</u> L.), a different genus altogether.

French sorrel likes a dry, friable soil and a sunny location. Garden sorrel preferes more moisture. Both may be grown from root division in the spring or fall. They are hardy, frost resistant plants and are easily started from seed, outside in March or April.

Furrows can be made in ordinary rich soil, one inch deep and plants should be thinned to stand 6" to one foot aprat. Mulch as soon as possible. Bell-shaped flowers, usually yellow-green with purple veins, form early in spring and blloom by May.

Seeds are a favorite food for gold and purple finches, so some form of control will be needed. The leaves and flowering stems should be cut back as hot weather sends them into early seeed production. You may get two harvests of seed and leaf in one season.

Keeping the seed pods removed will tend to rejuvenate the plant so it will keep producing green leaves into the fall. The roots will send up new shoots which will be better for greens than the heavy growth that may have become slug infested.

Plants should be replaced with new seedlings every three or four years as they take a lot out of the soil and sometimes rot at the root if left in the same bed.

Sorrel leaf can be harvested at any time the plant is growing. Best to use the leaves fresh as drying does not preserve their distinctive citrus-like flavor. The leaves can be cut with a side-bar cutter and dried via sun-cure methods in a windrow. Once dry, the leaves can then be picked up via vacuum/piggy-back systems (like from John Deere). Do not flail-chop the dried leaf, it shatters the leaf beyond marketing. The yield in dry leaf product is about 800 pounds per acre.

Marketing

Fresh leaves are used in salads, so there might be some direct marketing as a produce. Medicinally, sorrel is said to have diuretic, anti-scorbutic, and refrigerant properties and is given to reduce fevers and to quench thirst. As a produce, probably markets are limited and only bring $0.50 per pound.

The acidity of French sorrel leaves will turn metal knives black when used to chop them. Therefore, sorrel should not be cooked long or in an iron pan. Most uses for sorrel is as a spring tonic made in France. This might be the best way to market the leaves, as a cottage industry production of French Sorrel Soup.

Wholesale prices range from $0.65 per pound in 2-ton quantities to more than $1.80 per pound in 100-pound quantities. Most regional wholesalers will buy only one ton per year for marketing to retail health food stores and Coops. Retail prices are about $9.50 per pound.

The annual domestic demand for French sorrel is probably less than 10 ton for the health foods industry. Soup manufacturing is another matter. The French Sorrel Soup is quite popular in other parts of the world and could be developed in the United States fairly easily, once a source of supply was established.

Cottage Industry Example

The British make a sauce of the leaves by pureeing them in melted butter and adding flour for thickening and a little chicken

stock. It goes well with pork, fish or omelets. As in omelets, it is folded in when
turning the egg mixture in the pan.

A recipe for French Sorrel Soup:
2 handfuls of sorrel leaves
4 Tablesoons butter
3 Tablespoons flour
2 Tablespoons fresh lovage
Salt and Pepper
2 shallots, minced
2 Cups chicken stock
2 egg yolks
1 Cup cream
4 Tablespoons fresh chervil

Remove midribs of sorrel leaves by fold-
ing them and tearing from the top down. Chop
fine and cook in butter with minced shallots.
Sorrel will become a salad-green color and
puree itself in a few minutes.
Blend flour, chopped herbs, salt, pepper
and stock. Pour 1/2 Cup into beaten egg
yolks in a bowl. Return to pan, add cream
and heat thoroughly but slowly. The soup
may be put in a blender to chop herbs and
prevent lumps, as a time and work saver.
It can be served hot or cold.
If you manufacture this as a cottage
industry, you might market it to either an
airline company or even to a major soup manufacturer (like Lipton). The correct way to
begin would be to try it at several local
restaurants, moving then toward a chain of
stores (like Denny's). Once you had some
marketing data, packaging the dehydrated
contents into a package might be next. It
might even be sold frozen. It is already
sold in these two ways thru out Europe, and
is now imported for the "gourmet" stores.

LOW-COST SHELTERS & simple comforts easily
improvised anywhere: mountains, farm, city,
traveling. Plans 10¢ up. SASE for catalog.
Philomath, OR 97370

Wild Crafted Roots and Herbs - Wild crafted
roots and herbs - wholesale - guarenteed or
your money back. Root Diggin' Nation Herb
Co., P.O.Box 11120, Ferguson, MO 63135
(314 524-6680. (Networking for marketing and
transportation?)

**Organization for the Advancement
of Knowledge**

Oak Publishing
1212 SW 5th Street,
Grants Pass, OR 97526
Phone: 541-426-5588

Copyright 1986-2013 © Dr. Richard Alan Miller

Address Correction Requested

Return Postage Guaranteed

BULK RATE
U.S. Postage Paid
Grants Pass, OR
Permit No. 66

The Herb Market Report   Vol. 2 No. 8

THE HERB MARKET REPORT

for the herb farmer and forager   Vol. 2   No. 9   September, 1986

HMR INTERVIEW: Part II
Bill Mollison on Permaculture
and Ecosystems For the Future

This is a continuation of the interview with Bill Mollison when he was at The 2nd International Permaculture Conference in Olympia last August 8-10.

HMR: How do you envision the restructuring of our current monocropping industrialized farms, like the San Joaquin Valley of California, and do you see a timeframe for this?

MOLLISON: Yeah, I do. The modern industrial scientist is causing famine all around the world, and malnutrition locally. That's the two main products of monoculturing and you can add to that a chronic poisoning everywhere. That is, agriculture has floated free from its roots. Its purpose was to feed people "good food." It no longer does that. It doesn't relate to people's needs in any way.

What we're doing is re-relating the farm directly to people who need those good products. So we're setting up farm link networks with farmers and urban dwellers, pre-farming the farm so there is no risk to the farmer. And there are thousands of those. It takes 18-40 households, depending on the culture, to keep a family very wealthy on the land. This assumes that person is providing the needs of the household and not cheating or marketeering.

HMR: So pre-funding from urban dwellers is what you're suggesting?

MOLLISON: Very definitely. The timeframe is yesterday for many farmers. We are de-populating our farmland of highly experienced people at an alarming rate. You can't beat them at farm management. But, we're replacing them with farm machinery which causes unemployment which puts a charge on society to pay unemployment to farmers in the form of taxation. Wouldn't it be better if they were unemployed happily on the land and with their families? We could have intercepted that through a farm-link office

where any person could subscribe for say two acres of firewood planted by a farmer for $200 plus $50 for fire control. At the end of four years you get an average $4,000 income per acre and what you pay him is what he would get out of it in sheep which is $70 per acre a year (in Australia). Pay up front so he can afford to get that timber in there.

HMR: That's great. Let's move on, now. As an example, how would you deal with raccoons that are systematically destroying a farmer's crop of sweet corn? Would you stop raising the corn, would you feed the racoons, have dogs to chase the coons out, and now you're feeding dogs? How would you handle those racoons?

MOLLISON: I eat them. I get more protein out of the coons than I could ever get out of the corn. On one patch of my friend's in Vermont, we got 5 opposum, 2 coons, etc.. We worked it out and the protein yield was far higher than the corn could ever be.

HMR: Can you realistically give a workable plan to a large mechanized farm?

MOLLISON: Yes. But it would be really extraordinary, nothing that has ever been done with mechanization. I've been doing some large style drilling of tagastashe with large mechanized materials. And I can lay down a crop that you can pellet into feed at the highest yield of any unirrigated crop in the world. In between the tagastashe strips are tree-alfalfa strips. Mainly, I want to let thousand of amateurs loose on the world. I'm no longer interested in sitting somewhere and making a buck. To become competent it takes young people two to three years of working on these permaculture concepts.

HMR: Do you recommend a legal structure that lends itself to families or people pooling resources? I ask this because in PERMACULTURE II you mention the idea of gathering together with a few friends to build the alternatives you mention. This sounds like the original communal efforts of the 60's , trying to find a blending of egos and spiritual philosophies.

MOLLISON: It grew out of those inadequate attempts to form communities that were part of the 60's, most of which have broken apart. But, taking a very rational approach to community ownership for private use - that's the ideal. [Like a profit-sharing cooperative] you've got all the advantages of private useage, but you don't have the right-to-ruin given by private ownership.

The ideal way to work land is like a thing in England called common work right. A trust owns the land, and it only has three directors who can then appoint others. Nobody votes; it's not democratic. The only consensus we need is that we never come to consensus. Now, the trust governs its directors. Any person who can see a way to make a living on that land applies to the trust. The land lets (rents) a living to them, including if necessary a residential unit, but often they would like to live elsewhere. They then pay 10% aof the net to a common work fund which goes on developing other livings. In this way a small 200-acre farm in Kent employs 36 people full time on site and 95 off-site from the products produced on the site, and it's hardly developed at all!

One farm can employ hundreds of people. A beekeeper is essential to your small fruit grower. The milker can supply manure for energy for may people (methane, hot water and can-fuel). We run all tractors and cars on those systems. You have an energy man, a bee man, small tree man, worm man all working on the wastes from the digestor. Worms go to the fish ponds and triple their value. The casings go back in the glass house attached to perhaps a brick-making works, digging clay from the silage pits on the farm. You can think of other

projects.

HMR: What are the alliances you speak of with similar groups?

MOLLISON: A large group of Sufis are using Permaculture, likewise in the U.S. those interested in Biodynamics, the New Alchemy Institute, etc.. We would like to lie within every organization and still maintain our own teachings, so we are distinct in design.

HMR: So you are supporting regional networking, then?

MOLLISON: Yes, and we also have regional and independent design consultants. Nobody owns permaculture; it's a common copywrite of our trainees. And all of them are independent. It's not franchised. All our systems are independent legally structured. So, what you've got is a very large global cooperative of tiny businesses.

HMR: What forms of alternative property ownership do you prefer?

MOLLISON: I myself prefer to live on land in trust with a long-term purpose. I personally am allowed to lease (earned the right) for life, inheritable, transferable, a half-acre for a house and other land on an economic level that I am fit to use.

HMR: What is your main current of thought now, sort of your "hot" item?

MOLLISON: My real hot thing right now is that it's five minutes to midnight. We face a meltdown of icepacks and consequent searises. It's time to open the great debate: Can we survive? Nobody's sure we can. Start to turn the whole society toward structured 3% less trees and we all asphixiate. It is five minutes to midnight. What is the use of choking with a million in your pocket? Why didn't we have that million in survival, and survival means "trees." Now, why didn't we turn our mainstream agriculture into mainstream tree cropping? We're supporting it a $28-30 billion a year and that will just ruin America. If you don't green it, we're all dead! So the main thing now is let's take over the investment income of this country and turn it into ethical ends. We have $60 billion turned over here now in ethical investments and we can turn the rest over if we put it to the people.

HMR: Is it possible to reverse the damage

done from original agricultural practices, like erosion...?

MOLLISON: Take dieldrene. As far as erosion, we can build soil. There's no doubt about that. We have the techniques where there's enough of anything left to work from. We can hoe and create soils by the right trees. But, we can't unpoison the soil. We've found that years ago copper was used in Australia and it's still killing sheep, from before World War II. It's in the top 2 inches of the soil and we can't raise sheep for years, or eat an egg from that land for the next 200 years. What we've put on in the past we can't take off, but we need never put that stuff on. Those farms should be locked up as toxic or put into non-food production, namely forestry, perhaps for centuries.

HMR: What questions have I not asked that I should have asked you?

MOLLISON: What's the priority for young people who are going to be designers today? The real priority is to set up a money-handling system that services people, to set up investment trusts, development trusts, and commonly revolving funds that help people who believe in the future. If people can do that well, (and all our people do that well), they have endless capital and cease to become employees subject to client wishes and they become purchasers and developers of land. And that's what we must become to create the future. We can't passively leave it to someone else who knows nothing about land to determine the future. We must borrow the land and create the future. We can't afford the warehouses, the headless dinosaurs of yesturday. It's critical we take them out.

HMR: Thank you for a great interview. Where can we get further information?

MOLLISON: In the U.S.A., the Permaculture Institute of North America (PINA) on Whidbey Island in Washington. Contact the network this way for designers and ethical investment seminars in the next few months. Write me as the man who knows about Permaculture in Tasmania and it will reach me. Write to Tagari, P.O.Box 96, Stanley, Tasmania 7331, Australia. You may also wish to contact the International Tree Crops Institute U.S. A., Inc., Box 888-M, Winters, CA 95694

Special thanks to Ron Febus and Iona Miller for helping organized this interview.

NEWS RELEASE

Plastics, resins, and other substances may be manufactured from shrubs in the future. According to an article from "The Futurist," (March-April 1986), sumac, a perennial shrub common in the United States, contains hydrocarbons, oils, and complex molecules called polyphenols, all of which can be used to make drugs, pesticides, plastics, and other industrial products. According to the U.S. Department of Agriculture's Research Service, farmers could grow and harvest sumac easily and then send it to processing plants to have the polyphenols and oils removed for further manufacture.

It now appears that jobs will open up in the field of natural resources. According to the West Virginia University News Service, both government and industry may face a shortage of natural-resource professionals in coming years.

Enrollment in natural-resource programs for the nation peaked about seven years ago. Many were drawn to these majors by the worldwide interest in the environment. Forestry, wildlife, recreation, and ecology were a fad of the times.

The 1970s' enrollment in forestry programs, for example, was way out of line with career opportunities. Today's opportunities are widening, however. Such things as environmental protection, acid precipitation, enhancement of wildlife habitat, and providing for leisure and recreation are now long-term concerns of America that haven't been solved. As a result, the backlog of problems requiring natural-resources professionals is increasing daily.

- next month - Exclusive interview with Japan's Master Farmer Masanobu Fukuoka on THE NATURAL WAY OF FARMING.

NOTES FROM THE EDITOR

I recently had the pleasure of meeting the herbalist Dr. Paul Lee of the Platonic Academy (Santa Cruz). Of special interest was a list of immune-enhancing herbs herbs which should be considered viable alternative cash crops for the small farm. They are

Echinacea angustifolia is widely cultivated in the United States. Much of it is exported to Germany, where it is a primary ingredient in a number of herbal products being used for a new therapy - "Umstimmungstherapie," which means "returning the immune system."

Astragulus membranaceus is the medical "herb of choice" for the Chinese. It is an excellent immune-enhancer, and is especially valuable as an aid in protecting cancer patients from the side-effects of radiation and chemotherapy, both of which are detrimental to the immune system.

Ginseng and Eleutherococcus senticosus (sometimes called Eleuthero ginseng or Siberian ginseng) are the herbs of choice for immune enhancement in Russia, due to the research of I.I. Brekhman in Vladivostok.

The herb of choice in Europe for the prevention and treatment of heart conditions is Hawthorne (Crataegus oxycantha). It acts as a heart tonic, strengthening the contractility of the heart muscle and toning the arterial wall. Strong arterial walls help prevent the build up of plaque, a contributing factor in the development of arteriosclerosis. As a preventive measure, Hawthorne can be taken in capsule form or as a tincture (alcohol extract). Hawthorne is non-toxic, unlike Digitalis from Foxglove.

If you choose to cultivate any of these crops, marketing them should be no problem. OAK offices now have several standing orders for each, and we can assist in your marketing needs for a standard commission of 10% of gross sales. Technical information on several of these has also been prepared.

BABY'S BREATH PLANTS FOR SALE - One-year old Gypsophila paniculata var. "Bristol Fairy" for sale in quantities of 1,000 for $300, less shipping. Contact Colleen Podoll by calling (503) 592-2796. Member of SOHGA. (ed - these roots have long taproots and must be dug before November).

NEWS RELEASES

The articles on alternative agriculture are beginning to hit even the most prestigious of journals. For example, "Scientific American," (July, 1986) recently offered the following headline for the article titled "Potential New Crops:"

"Buffalo gourd, cranbe, jojoba and kenaf are approaching commercial production. A number of other plants show promise as sources of food and as industrial materials."

I have always made it a point to read "Scientific American" since High School. My first "science fair" project even came from a section titled "American Scientist" in the back of each issue. In another issue, (Jan., 1986), titled "The Chemical Defenses of Higher Plants," insight is offered on how you might apply new technology to your current farm plan via "permacultural" techniques. The headline reads

"Some plant-produced chemicals poison herbivores or repel them; others reduce plants' nutritive value or impede an insect's growth. Herbivors in turn have ways of exploiting these natural products."

HMR strongly recommends you begin to spend more time in the library this winter. The information is out there. You simply need to know what you are looking for and why.

HERB FARMING & FORAGING TAPES by Richard Alan Miller

If you haven't been able to attend a workshop yet, enjoy Rick's informative lecture style in your home or car! Most tapes contain pertinent questions and answers from participants, bring up points not necessarily covered in Rick's books.

THE FORAGE AND CULTIVATION OF EPHEDRA

Chinese Ephedra has been used medicinally for more than 5,000 years. In 2,700 B.C., Shen Mung, the father of Chinese medicine used the dried roots and stems as a decongestant to treat coughs, colds, headaches, and fever. It was during this time that it was given the name ma huang.

Most all varieties of Ephedra are currently marketed, although the primary crop is taken from Ephedra major Host (E. nebrodensis Tineo). Other cultivars used include E. gerardiana Wall.(E. vulgaris Rich.), E. intermedia Schrenk & Meyer, E. sinica Stapf, and E. equisetina Bunge.

E. Major is a tall, evergreen shrub which grows up to 6 feet in height as a wild plant in the Mediterranean areas of Spain, Sicily, Afghanistan and Pakistan. E. Intermedia grows up to 2 feet high, and ranges from Inner Mongolia to Pakistan. It prefers lower altitudes to the E. major.

E. gerardiana, a dwarf species (6-15 in.) is native to the northwest Himalayas at altitudes up to 16,000 feet in northern India, West Pakistan, Tibet, Szechwan and Yunnan Provinces of China. In Pakistan, it is less accessible than E. major and handicapped by more humid weather.

E. sinica and E. equisetina are both found at the 5,500-ft. level in northern China from Sinkian to Hopeh Province and north to Outer Mongolia. These species have been experimentally cultivated in Australia, Kenya, England and the United States. In this country, efforts were more successful in South Dakota, Utah and New Mexico. Labor costs were the only inhibiting factor which made it seem unfeasible. New techniques in harvest may make this a very attractive cash crop, however.

Most Ephedras are thick-stemmed, 3 to 5 inches at the base, with many slim, jointed branches and twigs having fine longitudinal ridges or ribs. The leaves are minute and scale-like, sheathing the nodes. The herb has both male and female flowers. The males containing stamins are found together on catkins, while the females containing pistils arise from a two-leaved flower branch that is supported on axillary stalks coming from the stems. The fruit consists of two pistil-like capsules containing a juicy cone-shaped seed in each capsule. The stems or branches are slender and erect with small leaves somewhat like scales on the stem.

Chemistry

The woody basal stems of Ephedra plants are very low in alkaloid content, while the roots and fruit are nearly alkaloid-free. The green branches and twigs of the Mediterranian and Asiatic species contain the alkaloids ephedrine ($C_{10}H_{15}NO$) and psuedoephedrine (isoephedrine) in varying amounts depending on the plant, the altitude at which it grows, and the time of year and weather of harvest.

E. major msy contain over 2.5% total alkaloids, nearly 75% of the total being ephedrine. E. intermedia is low in ephedrine but fairly high in psuedoephedrine. In E. gerardiana, total alkaloids vary from 0.8 to 1.4%, of which 50% is ephedrine. E. sinica contians roughly 1.3% total alkaloids (1.1% ephedrine), while E. equisetina has a total of 1.8% alkaloids (1.6% ephedrine). The pharmaceutical trade requires that dried ephedra contain no less than 1.25% ephedrine.

Ephedra has a strong pine odor and very astringent taste. Ephedrine and psuedoephedrinerine are very stable. For example, a solution of ephedrine hydrochloride sealed for six years will show no oxidation nor loss of activity.

Ephedrine acts much like epinephrine but has the advantage that it can be given orally as well as by injection. It is a mydriatic drug, stimulates the cardiac muscles, causes a marked rise in blood pressure and in pulmonary pressure. It is an effective dilator of the bronchioles, contracts the uterus, and is a diuretic as well.

Pseudoephedrine is weaker in action on the heart, is more potent diuretic and has no effect on the uterus. The two alkaloids seem equal in their effect on voluntary and involuntary muscles. They are quickly absorbed from the gastrointestinal tract and pass through the liver unchanged.

Cultivation and Harvest

Ephedra plants can be grown from seed, layering or dividing the rootstocks. They thrive best where the rainfall is less than 20 in. annually. The fruits are best gathered by hand, dried, and then the seeds extracted. Seeds are planted in early spring, directly in the field at 2.5 feet spacing and 0.5 in. deep, in rows 2.5 ft. apart.

The seedlings must be watered and kept weed-free during the first year. Harvesting begins when the plants reach four years of age and should take place in autumn, during the blooming season, when the alkaloid content is highest. Throughout the summer rains, alkaloid content declines, then gradually increases until it is double that of springtime.

Traditional forms of harvest used workers wielding hand sickles, cutting all stems that are less than 0.5 in. in diameter. The labor costs, havesting in this manner, make this crop not feasible. However, using a rotory mower, last year's growth is cut in the spring. The new growth can then be taken with a rotory mower in the fall, with a piggy-back trailer for cut material. A shear-cut is prefered (like a lawn mower action) to give a cleaner cut, as Ephedra tends to frey.

The material is then dried in the sun for fifteen days to reduce volumes by 50 to 60%. Drying by artificial heat for three hours at 120°F. has reduced alkaloid content from 1.2 to 0.3%. After drying, the stems are beaten with sticks to break off the joints and then screened to separate the unwanted joints from the internodes. These are then packed in bags or covered containers and stored in a dry atmosphere. Exposure to humidity during storage can result in complete loss of alkaloids.

Marketing

The dried material was formerly exported in bales. China was, until 1925, the only major supplier of Ephedra. India began exporting Ephedra from Baluchistan in 1928. That region is now part of West Pakistan, and that region has now become the leading source of supply for the world with this crop. Spain is only a minor producer.

Because of the variation in alkaloid content of the raw material, it has been found necessary to set up a factory in the major growing areas to process the plants and produce Ephedra Extract. The dry extract, containing 18 to 20% total alkaloids, serves as the source of the pure alkaloids.

In recent years, most of the ephedrine and psuedoephedrine used in the western world has been manufactured synthetically. In the 1950's, the price of synthetic ephedrine rose sufficiently to bring about an increased demand for the natural product, which some pharmaceutical companies still prefer. For one thing, synthetic ephedrine is not optically active. Also the reentry of Chinese Ephedra in the world market has lowered the price of the crude drug.

While there is a tradition of use throughout Europe and Asia for this crop, present-day practice in the United States uses ephedrine, orally or subcutaniously, as a prescription in cases of rhinitis, asthma, hay fever and emphysema. The relief is more enduring than that produced by epinephrine. After three or four days, patients may cease to respond. In such cases, dosage is suspended for a week or so, and then resumed with good effect.

Ephedrine salts in nasal sprays relieve congestion and swelling. Ephedrine is given subcutaneously to prevent hypotension during anesthesia. Orally, it has been used with success in treating certain forms of epilepsy, nocturnal enuresis, myasthenia gravis and urticaria accompanying angioneurotic edema. Psuedoephedrine, taken orally, is an effective nasal decongestant.

Prices for imported Ephedra begin at $0.45 per pound in 2-ton quantities, while 100-pound quantities will sell for more than $1.10 per pound in a C/S. The markets for this crop are extensive and growing. As an alternative cash crop for high-desert, low rainfall regions, it is a perfect choice for consideration.

Native Species

The ten species of <u>Ephedra</u> native to North America are said to contain no useful alkaloids. This has recently been shown to be false. Most native varieties (like Mormon Tea) contain some limited quantities of ephedrine, primarily containing D-norpseuodephedrine and tannin. They both cost the same, however, per pound when purchased from the health food store.

Domestic varieties have been used mainly in folk-medicine decoctions taken primarily as remedies for venereal diseases. Some U.S. companies currently market this crop as a beverage, hence the local names of Desert Tea, Mexican Tea, Mormon Tea and Whorehouse Tea. <u>E. viridis</u>, dried and packaged, is today widely sold by the health food industry as "Squaw Tea," for example. That market requires as much as 50 ton per year as a foraged crop from Utah and New Mexico.

The tannins from domestic species have also been used in tanning sheep skins. The ashes of the burned plant are blended with powdered chewing tobacco, especially in Pakistan.

Preparation

The Chinese technique is to bring a large pan of water to boil. Put one to two ounces of Mormon Tea (or <u>Ephedra</u>) into the boiling water and put a lid on. Allow to boil for 5 minutes, then turn heat down. Three to four cups of the liquid can act as a very powerful stimulant.

If the herb is left on the stove for several days, fermentation occurs. The water is usually brought to a boil at least once each day. After the fourth day, the brew becomes quite strong as a stimulant. Breathing is improved by placing Tiger Balm on the lip under the nose and inhaling the fumes of <u>Ephedra</u>. After five minutes of this, drink three to four cups of the liquid. The resultant increase in energy will be seen to directly relate to the ease in breathing.

If used in excess, there is the possibility of losing elasticity in the blood vessels and bronchial tubes. Also <u>Ephedra</u> can produce vertigo, nervousness, and insomnia with prolonged use. It should not be used if one suffers from high blood pressure, heart disease, diabetes, or thyroid problems.

FIRST STEPS IN DEVELOPING NEW FLORAL MARKETS:

The following outline was created for a student who had grown dried flowers for a local floral shop, and wanted to expand production and marketing:

(1) Complete a sales list of potential buyers. These come from a library of telephone books for major cities in the United States.

(2) Create a brochure of the products she had for sale. This probably should be 4-color photos, with wholesale breakdowns on prices/quantity, including packaging.

(3) Mail the brochure. This creates an updating on your mailing list into 3 main categories: (A-list of preferred customers who buy something, B-list show no response, and C-list who show no interest after 3 mailings).

(4) This means that the B-list wants to eventually become either A- or C-list. If they do not respond with 3 mailings, drop them from the lists.

(5) Ways to compile a B-list is via such resources as Yellow Pages search, researching magazine ads to see who is selling which products, and via buying mailing lists from others.

(6) The Sales Brochure will cost a minimum of $500 for the brochure and first mailing. This should include 200+ mailings and camera work.

(7) The wholesale pricing needs to include packaging costs and shipping alternatives in the Sales Brochure. The photos should reflect the produce grouping, establishing the quantities you wish to sell as a "unit." For example, how should you sell cattails? Or ferns?

(8) On some items you may wish not to include a price. Rather, you could indicate that price quote variations are available upon request.

Once a brochure of products and a valid mailing list have been established, both can be improved with insight and inputs. The key is in organizing your products in a brochure and the development of a growing mailing list of buyers. A series of cottage industries can then emerge where you manufacture your dried florals into arrangements.

BOOK REVIEW

POTPOURRI: A Collection of Potpourri Recipes. Hazel Abernethy. Rosefern Enterprises, Box 204, Marfa, TX 79843. 81pp (Spiral bind), c1983. $8.50 ppd.

This wonderful little text has become a welcomed addition to our library with the increased markets for potpourris. I have watched this market grow in the last four years to more than 400% since 1980. As a market, the field of potpourris is probably the fastest growing of all herb and spice markets today.

The text includes a brief history of this artform, useful for perspective on the current market directions for potpourris. The contents include blends and combinations, procedures, and most important, specific recipes. These include a number of the old recipes, and how to use such ingredients as flowers, herbs and spices, flowering trees and shrubs, and wild flowers.

The reason I like this book is for the descriptions on how to prepare most of these ingrendients for use. While most of this information is available from other sources, the organization makes it more accessable.

It would be nice to have more technical information on blending techniques from a chemistry perspective, but that is not the scope of this book.

As a sourcebook for potential cottage industries, however, this text becomes very useful in getting started. Without meaning to, it gives direction to the small farm on which crops should be considered for these markets. There are even recipes for such "in demand" items as herb pillows and so-called "moist potpourris" and colognes.

WORKSHOPS

Kansas City, MO - November 13, 1986. A one-day Farming Workshop, focusing primarily on marketing. For further information, contact Acres, USA at (816) 737-0064.

Spokane, WA - No date set. A one-day Foraging Workshop, oriented toward commercial production and processing. For further information, contact Leonard Hendrikx of The American Indian Community Center at (509) 535-0886.

Vancouver, B.C. (Canada) - A two day Farming and Foraging Workshop, featuring the herbalist Norma Meyers and marketing expert Richard Miller. For further information, contact Truman Berst at (503) 223-1099 or Norma Meyers (Canada) at (604) 872-7338.

Portland, OR - A two day Farming and Foraging Workshop, same as the Vancouver event. Use same contacts.

Organization for the Advancement of Knowledge

Oak Publishing
1212 SW 5th Street,
Grants Pass, OR 97526
Phone: 541-426-5588

Copyright 1986-2013 © Dr. Richard Alan Miller

Address Correction Requested

Return Postage Guaranteed

BULK RATE
U.S. Postage Paid
Grants Pass, OR
Permit No. 66

Potpourri from Herbal Acres

A quarterly newsletter for $15/year. Information-packed for cottage industries and the home gardener. Pine Row Publications, Box 428-OAK, Washington Crossing, PA   18977

The Herb Market Report   Vol. 2   No. 9

THE HERB MARKET REPORT

for the herb farmer and forager   Vol. 2   No. 10   October, 1986

HMR INTERVIEW:

Masanobu Fukuoka on The Natural Way of Farming

This is the second exclusive interview which "The Herb Market Report" was fortunate in obtaining. This was taken during The 2nd International Permaculture Conference, held August 8-10 at the Evergreen State College, in Olympia.

Masanobu Fukuoka is considered Japan's Master Farmer. His innovative thought, combining philosophy with agriculture, is outlined in his books, including THE ONE STRAW REVOLUTION and THE NATURAL WAY OF FARMING. Fukuoka teaches regenerative agriculture, and is a major inspiration to the permaculture movement.

His technical background includes training as a microbiologist. He worked for years as a plant disease specialist. Then he set about the task of rebuilding his father's farm, thereby evolving his unique method of natural farming. He speaks humbly of himself, but his methods have been embraced widely in the United States, particularly where rice is a major cash crop.

Fukuoka considers farming to be a spiritual path. This becomes quite evident, when like an oriental Buckminster Fuller, he begins scribbling cosmic glyphs on the blackboard and proclaims enigmatic truths. In Fukuoka's worldview, "There is no wide and narrow on the earth; there is no slow and fast in the blue sky."

Fukuoka's "green philosophy" can serve as an inspiration to all of us who feel a deep love for the land. His Zen perspective on farming is best summarized by the following quote:

"Ever since I began proposing a way of farming in step with nature, I have sought to demonstrate the validity of five major principles: no tillage, no fertilizer, no pesticides, no weeding and no pruning. During the many years that have elapsed since, I have never once doubted the possibilities of a natural way of farming that re-

nounces all human knowledge and intervention. To the scientist convinced that nature can be understood and used through human intellect and action, natural farming is a special case and has no universality. Yet the basic principles apply everywhere."

Like many a man-with-a-mission, Fukuoka-san declined an interview with his translator as intermediary. He preferred instead to expound his philosophy from the heart. He weaves together the opposites, relating the pragmatism of the most down-to-earth farmer with the lofty contemplations of a mystic. The sublime beauty of the resulting tapestry is evident in the photos he brings of lands currently being regenerated in Ethiopia and Somalia.

When Fukuoka began his discourse you could sense the sincerity and immediacy of his message. Human attitudes have a tremendous impact on our common environment. He challenges us all to refine our consciousness. Standing at the blackboard in traditional Japanese garb, Fukuoka starts his talk with a calligraphic flourish. Like a martial arts master, he seems to combine serenity with an acute alertness. Beginning from a still center he drew an upwardly-expanding spiral....

FUKUOKA: "Nowdays, everybody in the world is going in the direction of an ever-broadening spiral. Everyone seems to think 'the bigger the better,' 'more is better.' People think they can grow a lot in a large field or a small field. The city culture started from using the scythe, soil, and hammer. That was the beginning of civilization. Now, people think large machines are better. I wonder if that is true! Humanity has made a lot of progress. They climb up the mountains, higher and higher. What do you think is at the end? If the upward spiral reaches the limits of growth, things fall apart at the end. They separate.

"Even with humanity's knowledge, like physiology, science and construction, the trend is toward creating 'experts,' trained specialists with a narrow band of knowledge. [He draws a branching line on the board]. In the beginning it just separated into two things, then it branched out into four things, and eventually to eight things, and so on. This progression is also separation.

"Humanity's progression of development is also separating, just branching out and branching out. The more specialized the knowledge, the more the whole picture is lost, and things start to fall apart. [He draws a balloon]. This is the world of humanity's head. I think humanity's world is like a balloon and it will eventually explode. Knowledge is falling apart. Very few people are trying to prevent this, including hippies and other conscious people.

"In farming or agriculture the center is home farming, the garden or little-site agriculture. The ever-increasing upward spiral is large-scale agribusiness. Against the modern technological agriculture, organic agriculture is starting from the bottom, also permanent agriculture, what we call permaculture. Those movements are trying to go smaller and smaller.

"Big people have big farms and a lot of money, big house, and they think that is a happy life. But there is also another way - living in a small cabin in the mountains with a smaller garden. The things you have in a small house are light and wind, water, fire and earth. These are the basic five elements. Some people think this is O.K., like hippies or Indians or those who have a great spirit in their minds. They think this is fine. But is this also O.K.?

"To me, these two different ways (trying to get bigger or trying to get smaller) are also the same thing. Its all in the world of the head - a headtrip. So say 'protect nature.' Some say the little-sized garden is 'good.' All they are doing is expanding the world of humanity's know-ledge.

"Some people are going really fast; some are acting as brakes to slow them down. Many think large chemical agriculture is destroying nature. Other people, like hippies, are <u>trying</u> to protect nature. Those are the same! It's all their head-trips or intellect. If it stays like this, this world will keep expanding and things will eventually fall apart [entropy].

"In this world, this person and the other person talk, and nothing is said. There's a distance between those who have a western and eastern philosophy. They cannot talk anymore than President Reagan and Gorbachov can talk; that is the same thing. They think they talk about war and peace, but why do you they cannot solve the problems? They have to get back to the center, to our origin or they won't be able to talk, and find out.

"Where can they find the common ground to talk? In order to do that you have to jump off from the world of humanity's knowledge. No thinking! You have to enter from the world of thinking to the world of Nothingness. Outside of the five elements, that is the world of religion.

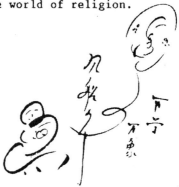

Figure I: Balloon of human knowledge connected to God by 'string' of philosophy.

[He draws a Buddha-like figure in the shape of OM]. "This is the God, right here. The God holds a baby [He draws a baby in God's belly; see Figure I]. The God's baby has a string attached to the balloon (world of intellect or knowledge). God's baby is Christ, Buddha, Lao Tse, or maybe Mohammed. All those babies know the God and human beings.

"The dialog between God and those babies is the religion. Christ and other babies are trying to tell the world of humanity that they are separated by the 'string' of philosophy. The knowledge that humanity has, even of nature, is only nature science.

"As the science of nature expands, the world of the head or knowledge just goes down [relates back to the descending spiral].

It expands and humanity goes down and down, into a confused world. It's not that you know things if you know or understand more. The more you pile up the books, the more you get confused and at that point you are really away from true nature. You just get confused. That is the world of culture or civilization, the world of the head or intellect.

On True Nature:

"Natural farming is not right or left, not more or less, not west or east. The world has not 'big' or 'small,' slowness or fastness. That is the world of true nature. Natural farming starts by catching the true nature. True nature is the world of Truth. You can almost say the world of Truth is the world of God. Everything starts from God; we call this center God.

"I like to think and talk what humanity should do right now! I went to Africa last summer. Eighty years ago Ethiopia and Somalia used to be forest like the State of Washington. During the last 80 years all around this land became a desert. [He pauses to show photos of arid landscapes, and the startling changes wrought by his regenerative program].

"Even though there is a lot of greenery here, in Washington, if things go like this, and we lose 3% of greenery from the earth, we will have an acute oxygen shortage. People will lose their lives. There is no time for biological research or assembling data. There is only one way to turn the desert into True Nature. [He draws an airplane on the blackboard]. Instead of using airplanes to drop bombs, or using the Space Shuttle, I would like people to use those things to sow seeds from the sky. Use your airplanes constructively.

"The large farms of the United States are made from oil. The corn growing there is made from oil [i.e. petrochemicals]. People in the U.S. are destroying 2 ton of soil to grow 1 ton of crops. You have to keep in mind that it is not that you're destroying your own place, but also other countries, like Africa. The hybrid seeds of the u.S. are trying to control the world, but also this is strangling your own neck. This invasion of seeds can be turned around; even the airplane used to drop the bomb can be used for peace.

"Most developed, specialized technology is the least developed technology. Genetic scientists just look at fragments of the plant, the genes. There is no life in just one spot of an entire plant. It is a mis-take that one variety of corn is planted in a large field. To mix everything, like trees, fruit, vegetables, and grains, so everything is growing together, that becomes the Garden of Eden.

"My natural farming has no distinction of trees, leaves, roots. Now scientists just see the leaves and fruit instead of seeing the whole plant, especially the root. The farmer just sees the fruit. Some people just see the rice. That is why the soil is depleted.

"If there is a mountain [there is, as he sketches one out] some people plant on the west, some on the east. Some people plant trees, some grow rice. People try to make this mountain green through different means, but it makes no sense. Some people say there ought to be a forest to enjoy. They try and catch the beauty of nature.

"Some people make a highway and try to climb up by car, so many people can enjoy nature. They say it's not good that one or two hippies only can enjoy nature. Some say the road destroys the cedar trees so it's better to build a rope bridge. Others say helicopters are better. Everyone has ideas on the same theme; to make this mountain green. But if they all try different things, what do you think is going to happen?

"Whether you consider those who try to protect the greenery or those who try to destroy the greenery, everything is destroying it. Knowledge is trying to stay away from nature. The center 9 worlds of the God) is True Nature.

"In their thinking they are trying to go back to that point, but they all go back to the headtrip. They are just catching the false or imitation God. You can't reach Buddha or Christ from the top of a mountain. Everyone is saying it's good to climb up there, but God is even above that! Just around the mountain is the world of intellect. People can learn wht Buddha or Christ said but they cannot see the God. The God doesn't exist in front of you. It's not the nature we are seeing. It's not just above us; the God is behind us.

"In the ancient times many people were in touch with God. They just forgot. They knew when they were babies. Babies have the most wonderful brain. Humanity forgot to see the God when they ate of the fruit of Knowledge. God didn't forget humanity; but humanity forgot God. You just have to remember!

"I'm just a man God was trying to catch fifty years ago. I'm just a man that es-

caped from God. I escaped from God because
it was too much responsibility, so I thought
I'd be just fine as a simple farmer. So I
betrayed the God. So in terms of knowledge
I don't have very much. I'm not even at the
foot of the knowledgeable. But I know foolish I am; I know that I don't know anything!
That's why I didn't say anything for 30
years, then seven years ago when I can to
the United States I started talking to people. I was going to end my life as a small
farmer without saying anything.

Figure II: World of intellect containing opposites.

"Although I wrote a few books, I'm just
writing to let you know that human knowledge
is all useless. Even today's interview, I
know that I can't say anything. It's kind
of sad, but I appeciate everybody's kind-
ness. I feel happy, very sad that I am just
a foolish farmer."

NOTES FROM THE EDITOR

The lack of effective cooperation among
researchers in the biological, physical and
clinical sciences is in part responsible for
the lack of successful development of new
plant drugs in the latter part of the 20th
century. This is also due to unrealistic
Federal regulations hampering research for
new drug research.

"The cost of bringing a new
drug to market has jumped from
about $50 million to more than
$90 million in recent years,"
said Pharmaceutical Manufacturer's Association President Gerald Mossinghoff.

Mossinghoff's rebuttal to Rep. Henry
Waxman's (D-Cal) complaint that prescription
drug prices have risen at more than twice
the inflation rate since 1981, while the
pharmaceutical industry has enjoyed profit
margins nearly triple that of the average
of other manufacturers.

As Duke pointed out in "Herbalgram,"
if it costs $90 million to prove a drug safe
for use in general consumption(FDA), where
would a drug company recoup its investment?
For example, devil's club root might be
shown to be an effective anti-aging drug,
but would not be able to get a patent to
protect its research investments. With this
simplified scenario, there would be no profit protection for a drug company in studying
herbal or natural drugs for market.

In a recent article in Economic Botany
40(3), Dr. Varro Tyler writes a most interesting perspective on "Plant Drugs in the
Twenty-first Century." He suggests that
this problem, along with other inhibiting
factors, will change as health-conscious
consumers demand more accurate information
and a wider availability of natural drug
products.

This is already shown to be true in
Germany, where there is probably more than
400% more natural-source drugs being marketed to the general public. Tyler paints an
optimistic outlook for the U.S.'s future in
these new plant drugs, however. With new,
innovative, and simplified methods of bio-
assay, applied analytical methods, and plant-
cell-culture systems, research andproduction
of new standardized drug plants will be
greatly facilitated via lower costs.

You may order Masanobu Fukuoka's books of
ONE STRAW REVOLUTION and THE NATURAL WAY OF
FARMING directly from Rodale Press, Inc.,
Emmaus, PA 18049.

WILDFLOWER SEED PRODUCTION AS A CASH CROP

Growing wildflowers for seed, promoted several years ago as an alternative cash crop, has developed into a full-scale industry for the United States. Of the more than 2,000 acres of flowers grown in Oregon, for example, more than 95% of that was wildflowers.

Flower seed production is a very specialized business requiring a high degree of management, some specialized equipment, and favorable soil and climatic conditions. While the primary industry is centered in California, commercial seed companies are interested in finding alternative production areas because of changing land use patterns.

Relatively small acreages are involved in growing many of the flower species, and nearly all are grown under a commercial seed company contract. In Oregon, fields under contract include bachelor button, corn poppies, baby blue eyes and several dozen other wildflowers. It's like a brushstroke of color on the landscapes throughout the Willamette Valley in Oregon.

The risks are high, but so are the rewards. Some seed has sold for as much as $12 per pound for hard-to-grow varieties that require a lot of care and weeding by hand. A more average price, according to the larger seed companies, run from $2 to $5 per pound. Of course, there are alternative marketing resources for those who would like to receive larger cash-yields for their efforts.

Growers should contract with 6 to 8 different seed companies when approaching these cash crops. The returns will vary with the kind of flower and yields, but on the average a grower can expect to gross more than $1,200 per acre. Expenses can often be high because of the special pains taken to cultivate and harvest these seed.

Cultural Methods

Probably about 20 thousand species of trees, shrubs, and herbaceous (nonwoody) plants in the United States are classified as wild. About 15 percent are well-established species that came from other countries or escaped from cultivation. Most of them are herbaceous.

A good number of them have leaves and flowers so attractive that many persons want to grow them in home gardens, along roadsides, and in other suitable places. You should seed field plots of 2 acres each for a three-year period to assess their seed production potentials and general adaptabilities to your area and to identify and study some problems that would be associated with commercial seed production.

Seedbeds can be prepared by plowing, disking, spring-toothing, and harrowing. Fertilizers should be broadcast during seedbed preparation in the amounts of 80 to 100 pounds of nitrogen, 60 to 80 pounds of phosphate (P_2O_5), 60 to 80 pounds of potash (K_2O), and 40 to 60 pounds of sulfur per acre. An additional 40 to 60 pounds of nitrogen might also be added during the growing season for some of the larger, long-season flower species.

Herbicides can be applied to individual crops that have been labeled for use with those forms of control. This should be done from studies based on each flower specie's tolerance as determined in previous greenhouse tests and published literature. Cultivation and a certain amount of handweeding will probably be required, especially in those flower species not using pre-plant, pre-emergence, and post-emergence herbicides.

Most wildflower seed will want to be treated with thirma (Arasan 75) dry fungicide or equivalant compound, and seeded with something like a Planet Jr. seeder (for small acreages). The row spacing should be 20 inches with row width to correspond to available cultivation equipment.

Stands of some of the larger flower species should usually be blocked or thinned to allow sufficient space among plants for optimum development of seed heads. Normally, one to three plants are left in clusters separated by a space of five to six inches in the row.

Overhead irrigation systems can be used to supply water, although furrow irrigation is often preferred. The sprinkler systems do not seem to cause excessive lodging of seed loss, or to be a contributing factor in foliar disease.

Honeybees should be provided for pollination. Bumblebees, other wild bees (Halictus sp.), certain moths, and hummingbirds are usually also present as pollinating agents.

Insect pests are usually not present in large numbers. Often one pound of Dylox per acre will provide effective control of such pests as lygus bugs. Powdery mildew will often be a problem with such crops as zinnias. To control it, dusting sulfur at the rate of 30 pounds per acre in late August is used in Oregon.

Such crops as dahlia, larkspur, snapdragons, and stock are often affected by root rots. This can be eliminated by cutting back on frequent irrigation practices.

Harvest Methods

Seed losses from shattering (seeds falling to the ground) is generally the main problem with many flower species as they mature. Wind and rain near maturity, handling during swathing or during elevation of swathed material into the threshing unit, and seed pods opening during drying in the swath are also major problems contributing to losses.

Many growers attempt to use as many different techniques to efficiently harvest seed as they can. One field of poppies in Oregon gets sprayed by an airplane with paraquat, a defolliant that destroys the body of the plant but leaves intact the thousands of poppy seeds inside each of their protective shells.

Some wildflowers are sprayed with a sticky, adhesive material until they are ready to harvest. This keeps the seed pods from shattering and losing their precious cash crop.

Other farmers have resorted to an expensive, but very effective, method of laying down wide sheets of butcher paper on the ground to catch the seed. The cost usually run up to $150 per acre for the paper alone.

The seeds are then allowed to dry on the paper for up to a week, and are then retrieved. The paper is then plowed into the ground. This technique can often triple a grower's yield. A 40-inch-wide plot-type combine is used to thresh the seed, either as a stationary machine for plant materials on tarps, or as a combine for those flower species that should be direct-harvested.

Commercial swathers are sometimes equipped to lay the plant material on a 48-inch or wider strip of paper that is unrolled behind the cutter bar. When the material on the paper has dried, a combine harvester separates the seed from stems, leaves, chaff, and paper.

Seeds mostly can be collected about a month after the flowering. The seeds of most wildflowes vary so much in size, you may need more than three sieves to separate the various sizes. Often seeds in the smallest sieve may be immature and give a less germination than is allowed by the contract for sale.

The Forage of Wildflower Seed

When foraging in the wild for your seed stocks, you should not overlook those seed with fleshy coverings. The covering can be removed by soaking the seed in warm water for 10 to 15 minutes. Then the seeds are placed in a sieve with a mesh smaller than the seeds. The coating is scrubbed off with a stiff-bristled or wire brush.

A few species, particularly annuals or biennials (like the daisy-fleabane and fringed gentain), may germinate and develop leaf rosettes in the fall.

Seeds of wildflowers in most temperate regions require one winter in the ground before germination. If they do not get the right conditions of moisture and temperature to germinate the following spring, they must go dormant and not germinate until conditions are right - maybe in another year or two!

Some wildflowers are difficult to establish if the roots are disturbed in transplanting. The seeds of such species should be planted in a small, tough fiber paper pot. This should be placed in the ground in the spring when the seedlings are 3 to 4 inches tall or long. Be sure to "harden" the plant outside before transplanting.

Some wildflowers have a marked preference for soils that are loamy or sandy, dry to damp or wet, acid to alkaline, and open to dense woodland conditions.

The following is a list of some of the more popular and attractive wildflowers:

Northeastern Region

Meadow anemone (Anemone canadensis)
Wild columbine (Aquilegia canadensis)
Butterfly-weed (Asclepias tuberosa)
Marshmarigold (Caltha palustris)
Dwarf-cornel (Cornus canadensis)
Pink ladyslipper (Cypripedium acaule)
Trailing-arbutus (Epigaea repens)
Trout-lily (Erythronium americanum)
Wintergreen (Gaultheria procumbens)
Closed gentain (Gentaina andrewsii)
Fringed gentain (Gentaina crinita)
Wild geranium (Geranium maculatum)
Beach pea (Lathyrus maritimus)
Tigerlily (Lilium superbum)
Cardinal flower (Lobelia cardinalis)
Oswego tea (Monarda didyma)
Rosebay (Rhododendron maximum)
Golden ragwort (Senecio aureus)
Trillium (Trillium grandiflorum)
Blue violet (Viola papilionacea)
Birdsfoot violet (Viola pedata)

Southeastern Region

Yellow jassamine (Gelsemium sempervirens)
Purple gerardia (Geranrdia purpurea)
Puccoon (Lithospermum canescens)
Passionflower (Passiflora incarnata)
Scorpionweed (Phacelia bipinnatifida)
Meadowbeauty (Rhexia mariana)
Firepink (Silene virginica)
Goatsrue (Tephrosia virginiana)
Aarons-rod (Thermopsis caroliniana)

Plains Region

Sandverbena (Abronia fragrans)
Pasqueflower (Anemone pulsatilla)
Poppy-mallow (Callirhoe involucrata)
Indian paintbruch (Castilleja sp.)
Purple cactus (Coryphantha vivipara)
Plains-gentain (Eustoma russelliana)
Bindweed-heliotrope (Euploca sp.)
Bluebonnet (Lupinus texensis)
Blazing-star (Mentzelia decapetala)
Wild four-o'clock (Mirabilis nyctaginea)
Evening-primrose (Oenothera lacinata)
Pricklypear (Opuntia polyacantha)
Beardtongue (Penstemon grandaflorus)
Texas-sage (Salvia coccinea)

Rocky Mountain Region

Sego-lily (Calochortus nuttallii)
Sulfurflower (Eriogonum umbellatum)
Skyrocket (Gilia aggregata)
Panicled bluebell (Mertensia paniculata)
Locoweed (Oxytropis lamberti)
Shrubby cinquefoil (Potentilla fruticosa)
Spiderwort (Tradescantia scopulorum)
Globe-flower (Trollius laxus)

Southwestern Region

Century-plant (Agave americana)
Pricklypoppy (Argemone mexicana)
Barrel cactus (Ferocactus wislizeni)
Blanketflower (Gaillardia pulchella)
Gaura (Gaura parviflora)
Pincushion cactus (Mammillaria sp.)
Fishhook cactus (Thelocactus uncinatus)
Spanish-bayonet (Yucca baccata)

Pacific Region

Firecracker plant (Brodiacea ida-maia)
Tall clarkia (Clarkia pulchella)
Springbeauty (Claytonia linearis)
Chinese-house (Collinsia bicolor)
Wallflower (Erysimum asperum)
California-poppy (Eschscholtzia sp.)
Summer's-darling (Godetia amoena)
Baby-blue-eyes (Nemophila insignis)
Owlclover (Orthocarpus purpurascens)
Prostrate verbena (Verbena prostrata)

HERB FARMING & FORAGING TAPES by Richard Alan Miller

BOOK REVIEW

Economic Botany, a Journal published for The Society for Economic Botany by The New York Botanical Gardens, Bronx, NY 10458. $40.00 per year/quarterly.

This is one of my most prized scholarly journals on herb and spice research. It is published for The Society for Economic Botany, a group of individuals who are making these alternative cash crops feasible, from a marketing perspective alone (ie. application and use).

Now in its 40th year, this quarterly publication contains technical papers on current research in ethnobotany, oil crops, and medicinal plants. It's second title to Economic Botany is "Devoted to Past, Present, and Future Uses of Plants by Man." The emphasis of the articles and papers are on the uses of plants

If I had to recommend only one scientific journal, this is it. The New York Botanical Gardens (publisher) is also worth following as far as activities. In June, for example, they held the 27th Annual Meeting of the Society. This was an event

as symposiums are concerned. I even contributed a paper on the potential of herbs as a cash crop.

Membership in the Society for Economic Botany is open to all individuals. Regular membership is only $20.00 per year (includes subscription to Economic Botany). This is obviously a better deal than simply subscribing to the journal by itself. For further information on the society, write Dr. Edward M. Croom Jr., Research Institute for Pharmaceutical Sciences, University of Mississippi, University, MS 38677.

WORKSHOPS

Kansas City, MO - November 13, 1986. A one-day Farming Workshop, focusing primarily on marketing. For further information, contact Acres, USA at (816) 737-0064.

Spokane, WA - No date set. A one-day Foraging Workshop, oriented toward commercial production and processing. For further information, contact Leonard Hendrikx of The American Indian Community Center at (509) 535-0886.

Vancouver, B.C. (Canada) - A two day Farming and Foraging Workshop, featuring the herbalist Norma Meyers and marketing expert Richard Miller. For further information, contact Truman Berst at (503) 223-1099 or Norma Meyers (Canada) at (604) 872-7338.

Portland, OR - A two day Farming and Foraging Workshop, same as the Vancouver event. Use same contacts.

Organization for the Advancement of Knowledge

Oak Publishing
1212 SW 5th Street,
Grants Pass, OR 97526
Phone: 541-426-5588

Copyright 1986-2013 © Dr. Richard Alan Miller

Address Correction Requested

Return Postage Guaranteed

BULK RATE
U.S. Postage Paid
Grants Pass, OR
Permit No. 66

The Herb Market Report   Vol. 2 No. 10

Re-subscribe

THE HERB MARKET REPORT

for the herb farmer and forager   Vol. 2   No. 11   November, 1986

BOTANICALS IN COSMETICS

Many of the crops discussed previously in this newsletter were oriented primarily toward the food and drug markets. There is another market which is fast becoming significant enough to also be considered when choosing alternative crops for the small farm.

Cosmetics and toilertries containing botanicals, often referred to by the consumer as "natural," "organic," and "herbal," are now attracting a growing number of the larger cosmetic industries to use these "new" ingredients. It is seen as a means to spark new life into sagging sales of cosmetics and toiletries over the last several years.

Botanicals have been used for medicinal and cosmetic ingredients since ancient times, however. For thousands of years, man has applied fruits, vegetables and herbs directly to the skin for a multitude of purposes. Honey and barley was used to soften skin, while oils and milk were use in Egyptian times to soothe and beautify.

In the South Seas, papaya was made into a popular cream, while henna (now again quite popular) was also used in ancient Egypt as a hair dye and nail polish. Our customs seem to cycle in the uses of certain botanicals, certainly.

The list of herbs, flowers and fruits that are often suggested in homemade concoctions is endless: Chamomile, rose oil, lavender, mint, rosemary, thyme, cucumber, apricot, pear, sesame oil, lemon, comfrey, and even aloe vera.

Most of these products, in recent years, come from smaller companies, appealing to the same demographics as that of the health foods. While these products have been sold primarily through specialty stores, the new trend is toward mass-market channels. The addition of aloe vera extract into the ingredients of such established brands as Jergens and Pacquin indicates the growing interest among all consumers in the U.S.

The three largest selling botanicals in the cosmetic industry today are unquestionably alow vera, jojoba and henna. However, other plant names are not only appearing in ingredient listings, but are being highlighted in advertising for their beneficial qualities.

The recent trend began back as far as the early 1970s, waning somewhat* and is now resuming with an even stronger following. Ten years ago, when the use of botanicals first became a factor in marketing, there was some initial concern among the larger producers that the "naturals" might become a threat to overall sales.

The philosophy of the cosmetic giants at that time was that these were simply another way to offer the user a method to achieve the same basic results achieved with chemically prepared ingredients. The unreliability of the botanical supplier had serious drawbacks to the larger manufacturer.

Pasqueflower
Anemone patens

Many in this industry also felt that sales could be minimal because they were dependent on the whims of a small "cultist" society that was not interested in anything

---

* Many botanical marketers see this waning as the time some of the larger tea manufacturers changed their formulas as a cost-reduction measure. This resulted in teas which the consumer quickly lost interest.

manufactured. The movement then was that only goods made with ingredients that came from the earth should be used, not from the laboratory.

Today, most consumers now realize that even products heavily relying on natural herbs must often include some chemicals as preservatives for adequate shelf life. If you don't believe this, look at the labels on the products currently in your bathroom. While purism is still an important issue, it is not the trend for the mass markets.

The one large company that can be attributed with the expansion of general interest in herbals in a big way at the time was Clairol (with their Herbal Essence shampoo). With this success, Gillette Company then followed with a hair care line under the name Earth Born.

Other companies chose to incorporate certain botanicals in their fragance lines strictly for scent, rather than using them in cosmetics and toilertry products. It should be remembered that at the time, Clairol was very careful not to highlight and specific herb. This, of course, has radically changed in recent years.

Some Definitions

Phytognosy is a term formed from two Greek words: "phyto" means plant and "gnosis" means knowledge. Cosmetic phytognosy is thus defined as a branch of cosmetic science dealing with the biochemical and physicochemical properties of plant-derived ingredients for use in cosmetics.

This also indicates that phytognosy is a study of cosmetic functions which have their origins in the plant kingdom. Pharmacognosy, on the other hand, is the highly specialized branch of pharmaceutical sciences dealing with both plant and animal-derived drugs.

Although cosmetic science is generally regarded as a discipline separate and distinct from pharmaceuticals, phytognosy does share some of the conceptual principles of pharmacognosy. For example, whereas some of the functional attributes of certain phyto ingredients have their roots in botanical folklore, phytognostic cosmetics are based upon plant-derived ingredients with efficacy established scientifically.

Recent renewed interest in the so-called natural foods, drugs and cosmetics has stimulated the public to learn more about the functional attributes of these botanical wonderments. As a result, a vast literature on natural materials and natural cosmetics has been written by consumers for the purpose of informing other consumers.

In these writings, beliefs, opinions, and testimonials may often be substituted for proven scientific facts. It is therefore important to place the science of cosmetic phytognosy in proper perspective and to differentiate it from the compounding of herbal forklore - usually not based upon scientific evidence.

Classifications

The vast majority of botanical ingredients for use in cosmetic phytognosy may be classified into one of six different chemical categories. They are 1) carbohydrates, 2) glycosides and tannins, 3) lipids, 4) volatile oils, 5) steroids, and 6) vegetable-derived phosphatides.

Carbohydrates may be classified into two broad groups: sugars and polysaccharides. Sugars and sugar-containing phyto ingredients may be function as demulcents for use in cosmetic phytognosy. Being metabolically related to sugars, certain plant-derived acids (ie. citric and lactic) find application as nontoxic acidulants or buffer system components to control acidity.

Strach is probably one of the most widely distributed organic compounds in the plant kingdom and is an example of a polysaccharide with unique "slip" when rubbed on the skin.

Gums are natural plant hydrocolloids which are produced in higher plants. They may be classified as polysaccharide type materials and are usually heterogeneous in composition. Gums find diverse applications in cosmetic phytognosy and may function as emulsifiers, gelating agents, skin-feel modifiers, suspending agents, thickener and stabilizers.

As examples, skin-feel modifiers include corn and starch, while gums come from trees (acacia), marine products (kelps), and seeds (guar and locust bean). Numerous plant extracts contain pectins, used as a thickening agent and stabilizer.

Glycosides and tannins are complex substances that are widely distributed in plants. Glycosides are compounds which include constituents with known therapeutic value. They are regarded as substances which yield one or more sugars upon hydrolysis.

The fresh mucilaginous juice of the aloe vera leaf (Aloe barbadensis Miller) contains a variety of ingredients, including a number of anthraquinone glycosides. The principal one, barbaloin, has known cathartic properties.

Used for centuries in the treatment of burns, abrasions and skin irritations, the gel of the aloe vera plant would, of course, have immediate utility in cosmetic phytognosy. The problem then arises as to defining the active ingredient. The leading school of thought is that there is no key active substance but rather a synergistic combination of different comstituents.

Glycyrrhiza (licorice root) contains a saponin-like glycoside, glycyrrhizin. Upon hydrolysis, the glycoside is converted to glycyrrhetic acid (plus two molecules of glucuronic acid). This root is considered useful because of its demulcent properties and glycyrrhetic acid has been shown to have anti-inflammatory properties.

Tannin-containing plant materials with relevance to cosmetic phytognosy include witch hazel leaf. Infusion or decoction of the leaf is known to yield hamamelitannin, a constituent with useful astringent properties.

Lipids are a rather diverse group of substances, the simpler of which have functional importance in cosmeti phytognosy. They are primarily esters of long-chain fatty acids and alcohols (or closely related derivities). Fixed oils and fats (as well as waxes) belong to this phytognostic ingredient category.

Olive oil and peanut oil are phyto sources for fats and fixed oils, often separated from the crude vegetable source by hydraulic pressure.

Seeds generally contain larger quantities of fats and oil than the other parts of the plant. In the case of the castor bean, 45-55% of the seed composition is a fixed oil (castor oil). Like other natural vegetable oils, castor oil contains a mixture of triglycerides. In general, when applied to the skin, the vegetable oils are easily absorbed and show excellent spreadability.

Fats differ from fixed oils only with regard to melting point. Fats are semisolid or solid at room temperature, whereas the glycerides of fatty acid fixed oils tend to be liquids.

Waxes may be defined as esters of high molecular weight fatty acids and fatty alcohols of the straight chain variety. Jojoba oil is a typical vegetable wax, now used as a skin-feel lubricant, emollient, and hair conditioning agent.

Jojoba oil may be regarded as a liquid wax containing linear esters of unsaturated long-chain fatty acids and alcohols. Unlike other waxes, jojoba oil is a liquid which is readily absorbed into the skin. It also appears to be compatible with the skin's natural lubrication chemistry and is highly resistant to rancidity and degradation at elevated temperatures.

Volatile Oils include odorous principles which are found in various parts of plants. Also called essential oils, these are the odoriferopus "essences" of plants. In the simplest sense, the function of volatile oils in cosmetic phytognosy is one of fragrance. Certain types of volatile oils are also known to have antiseptic, disinfectant and deodorant properties.

The types of constituents found in volatile oils are quite numerous and diverse. This presents some difficulties in the assignment of a chemical classification relavant to cosmetic phytognosy. One approach is to classify them with respect to the presence of significant general organic groupings: hydrocarbons, alcohols, aldehydes, ketones, phenolds, and esters.

As examples of each: Pine tree (hydrocarbon) is used as a counterirritant; rose oil (alcohol) is a fragrance; lemon grass (aldehyde) is an insect repellant; wormwood (ketone) is a counterirritant; thyme oil (phenol) is an antiseptic; and lavender oil (ester) is a fragrance.

Steroids are a class of natural products which include phytosterols (plant-derived sterols). Soybean oil distillates are a rich source of these sterols. These materials have been shown to have useful properties in the formulation of phytocosmetic emulsions. Examples of soy sterols are Sitosterol, Campersterol and Stigmasterol.

Vegetable-derived Phosphatides is the last general chemical grouping with cosmetic phytognosy significance. Vegilecithin is a term now used to describe vegetable-derived lecithin. Commercial soybean lecithin is a mixture of phosphatides with useful emollient and surface-active properties.

The hydroscopic characteristics of lecithin give it a humectant aspect which has led some manufacturers to use it as a moisturizer. Natural soybean lecithin also contains up to 20% phosphatidyl choline.

Ingredients

There are basically six different plant-derived ingredient forms for use in the cosmetic industry: 1) fresh plants, 2) dried phyto materials, 3) acellular products, 4) galenical preparations, 5) processed extracts, and 6) pure compounds.

Fresh plant materials are primarily used in cosmetic folklore preparations, and do not as a rule serve an important role in cosmetic phtognosy. The exception is in the perfume industry, where volatile oils from fresh materials (such as flower petals) are preferred for their "natural" essences.

Phyto materials obtained from tropical regions are usually sun-dried. Oven-drying may degradate or ruin color for such crops as flowers and leaves. Air-drying works best for automation, without the use of heat. If the active constituents are liberated by enzymatic processes, slow drying may be more appropriate.

Gums and fixed oils are considered as a form of acellular phyto products. They are derived from appropriate botanical sources by such physical processes as expression, steam distillation, or cold extraction (ie. "enfleurage").

Galenical preparations are defined as extracts from plant materials. These techniques include infusion, decoction, maceration, percolation, and continuous hot extraction.

Processed extracts are extracts which have been standardized in such a manner that the concentrations of the active principles are known. This is thus an intermediate stage between a simple extract and a pure compound.

The following discussion on cosmetic phytognosy was given for a broader definition on plant chemistry and their various groupings. With chemical background on the plant, often this information will help direct the small farmer toward better marketing options. How about balsam (soap) root?

NEWS RELEASE

Procter & Gamble is launching a new canola-based salad and cooking oil. The canola (rapeseed) beans used are low in e-rucic acid (thought to be associated with heart muscle problems), and contains about half the saturated fats of conventional cooking oils.

Although canola is one of the most popular crops grown worldwide, U.S. farmers have not grown much, because until now there was only a minor domestic market. With the introduction of this new oil, that is no longer the case, and rapeseed may become a major alternative cash crop.

Kraft made the right move at the right time when it bought Celestial Seasonings for an estimated $50 million two years ago. Sales of herb teas, now more than $90 million a year, are growing at a rate of more than 10 percent annually. Celestial Seasonings now represents about one half that market.

It should be remembered that more than 80 percent of the ingredients used are currently imported from Europe and Asia. More than 50 percent of these could be cultivated domestically by small farmers in the U.S.

The leading tea ingredient flavorings include chamomile, peppermint, comfrey, alfalfa, red clover flowers, and spearmint. All of these are now being grown to a limited extent by small farms as feasibility studies for eventual expansion. The key seems to be toward new flavor combinations not yet available in the marketplace.

NOTES FROM THE EDITOR

Please excuse the delay in getting this newsletter out. I have been traveling the last two months, and have not yet begun to catch up on the various correspondences and reports requested by the growing number of new farmers in this field.

For those living in the Midwest: There is a world shortage for burdock root now. This noxious weed likes to intercrop with corn, and can be easily harvested before the snows. If you would like further information, please call or write OAK offices. We have numerous buyers requesting domestic sources for 1987.

- continued on page 7 -

HOW TO GROW PLANTS WITHOUT A GREENHOUSE

by John and Martha Vaughn*

With thousands and thousands of farmers going bankrupt and most of agriculture in general in a deep Depression, we decided to write this booklet.

We know that the majority of farmers are looking for a cash crop to help their cash flow until there is a turn around in corn, beans, wheat, and livestock prices. This method of starting plants and transplants that we have outlined is the best known and has been used for over 200 years and is still in use in twenty or more States today.

Most all kinds of plants can be started and grown by the Bed method such as vegetables, herbs and spices, flowers, tobacco, strawberry, huckleberry, etc.

Plants are already conditioned for outside temperatures and are ready to transplant in the field by planting time. Here in northwest Missouri we usually start in May.

If you are raising transplants to sell to other growers such as vegetables or flowers and bedding plants, this is an excellent source to quick income. We hope this information will help your family to survive these troubled times in agriculture.

Site Selection

Site selection is important. Avoid wet areas. Choose a south slope if possible, nearly level ground with some slope or drainage is OK if there is some wind protection on the North and West. Full sun is a must. Use good soil like you were selecting a garden site.

Soil needs good drainage and tilth. Adding organic matter, compost, seaweed, grass clippings, plowing under a green manure crop are all excellent ways to improve the soil.

Beds must be kept moist so if your site is close to a water source such as a pond, spring, stream or water line it will save some work time.

If you have been using heavy applications of Herbicides on areas near or may have run off on your site, be cautious.

Preparing the Seed Bed

Now that you have selected the site you are ready to prepare the soil. Number one do a toxicity test. If your soil is laced with pesticides select a different site. Next is a good soil test, not just NPK, get the traces too. Be sure and test for pH soil and your water supply also, you should continue to test water pH as long as you are watering your plant beds and in your transplanters where you set our your plants. Many plants have been ruined by bad water pH and toxic material. These are all precautions to save you time and money.

The common practice of preparing soil is plow, disc, harrow. This is fine. If you don't have these tools but have a good tiller, the tiller will do a good job by itself.

Don't run out and buy anything you don't need. Many seed beds have been made with nothing more than a spade and garden rake.

Your soil should be worked from six to eight inches deep. If you are low on organic matter, work some in as you go about preparing the seed bed. Your bed should be worked as fine and smooth as possible.

Your prepared be should be 15ft x 105ft. This gives you some lea way if you are out of square as the sheets are square.

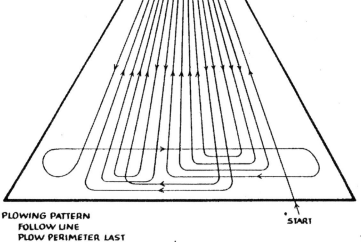

PLOWING PATTERN
FOLLOW LINE
PLOW PERIMETER LAST

START

* John and Martha Vaughn took an ACRES workshop on herb/spice farming two years ago and now market some of their crop through a coop formed in their region. They can be reached by sending an SASE to R. 1, Box 161, Dearborn, MO 64439.

Materials for Making Beds

Standard seed bed size is 12ft x 100ft. They will produce plants for one to six acres depending on the variety of plants and the amount of plants required per acre.

Numer one is a gas sheet 12ft x 100ft.

Number two is gas for weed control, used just before planting of seed. Twelve cans per bed required. This control, properly used, will save you at least one hundred hours of hard weeding which is hard work.

Before this method was used, farmers would prepare the bed, then pile hugh brush piles over it and burn. The heat would kill the weed seeds near the top and some times give good control.

I suppose in some areas of growers this is still practiced. I haven't seen it for thirty years or so.

Number three is your cotton or remay that is used to cover the bed after it is seeded. Standard size 12ft x 100ft.

Number four is a spool 250ft long of small wire, like electric fence wire. This goes down both sides of the bed and across each end.

Your cotton is fastened to this usually with a hog ringer and hog rings, this is the quickest.

You need four strong wood stakes about 2ft long for each corner of the bed and fifty small stakes about one inch size to stake the sides and ends. This will keep the cotton above the bed. After you have your cotton on the bed you may cut any stakes off that are above the sheet.

Number five is medium for mixing with the seed so as to be able to seed evenly over the entire seed bed. We like to use a bag of pulverized limestone and a bag of mill organite. Mix these two together in a large tub.

Next add your seed and mix and mix some more. Do a good job on this.

Number six is an 18 inch to 24 inch lawn fertilizer spreader, the 2-wheeled kind that you pull. You set the flow so as the two bags of medium with seed for one bed will cover the entire seed area. You need to test this flow amount by mixing an extra bag of each medium without seed in it and make a test run the length of your bed one time.

Then weight or measure what it took for one run. If the spreader was a 24 inch model and you used 1/6 of your medium, you have it set right. We like to use 1/12

of the medium then spread it twice. We think we get it more uniform.

Number seven is your seed. Many of the herb seed are tiny, running 500,000 seeds or more per oz. This is why you have to use a good medium to mix the seed it. Be sure and know your seed count per oz. so as to know how many seeds are needed per acre of plants.

Number eight is your weed control gas. Tubes for applying the gas under the gas sheet. We like to use 12 tubes, some people get by on less. In addition to the tubes, you need an adaptor for hooking up the gas cans.

Making the Bed

Now that you have the bed prepared and you have your materials on hand, you are ready to start.

Your bed can be made anywhere from early August up to seeding time for spring planting. We make ours in the fall whenever the soil is workable and moist. If it is too dry, sprinkle it down so you have enough moisture. Some years we are too busy in the fall and we have made beds in Feb. and March.

To lay out your bed, drive two stakes 12 ft apart on one end of bed. Measure 100 ft to the other end and drive two more stakes 12 ft apart. To check if the four stakes make a true rectangle, measure across opposite corners. If the distance is equal it is square, if not adjust your last two stakes till you have the same measurements.

Run a string around the four stakes for a guide to dig a trench 10 or 12 inches wide and 8 inches deep. Keep straight by following the string line.

Spread your gas sheet over the bed, lay the edges in the trench and cover plastic in trench with the dirt from the trench you dug. Fill level with bed. Tighten sheet as you fill. When your trench is full, walk around it and tromp down. This holds it all winter till seeding time.

If you don't make your bed till seeding time, do it the same way. At seed planting time we check for any holes that may be in the gas sheet. If you have any you may use duct tape to repair. You can't have any leaks, be sure to look good.

Seeding Time of Beds

After checking the gas sheet for any holes and leaks, you are ready to gas the bed.

Dig holes or tunnels under the edge of the gas sheet for the gas tubes. You need to space 5 on each side of the bed evenly.

Put one hole under each end in the middle for the end gas tubes. You now have twelve tubes stuck under your gas sheet.

Leave about a third of the length of the tube on the outside of the bed for connecting to the adaptor. Form dirt around tube, pack down gas tight and you are now ready to apply gas. Be sure you can blow air through tubes.

Check all twelve tubes and place a piece of tape over end of eleven tubes. Connect the adaptor to number twelve, put can of gas in adaptor and release gas. When can is empty, remove adaptor. Place piece of tape over end of tube. Go on to the next tubes and so on till you have used twelve cans.

Leave gas under sheet two days or till you are ready to seed. When you are ready to seed, remove gas sheet in the morning and air out bed for four or five hours. This will aerate and remove any excess moisture that may condense under the sheet.

You may want to rake the bed lightly with a garden rake. Mix your medium and seed, put in spreader and apply. Rake lightly after seeding and put on your cotton sheet. Be sure to stretch snug.

If you have an insect problem, it is necessary to remove the sheet to apply your insect control.

Watch you beds closely for moisture, insects, and weeds. Your gas should give good control on weeds, but some times there are some tough ones that get by. We use a long plank, like a 2 x 2, that will reach across the bed to sit on when weeding. This plank needs to be set on blocks or something to raise above plants by about one foot.

When plants are ready to set in field, we like to remove the cotton during the middle of the day for a few days to temper the plants. The day you pull plants, water the bed early in the morning so the ground is soft for pulling.

Let the plants dry off for an hour or so and you are ready to pull. Place your plants on damp burlap bags till you can barely roll the sack around the plants. Pin with 16-penny nails for easy handling. Place in the shade to keep moist and cool. Don't pull more plants than you can set that day.

After pulling each day, recover the bed.

Your total cost for supplies of making one twelve by 100 ft bed will be under $135, not counting your seed cost, which will vary.

We raise enough plants per bed to set from 2 to as man· as 7 acres. However, we always make extra beds.

You may want to plant some garden crops under the edge of your bed, such as radishes, spinach and lettuce. Lettuce still stay tender under cotton until July here in the N.W. Missouri.

Sources of Supplies and Seeds

Phonix Farm & Garden Supply Co.,
311 West 72nd St.,
Kansas City, MO   64114
  Earth-Rite "C"
  Jersey Green Sand
  Soft Phosphate
  Bone Meal
  Nitro 10
  Kelp Meal
  Maxicrop
  Diatomaceous Earth
  Garden Dust
  Fish Emulsion

Necessary Trading Co.,
New Castle, VA   24127
  Rotenone - Pyrethrin
  B.T.
  Red Devil Dust

Bio-Organic Labs,
R#1   Box 161,
Dearborn, MO   64439
  Gas, Gas Sheet, Cotton, Mill
     Organite, Pulverized Limestone
  Gas Tubes and adaptor for seed beds
  Bio-Plus products
  Pyrethrin Dust
  Blood Meal
  Granite Dust
  Nicotine extract

- continued from page 4 -

For those living on the West Coast:
Cascara buying stations should begin to form now. There were some shortages this last year and several German buyers would like to develop contracts fro 1987 crops at this time.

I will be quite busy in February: The Spokane Indians and Washington State University would like me to make a 1-day presentation on processing and automation-harvesting techniques. The event is planned February 19-22 in Spokane. For further information, contact Raymond Rayes at (509) 535-0886. The emphasis is on foraging.

I will also be speaking several days at the AERO (Alternative Energy Resource Organization) Conference held at Montana State University in Bozeman on February 5-7. This could be one of the more important conferences held this year, I'm excited to meet some of the other speakers. For further information, contact Nancy Matheson at (406)-442-7158.

BOOK REVIEW

HERBS, SPICES AND MEDICINAL PLANTS: Recent Advances in Botany, Horticulture, and Pharmacology - Volume 1, edited by L. Craker and J. Simon. Oryx Press, 2214 North Central at Encanto, Phoenix, AZ 85004. c1986. 359pp. $ 65.00

The continual search for and growing interest in natural plant products for use in the flavor and medicinal industries has created an ever-increasing demand for recent and accurate information on plant culture and pharmacology.

To supply readers with original information that review and summarize the most recent scientific literature on this topic, The Oryx Press has recently published Volume 1 of HERBS, SPICES, AND MEDICINAL PLANTS.

Edited by Lyle Craker and James Simon, this new book is the first in a series of annual volumes developed to explore various aspects of the botany, horticulture, and pharmacology of herbs, spices and medicinal plants.

The first volume covers eight subject areas. Written by prominent experts from around the world, the work includes such topics as botanical nomenclature of culinary herbs and potherbs, biochemical pharmacology of plant alkaloids, and production ecology of secondary plant products.

The book's usefulness is enhanced by numerous charts and detailed illustrations. Each chapter concludes with an extensive list of additional references. While this text is technically oriented, it is an essential resource when considering alternative crops such as herbs, spices and medisional plants.

Organization for the Advancement of Knowledge

Oak Publishing
1212 SW 5th Street,
Grants Pass, OR 97526
Phone: 541-426-5588

The Herb Market Report   Vol. 2 No. 11

Address Correction Requested

Return Postage Guaranteed

BULK RATE
U.S. Postage Paid
Grants Pass, OR
Permit No. 66

**Please excuse us
for being late this month.**

THE HERB MARKET REPORT

for the herb farmer and forager   Vol. 2   No. 12   December, 1986

FOREST PHILOSOPHY
by Curtin Mitchell*

(The following article was first published in "Permaculture with Native Plants," a newsletter for developing appropriate use of multiple resources in Pacific NW forests.)

"Many people on the Net are involved and committed to advancing knowledge of native plants, thus this Newsletter expresses only the tip-of-the-iceberg. It is important to share information about growing native plants in the garden and this is an excellent way to develop appropriate use of forest resources.

"This may be the foundation of Forest Farming in the future. One of the advantages of this somewhat slow approach to Forest Farming is that it encourages and allows the development of a philosophy to guide the use of forest resources.

"In previous Newsletters we have shared ideas about appropriate and sustainable use of the forest. We have discussed strategies for the long term survival, such as, steady-state maintenace as well as how forests survive catastrophies. We have also considered different approaches to land use, from the aesthetic enjoyment of nature to "rip-off" methods and have suggested a blended method.

"At this time I'd like to take the liberty of extending these ideas into the forseeable future.

"In the Pacific Northest about forty percent of the land appears best suited to permanent forest. It is the character of these lands that are of concern. These forested areas are a mosaic of forest types, such as, spruce-hemlock, pine or fir-cedar as the dominant tree species.

"Some people estimate there are as many as 200 different types of forest in this region, with each forest type containing hundreds of species in its plant community. In some cases these plant communities have persisted for thousands of years, relatively unchanged. These are sustainable systems! As we small and puny humans stand amid the forests, it behooves us to understand them before we intentionally or unintentionally change or destroy them.

* "Permaculture with Native Plants"
Box 38, Lorane, OR   97451

"The forest may be seen as a complex biologic machine, analogous to a chemical factory, with sun, rain, air and soil as the necessary "raw" materials. The forest is quiet, clean, beautiful and completely solar-powered. This factory can reproduce itself with recyclable parts.

"The forest surpasses the most complex chemical factory or oil refinery, which are noted for making hundreds of useful products from raw materials. The forest community, with hundreds of species, produces thousands of potentials products; yet we live amid these forests almost as savages, largely ignorant of their potential. At the same time we are dismantling our forests faster than we are learning of the potential they hold. We literally, 'can't see the forest through the trees' and some foresters (sic) vision is limted to one or two species of tree!

"It borders on the immoral to live amid regional abundance and worry about how economically depressed we are. We must crawl before we can walk and we must begin from where we are. Yet we seem to have lost our way before we have begun. From the meager beginnings of our Network, several approaches to the appropriate use of the forest is possible.

"One possibility for using the forest sensibly, is what I call the Multistory Model of Forest Farming. Some will say it is a poor beginning, others will see it as an unrealistic dream.

"The Multistory Model involves using

native plants within each forest type. One example would be an overstory of douglas fir, with an understory of hemlock, cedar or yew. A third story would be smaller trees or tall shrubs, such as seviceberry, hazel, vine maple, osoberry, ocean spray or tall Oregon grape.

"A fourth story could be shorter shrubs, such as snowberry, salal or braken fern. Below this could be a fifth story or sword fern, kinnikinnic, Claytonia, wild ginger or prince's pine with mushrooms, which require no sunlight, under them.

"Using this model we have identified forty-three species of native or naturalized plants which have a current market. No expensive market development is needed. Many of these plants are currently imported, often from third world countries. It seems we have neither the knowledge nor motivation to provide for ourselves. In some cases it is cheap in the short-run to live off the backs of people in other countries, however times-are-a-changin'.

"We need to inventory our forest to identify all possible species which have current or forseeable future use, with special emphasis on shade-tolerant species. We need detailed information on the requirements of each species, such as soil type, elevation, light and mositure requirements. Each plant must be scrutinized as to how many ways it can be used. New products need to be developed. For example, we need to substitute for coffee and chocolate immediately. At the same time we must evaluate the rarity of each speices so that we don't kill the golden goose in our pursuit of Forest Farming.

"Each landowner or renter needs detailed information on their plant community. What species are present, what is the successional stage, and what species will grow on these sites? This knowledge, along with soil type, elevation, aspect, etc. would be a beginning. Once the inventory is finished, intelligent projections may be made. The projections should include what nature is doing and will do, so that nature's scenario may be seen. In many cases the best strategy may be to let nature plant and grow, while we concentrate on intelligent harvesting. Other projections and strategies of selective weeding, cultivation or even irrigation may be considered.

"The harvesting, storage and processing methods need to be determined. Techniques of cold storage, drying and milling need to be learned or relearned. The economics in terms of labor, tools and equipment must al-so be determined, and last but not least is the need for marketing.

An understanding of forest dynamics, such as plant interaction, is an integral part of the forest philosophy. The principles of permaculture need to be understood and applied to insure the sustained production and use of forest resources. The necessity of maintaining diversity, enriching the plant community, should be understood by every school child. In short, the role of all components of the forest should be understood and appreciated. One example of our lack of understanding revolves around the role of brush in young forests. Conventional forestry views abundant brush, which follows clear-cutting, as unwanted competition for the newly planted trees. Without commenting on clear-cutting as a practice, or planting trees on these clear-cuts, we must develop an understanding of the role of brush species in the later health of the forest. These aggressive species hold soil and nutrients on site and capture sunlight, and even moisture which would otherwise be lost. Brush also provides useful competition, partial shade and longer term fertilization of the forest. The role of brush species in the long-term health of the land must be better understood and re-emphasized. Another alternative is to recognize the brush as a resource or source of useful products. Over thirty of the species we have identified, with a current market, could be considered brush species. The use of these species needs further exploration.

"Permaculture principles, such as doing only what is necessary, stacking functions, and repeat or redundant functions, as well as the diversity of connections need to be applied to the forest farm. The ideas of "beginning at the doorstep" and the function of the forest edge need further development. Forest philosophy embraces the principles of permaculture, understanding natural plant communities, appropriate land use, developing useful products and will lead to a sustainable economy. Forest Farming based on this philosophy begins with backyard gardeners and will involve horticulturists, botanists, ecologists, biochemists, nursery workers, seed collectors, harvesters, warehousers, processors, marketers and perhaps even foresters.

"This outline of Forest Philosophy-Farming is intended as a first approximation, a working statement for the future of the forest lands of our region. If you are outraged by this statement, please respond with criticisms, comments, or an alternative statement. This statement needs refinement."

"THE HERB MARKET REPORT"
Crop Reports

For the last two years, OAK offices have prepared a number of FARM PLANS for specific individuals in different parts of the U.S. and Canada. As a result, a large number of technical resources were compiled on specific crops for those regions.

These individual CROP REPORTS may vary in content and scope, primarily because the information does not yet exist or the search is not yet complete. All, however, have a similar format regarding content. They include

* A one-page overview on the crop, including marketing options and competition and a statement on machinery needs.

* Several overviews on various cultivars, their range and soil requirements, and technical papers on cultivation and harvest.

* A DIALOG computer search on specific technics for cultivation and marketing.

* A computerized SEED RESOURCE LIST on price comparison to more than 300 seed companies on specific cultivars on each crop. This sells for $10/crop (See HMR Vol.2,No.1 for example) by itself.

* A list of specific small and large buyers for the crop.

The individual CROP REPORTS are now available from OAK at $20 each. The list is growing every month. Those available at this time are

ALOE VERA	KELPS
ANGELICA	LEMON BALM
BABY'S BREATH	LOVAGE
BASIL	MARIGOLD
BERGAMOT	MAYAPPLE
BLACK CUMIN	MINTS (Including APPLEMINT and others)
BLOODROOT	NUTMEG and MACE
BORAGE	OREGANO
BURDOCK	PARSLEY
CAPSICUM (and PAPRIKA)	PASSION FLOWER
CARAWAY	PENNYROYAL
CARDAMOM	PEPPER (BLACK and WHITE)
CASTOR BEAN	PEPPERMINT (see MINTS)
CATNIP	PIMENTO (ALLSPICE)
CHAMOMILE (GERMAN and ROMAN)	PSYLLIUM
CHILLIES (see CAPSICUM)	PURSLANE
CHIVES	RED CLOVER
CINNAMON and CASSIA	ROSEMARY
CLOVE	SAGE
COLTSFOOT	SAFFRON
COMFREY	SAVORY (WINTER and SUMMER)
CORIANDER/CILANTRO	SPEARMINT (see MINTS)
DANDELION	TARRAGON
DILL	THISTLE (BLESSED)
ECHINACEA	THYME
FEVERFEW	TUMERIC
GINGER ROOT	VALERIAN
GINSENG	VANILLA BEAN
HIBISCUS	WILD INDIGO
HOREHOUND	WORMWOOD
JOJOBA	

NEWSLETTERS OF INTEREST
for The Herb Farmer and Forager

QUARTERLY NEWSLETTER,
American Herb Association,
P.O.Box 353,
Rescue, CA   95672

ACRES, USA,
P.O.Box 9547,
Kansas City, MO   64133

ALTERNATIVE AG NEWS,
Institute for Alternative Ag, Inc.,
9200 Edmonston Road, Suite 117,
Greensbelt, MD   20770

APPALACHIAN HERB NETWORK NEWSLETTER,
Route 5, Box 423,
Livingston, KY   40445

ASHS NEWSLETTER,
701 N. St.Asaph Street,
Alexandria, VA   22314

THE BOTANICAL GROWER,
High Country Botanicals,
121 West Howard Street,
Boone, NC   28607

BUILDING ECONOMIC ALTERNATIVES,
Co-Op America,
2100 M Street, N.W., Suite 310,
Washington, D.C.   20063

THE BUSINESS OF HERBS,
P.O.Box 559,
Madison, VA   22727

CANADIAN PHARMACEUTICAL JOURNAL,
Toronto, Canada
(see HERBALGRAM)

CoEVOLUTION QUARTERLY,
Box 428,
Sausalito, CA   94966

COLTSFOOT,
Route 1, Box 313A,
Shipman, VA   229171

COUNTRY HERBAL,
Box 370,
Victor, MT   59875

COUNTRYSIDE JOURNAL,
Highway 19 East,
Waterloo, WI   53594

THE CULTIVAR,
Agroecology Program - College 8,
University of CA,
Santa Cruz, CA   95064

HERBALGRAM,
Herb Research Foundation,
P.O.Box 2602,
Longmont, CO   80501

HERBALISTS OF THE PACIFIC STATES,
P.O.Box 10431,
Portland, OR   97210

THE HERB MARKET REPORT,
The Organization for the Advancement
          of Knowledge, Inc.,
1305 Vista Drive,
Grants Pass, OR   97527

THE HERB REPORT,
P.O.Box 95333,
Stuart, FL   33495

THE HERB QUARTERLY,
Box 275,
Newfane, VT   05345

THE HERB, SPICE & MEDICINAL PLANT DIGEST,
USDA,
University of Massachusetts,
Amherst, MA   01003

HORTIDEAS,
Route 1, Box 302,
Gravel Switch, KY   40328

ILEIA NEWSLETTER,
P.O.Box 64,
3830 AB Leusden,
THE NETHERLANDS

INTL PERMACULTURE JOURNAL,
Permaculture Inst. of N.A.,
6488 Maxwelton Road,
Clinton, WA   98236

JOURNAL OF HEALTH AND HEALING,
Box 109,
Wildwood, GA   30757

LADYBUG SOCIETY,
218 Seventh Street,
Boonville, MO   65233

THE LAND REPORT,
The Land Institute,
Route 3,
Salina, KS   67401

LIVING OFF THE LAND,
P.O.Box 2131,
Melbourne, FL   32902

MESSAGE POST,
P.O.Box 190,
Philomath, OR   97370

NATIONAL GREENHOUSE INDUSTRY,
P.O.Box 217,
Mills, WY   82644

NEW DIRECTIONS IN AGRICULTURE,
Intl. Alliance for Sustainable Ag,
1701 University Ave., SE, Room 202,
Minneapolis, MN   55414

THE NEW FARM,
222 Main Street,
Emmaus, PA   18049

NORTHWEST WOODLANDS,
4033 S.W. Canyon Road,
Portland, OR   97221

ONTARIO HERBALIST ASSOC. NEWSLETTER,
General Delivery,
Jackson's Point,
ONTARIO, CANADA   LOE 1L0

OREGON SMALL WOODLANDS ASSOCN.,
1149 Court Street, N.E.,
Salem, OR   97301

ORGANIC MARKET NEWS,
Steering Committee for Sust. Ag

PACIFIC FISHERIES ENHANCEMENT,
P.O.Box 5829,
Charleston, OR   97420

PERMACULTURE ACTIVIST,
6488 Maxwellington Road,
Clinton, WA   98236

PERMACULTURE WITH NATIVE PLANTS,
Curtin Mitchell,
Box 38,
Lorane, OR   97451

POTPOURRI FROM HERBAL ACRES,
Pine Row Publications,
Box 428,
Washington Crossing, PA   18977

RAIN UMBRELLA, INC.,
3116 North Williams,
Portland, OR   97227

THE REGENERATION PROJECT,
Rodle Press,
33 East Minor Street,
Emmaus, PA   18049

RURAL EDUCATION CENTER PERSPECTIVES,
Stonyfield Farm,
Wilton, NH   03086

SISKIYOU COUNTRY,
P.O.Box 989,
Cave JUnction, OR   97523

SMALL FARM ADVOCATE,
P.O.Box 405,
Walthill, NE   68067

STEERING COMMITTEE FOR SUSTANIABLE
        AGRICULTURE,
P.O.Box 1394,
Davis, CA   95617

UPDATE ON HERBS,
215 John Street,
Santa Cruz, CA   95060

NEWS RELEASES

There may now be an a control for velvetleaf,(a serious weed to control with soybean farmers). Gayland F. Spencer (USDA's Northern Research Center) reports that the extract from the wild Uruguayan plant (Eryggium paniculatum) prevents the germination of the pest-plant's seed. Field trials are already in print.

A recent article in TIME MAGAZINE, dated December 15, 1986 was titled "Fertile Fields of Ginseng." The article read "How can farmers boost their sagging income? They can get out of surplus crops like wheat and get into something really different, like raising llamas or growing ginseng. That, at least, was the advice given 5,500 farmers from 42 states who gathered last week in Des Moines for Adapt 100, a conference sponsered by Successful Farming magazine that presented 100 novel ideas for ailing farms. "One speaker showed how eight deer can be raised for venison at the cost of feeding one cow. Other topics covered: growing garbanzo beans, converting corn into lighter fluid and raising edible snails and crayfish. The farmers were interested, though some where skeptical. 'A lot of good ideas got thrown around here,' said Ed Ackerman of Minnesota. 'But the bottom line is profit. Anyone can raise a crop, but you can't succeed unless you can sell it.'"

THE FORAGE OF BLACK (and BLUE) COHOSH - HERBS FOR THE FEMALE

Black cohosh (Cimiciffuga racemosa [L] Nutt. has been known in the South for centuries by a number of names. Black snakeroot, bugbane, rattleweed, and squaw root are just a few. It was first named Chistophoriana canadensis racemosa by Plukenet in 1696. It is an American herb, introduced into medical practice in America in 1828 by the herbalist Garden, and was used briefly in Europe from 1860.

While the markets for this root is now only used by Anglo-American herbalists of the Physiomedical schools, there is a new interest for this and other related crops in Asia and the Middle East. It is now believed that the markets could expand into Europe, with availability.

The medicinal part of black cohosh consists of the dried rhizome and roots. The plant is a perennial shrub that can grow to eight feet in height. Each of the leaf stems hold two, three, or five leaflets. The plant is topped with a slender spike of small, white flowers. The root is knotted.

The plant is indigenous to Canada and the eastern United States, especially Massachusetts, Ohio, Indiana and Georgia. It prefers rich, open woodlands (hardwoods) and cleared hillsides. The root is harvested in the Autumn, when the ground softens for easier root-gathering efforts.

Black cohosh has never been cultivated as a special crop, probably due to the limited markets for the root. It is quite cultivatable, however, in its natural habitat. Because it is a perennial and deciduous, and a profuse bloomer, cultivation of this plant would be beneficial to the area. It is extra hardy and thrives in moist shaded areas.

Chemistry and Uses:

Most all species of Cimicifuga spp. contain isoferullic, palmitic, and oleic acids, as well as tannins, recemosin, 15-20% cimicifugin, and other triterpine glycosides. Only the cimicifugin is active.

A water-insoluble but chloroform-soluble resinous fraction has been reported to have hypotensive activities on animals and to have peripheral vasodilatory effects on man. The plant has also exhibited hypoglycemic and antiflammatory activities on animals.

Black cohosh is used as an antirheumatic, anti-tussive (prevents coughing) sedative and emmenagogue (promotes menstrual discharge). It is used in cases of rheumatism, rheumatoid arthritis, intercostal myalgia (muscular rheumatism), whooping cough, chorea (in children, involuntary and uncontrollable movements of face or extremities), tinnitus aurium (ear-ringing sensation due to disease of the auditory nerve), dysmenorrhoea (poor monthly periods) and cramping pains in the womb. It is especiallly use in cases of rheumatoid arthritis.

Black cohosh may be combined with buckbean or wild celery in rheumatism. It may also be used with zanthoxylum bark in tinnitus.

Dr. John Lloyd reports that the Indians indroduced this drug to early American medicine, and it was discussed by early writers on materia medica, none of whom "added anything not given by the Indians as far as the field of action of the drug is concerned," except for some 19th Century instances of the use of this plant for treating smallpox.

As the name squaw root suggests, a common name of black cohosh, Indians used this plant as a female remedy, also for debility, to promote perspiration, as a gargle for sore throat and for rheumatism. The Penobscots drake it for kidney trouble or exhaustion.

Dr. Barton considered black cohosh a valuable medicine for relief of rheumatism. He called the root astringent and held that a decoction of it was beneficial in sore throats. Dr. Clapp called it "unquestionably one of the most valuable of our indigenous medicinal plants."

Black cohosh was official in the USP, from 1820 to 1936, and in the NF, from 1936 to 1950. Most of the effects from the chemistry are likely due to its bitter nature and its astringency. Toxicity data are conflicting. Some sources (based on animal studies) suggest that the plant is nontoxic, while other sources ascribe considerable toxicity to black cohosh. Its emetic action is not considered violent, and is probably the result of mild gastrointestinal irritation.

It should be noted that in traditional Chinese medicine, other Cimicifuga species such as C. foetida L., C. dahurica (Turez.) Maxim., and C. simplex Womsk. have been used for centuries for similar purposes.

BLUE COHOSH ROOT

About 80 years ago, blue cohosh (Clauophyllum thalictroides (L.) Michx.. was included in the U.S. Pharmacopoeia and was considered worthy of detailed studies. Known as squaw root or papoose root, it found use in obstetic and gynaecological conditions.

American Indian women drank an infusion of the root for two weeks prior to childbirth, which was usually painless. This herb has also been called blue or yellow ginseng. Its use is now restricted to herbal medicine.

Blue cohosh is a low growing perennial herb, with horizontal, branching rhizome bearing slender roots. It can reach a height of 3 feet, although it usually is only one foot high. The stem terminates into a large sessile tripinnate leaf. Other leaves, 2 to 3 to each plant, are pinnate, with leaflets being oval.

It grows wild throughout the eastern parts of the United States and Canada, especially in moist woodlands and mountain glades. It can be found as far south as Florida and west to Wisconsin and Texas. The part harvested is the dried rhizome, sometimes refered to as "root" in the literature.

Chemistry and Uses:

Besides phosphoric acid and a green-yellow dye, blue cohosh contains the saponin leotin, and the alkaloid methylcystine. Recent studies with C. robustum Maxim. in the USSR have found it to be rich in triterpene glycosides (caulosides A, B, C, D, E, F, and G), most of which have hederagenin as their aglycone. They possess fungicide activities.

There does not seem to be many in-depth scientific studies on the pharmacological properties of blue cohosh, except that an alcoholic extract of its aerial parts after treatment with petroleum ether has recently been demonstrated to have antiflammatory properties in rats.

The roots and berries of this plant have been used as a menstrual aid and as an aid to childbirth. Heat detoxifies the berries. It has even been used as a substitute for coffee in some parts of the Appalachians.

Toxic symptoms include nausia, vomiting, and gastritis. Greater amounts may cause headaches, thirst, dilated pupils, muscle weakness, incoordination, cardiovascular collapse, and covulsions.

Since the number of berries and amount of root necessary to produce these symptoms is unclear, exposure to the uncooked plant should be treated with emesis and activated charcoal. Severely ill patients should be observed and provided with supportive care.

Blue cohosh is usually sold as a crude botanical and as an extract. Crude forms were formerly official in N.F.. It is now considered a dangerous drug plant with good market potentials, especially in Europe.

PROXIMATE COMPOSITION OF GROUND SPICES. 100 GRAMS. EDIBLE PORTION

Spice	Water	Food Energy	Protein	Fat	Total Carbohydrate	Fiber Carbohydrate	Ash	Calcium	Phosphorus	Sodium	Potassium	Iron	Thiamine	Riboflavin	Niacin	Ascorbic Acid	Vitamin A Activity
	Grams	Cal.	Grams	Grams	Grams	Grams	Grams	Mg.	Mg.	Grams	Mg.	Mg.	Mcg.	Mcg.	Mg.	Mg.	Int'l Units
Allspice	9.0	380	6.0	6.6	74.4	21.6	4.2	0.8	110	80	1.1	7.5	100	60	2.9	39	540
Basil Leaves	6.0	325	12.0	3.6	61.7	20.5	16.7	2.1	470	40	3.7	42.8	150	320	6.9	61	15000
Bay Leaves	4.5	410	7.5	8.8	75.4	25.2	3.7	1.0	110	20	0.6	53.3	100	420	2.0	47	6180
Caraway Seed	6.0	465	21.0	23.1	43.5	10.4	5.6	0.7	500	20	1.9	8.5	380	380	8.1	N	360
Cardamom Seed	8.0	360	10.0	2.9	74.2	9.9	4.7	0.3	210	10	1.2	11.6	180	230	2.3	N	N
Celery Seed	5.0	450	18.0	22.8	43.8	12.9	10.2	1.8	550	170	1.4	44.9	410	490	4.4	17	50
Cinnamon	10.0	355	4.5	2.2	79.8	20.3	3.5	1.6	50	10	0.4	4.1	140	210	1.9	40	260
Cloves	5.0	430	6.0	14.5	68.8	11.1	5.0	0.7	110	250	1.2	9.5	110	N	1.5	81	530
Coriander Seed	6.0	450	12.0	19.6	56.5	31.5	5.3	0.8	440	20	1.2	5.9	260	230	2.5	N	N
Cumin Seed	6.0	460	18.0	23.8	44.6	9.1	7.7	0.9	450	160	2.1	47.8	730	380	2.5	17	1270
Dill Seed	8.5	435	13.0	17.9	56.4	20.7	6.0	1.6	210	10	1.1	11.8	420	280	2.8	N	50
Fennel Seed	6.0	370	9.5	10.0	60.8	18.5	13.4	1.3	480	90	1.7	11.1	410	360	6.0	N	135
Garlic Powder	5.0	365	17.5	0.6	73.3	1.9	3.2	0.1	420	10	1.1	3.5	680	80	0.7	N	N
Ginger	7.0	380	8.5	6.4	72.4	5.9	5.7	0.1	150	30	1.4	11.3	50	130	1.9	N	150
Mace	4.5	565	8.0	38.8	46.1	4.8	2.3	0.2	110	70	0.5	11.3	370	560	1.2	N	800
Marjoram	6.5	365	12.5	6.8	64.4	16.7	9.7	2.5	230	110	1.4	72.7	290	320	4.1	51	8070
Mustard Powder	3.0	580	32.0	42.6	18.5	1.9	4.0	0.3	790	10	0.7	8.3	650	450	8.5	22	60
Nutmeg	4.0	565	7.0	38.9	47.3	3.1	2.0	0.2	200	10	0.4	2.2	360	250	9.4	N	100
Onion Powder	4.5	370	10.5	0.8	80.5	6.4	3.5	0.3	290	40	1.0	2.2	420	60	0.6	15	N
Oregano	8.0	360	12.0	6.4	64.9	11.0	9.0	1.7	200	20	1.7	53.3	340	N	6.2	N	6900
Paprika	7.0	390	14.0	10.4	60.3	19.2	8.6	0.2	300	20	2.4	23.1	600	1360	15.3	59	58000
Parsley Flakes	4.0	355	22.0	5.6	54.3	8.7	14.1	1.2	310	540	3.6	14.5	170	1230	7.9	392	23300
Pepper, Black	8.0	400	10.0	10.2	66.5	10.0	4.6	0.4	160	10	1.2	17.0	70	210	0.8	N	190
Pepper, Chili	6.5	415	14.0	14.1	58.2	15.6	7.2	0.1	320	10	2.1	9.9	590	1660	14.2	64	51800
Pepper, Red	6.0	420	16.0	15.5	54.3	26.0	8.0	0.1	320	10	2.1	9.9	520	910	13.6	29	31400
Pepper, White	9.5	395	12.0	8.0	69.0	4.5	1.0	0.2	150	10	0.1	6.9	20	130	0.2	N	N
Poppy Seed	3.5	530	23.0	35.5	30.2	8.7	7.5	1.6	880	10	0.8	.99	690	180	0.9	N	N
Rosemary Leaves	5.5	440	4.5	17.4	66.4	19.0	6.0	1.5	70	40	1.0	33.0	510	N	1.0	61	3100
Sage	5.5	415	10.0	14.1	62.3	16.0	7.7	1.8	90	10	1.0	27.3	750	340	5.7	40	5900
Savory	9.0	355	7.0	5.2	69.9	15.3	8.7	2.2	140	20	1.1	37.8	370	N	4.1	N	5100
Sesame Seed	3.0	480	24.0	22.4	47.1	37.7	3.6	0.1	790	30	0.4	6.2	800	1.90	5.7	N	65
Tarragon	4.5	365	24.0	7.3	51.5	6.8	12.3	1.3	310	70	3.2	35.7	250	1340	8.9	N	4200
Thyme	7.0	340	7.0	4.6	68.3	24.3	13.2	2.1	200	80	0.9	135.0	510	400	4.9	N	3800
Turmeric	6.0	390	8.5	8.9	69.9	6.9	6.8	0.2	260	10	2.5	47.5	90	190	4.8	50	N

N = Non-measurable: values are below minimum levels found by AOAC methods (40 mg. riboflavin, 12 mg. ascorbic acid, 50 IU vitamin A per 100 g. of spice).   Mg. = Milligrams (0.001 grams).   Mcg. = Microgram (0.000001 grams).

Organization for the Advancement of Knowledge

Address Correction Requested

Return Postage Guaranteed

BULK RATE
U.S. Postage Paid
Grants Pass, OR
Permit No. 66

Oak Publishing
1212 SW 5th Street,
Grants Pass, OR 97526
Phone: 541-426-5588

The Herb Market Report   Vol. 2   No. 12

Index

Included in this index are
Vol. 1 - 1985
Vol. 2 - 1986

Dr. Richard Alan Miller

Dr. Richard Alan Miller

L

"Ladybug," 2-5-(7)
Laminaria, (green algae), 1-11-(6)
Lapathum acutum, 1-7-(1)
Lentinus edodes, 2-3-(6)
licorice root, 1-4-(1)
lipids, 2-11-(3)
Lippia graveolens, 1-5-(2)

M

Macrocyctis, (algae), 1-11-(6)
"Magical And Ritual Use Of
　　Aphrodisiacs," 1-9-(4)
ma huang, 2-9-(5)
management skills (test), 1-5-(6)
manure resources, 1-12-(3)
marigold, 1-12-(3)
markets
　　(herbs and spices), 1-1-(3)
　　(conclusions), 1-9-(4)
　　(considerations), 2-3-(3)
　　(floral), 2-9-(7)
　　(peak harvests), 1-10-(7)
　　(Egypt), 2-6-(7)
　　(France), 1-6-(3)
　　(Germany), 1-6-(3)
　　(Israel), 2-6-(9)
　　(Japan), 1-8-(3)
　　(United Kingdom), 1-7-(3)
　　(U.S.A.). 1-4-(3), 1-7-(4), 1-9-(5),
　　　　2-2-(6), 2-4-(4), 2-5-(7)
Matricaria chamomilla, 1-3-(5)
Mentha citrata, 1-6-(4)
Mexican oregano, 1-5-(2)
Mollison, Bill, 2-8-(1), 2-9-(1)
Monarda didyma, 1-6-(5)
Monarda fistulosa, 1-5-(2), 1-6-(5)

*Monarda punctata,*1-6-(5)
mormon tea, 2-9-(5)
mullein, 1-1-(2)
mushroom cultivation, 2-2-(8)

N

natural farming, 2-8-(1), 2-9-(1), 2-10-(1)
"Natural Way Of Farming," 2-10-(1)
nettle, 2-5-(5)
newsletter directory, 2-12-(4)
nori kelp, 1-12-(5)

O

oak mushroom, 2-3-(6)
Ocimum basilicum, 2-2-(1)
Oximum spp., 2-2-(4)
Oenothera biennis, 1-10-(5)
"One Straw Revolution," 2-10-(1)
"OPD," 1-8-(6)
Oplopanax horridum, 2-1-(5)
Origanum heracleoticum, 1-5-(1)
Origanum hirtum, 1-5-(1)
Origanum majorana, 1-5-(2)
Originum onites, 1-5-(2)
Origanum sipyleum, 1-5-(2)
Origanum virents, 1-5-(2)
Origanum vulgare, 1-5-(1)
Oxalis acetosella, 1-8-(7)

P

Palmer's grass, 2-5-(2)
Panax quinquefolium, 2-1-(4)
pau d'arco, 2-1-(6)
Peace Seeds, 2-4-(3)
Peaceful Valley Farm Supply, 2-5-(7)
"Perfumer & Flavorist," 2-4-(8)

Dr. Richard Alan Miller

Dr. Richard Alan Miller

For More Information

See our full list of publications
available for purchase, and Dr. Miller's
event schedule and consulting services
at www.richardalanmiller.com

Oak Publishing
1212 SW 5th Street,
Grants Pass, OR   97526
(541) 476-5588
(541)476-1823 (fax)
Rick@nwbotanicals.org

Dr. Richard Alan Miller

Services

www.richardalanmiller.com

Agricultural Consultant | Research | Lectures | Workshops

The following is a partial list of services available with full listing and contact information available online.

Phone Consultation

Dr. Miller is available for private phone consultations to address your specific needs for information. This could include such topics as grading crop samples, discussing specific markets, or what needs to be changed in the combine to separate leaf from the stalk.

It is recommended before booking time with Dr. Miller, that you read the relevant material in both his book, *The Potential Of Herbs As A Cash Crop*, and his newsletter, *The Encyclopedia of Alternative Agricultural.* These resources will help you ask the right questions and save time.

Farm Plans

Farm Plans include nine technical crop reports and additional information on several other crop alternatives. The report includes timetables, spirochetes with anticipated costs, incomes, volumes, markets, seed sources, expansion programs, projected gross receipts, etc. Recommendations and cottage industry suggestions will be based on current or future market trends, and your resources. When you order a farm plan, we need to know the following:

Dr. Richard Alan Miller

(1) List of capital equipment

(2) What equipment is in the neighborhood which might be leased

(3) Detailed soil descriptions of the land in question for use from SCS

(4) Crop and spray history of the soils in question

(5) How much money do you have to begin this venture

(6) What grows well in your garden

(7) Goals and direction

(8) A video of your farm and resources (or photographs)

Technical Crop Reports

Crop reports include life zone, description, history as a crop, chemistry, and form of usage. The field production section includes seed sources, propagation and cultivation, fertilization and irrigation needs, weed control, insect and disease problems, harvesting, yields, drying, processing, storage and marketing.

They also include a full computer search - using DIALOG (AGRICOLA and CRIS) - of all articles written on this crop. Some reprints of technical papers important to this subject are included in this report.

Outside Consultant

Dr. Miller is available to write grants and business proposals, design and supervise the development of specialized processing facilities, set up farming networks and new sources of supply, develop new markets and broker current inventories, and offer advice on botanical markets.

His expertise lies in the marketing and processing of herbs and spices as alternative crops in an agricultural diversification program designed for rural economic development. His markets include foods, drugs, cosmetics, and dried florals. Mr. Miller is considered a world authority in these markets.

Please go to www.richardalanmiller.com for pricing and availability.

Dr. Richard Alan Miller

Books

The Encyclopedia of Alternative Agriculture:
for Urban and Semi-Rural Communities

The Herb Market Report newsletters, teaching the basics for how to "small farm" field crops correctly, and be successful, were written before computers, or before the internet. While the data charts may not be current, the information about the herbs themselves is still a valuable resource.

Now available as a set of five books, the newsletters are archived, two years per book. Full color, delux soft cover, with actual original pages from the newsletter in black and white on the interior they bring a wealth of information carefully researched over ten year period, by Dr. Miller. Book 1 is the first ready for sale, the other four as they are completed.

Book 1, Vols. 1 & 2
Full color, soft cover, black and white interior, large format 8.5" x 11"; 216 pages

Herbs featured in Book 1: Catnip Herb; Cascara Segrada Bark;Roman Chamomile; Licorice Root; Horsetail; Oregano; Baby's Breath; Sword Ferns; Bergamont and the Eau de Cologne; Connoisseur's pot-pourri; Yellow Dock; Chicory Root; Thyme; Seeds from Forest Trees; Specified Essential Oils; Seaweeds; Marigolds; Nori Kelp. **Some regular feature articles include:** Major Markets; Cottage Industry; Book Reviews; Forage and Cultivation; Sources of Seeds; Selection of Good Cropland; Collection Techniques; Foragers Turn Weeds into Cash Crops

$24.95

A companion guide to the encyclopeia set of books:

Native Plants of Commercial Importance
by Dr.Richard Alan Miller

Here is an information-filled look at how to supplement rural incomes by the harvest of native plants from the region. Among the wild plants of North America are many which have long been used in medicinal, cosmetic, food and floral industries. Some of them are used in sufficient quantities to make them commercially important.

Dr. Richard Alan Miller

The book describes these and other forest products, dividing North America into five regions: Northeast, South, Midwest, Southwest and the Northwest. Each region contains a descriptions of 10 common crops now harvested, with detail and a special appendix on marketing. Reforestation is stressed to make each crop renewable and self-generating as a natural resource. This technique has led to the new concept of Forest Farming.

The future of foraging as a source of supplementing one's rural income lies with our ability to recognize natural resources.

Softcover. Color cover, illustrations by Connie Nygard; black and white interior; 340 pages.

$20.00

Dr. Richard Alan Miller

CPSIA information can be obtained at www.ICGtesting.com
Printed in the USA
BVOW051909220413

318810BV00002B/3/P